Applied Data Analysis for Process Improvement

Also available from ASQ Quality Press:

The Certified Six Sigma Black Belt Handbook
Donald W. Benbow and T.M. Kubiak

Applied Statistics for the Six Sigma Green Belt
Gupta Bhisham and H. Fred Walker

Design of Experiments with MINITAB
Paul Mathews

Six Sigma for the Shop Floor: A Pocket Guide
Roderick A. Munro

Six Sigma for the Office: A Pocket Guide
Roderick A. Munro

Defining and Analyzing a Business Process: A Six Sigma Pocket Guide
Jeffrey N. Lowenthal

Six Sigma Project Management: A Pocket Guide
Jeffrey N. Lowenthal

The Six Sigma Journey from Art to Science
Larry Walters

The Six Sigma Path to Leadership: Observations from the Trenches
David H. Treichler

Failure Mode and Effect Analysis: FMEA From Theory to Execution,
Second Edition
D. H. Stamatis

Customer Centered Six Sigma : Linking Customers, Process Improvement,
and Financial Results
Earl Naumann and Steven Hoisington

Design for Six Sigma as Strategic Experimentation: Planning, Designing,
and Building World-Class Products and Services
H.E. Cook

To request a complimentary catalog of ASQ Quality Press publications,
call 800-248-1946, or visit our Web site at http://qualitypress.asq.org.

Applied Data Analysis for Process Improvement

A Practical Guide to Six Sigma Black Belt Statistics

James L. Lamprecht

ASQ Quality Press
Milwaukee, Wisconsin

American Society for Quality, Quality Press, Milwaukee 53203
© 2005 by American Society for Quality
All rights reserved. Published 2005
Printed in the United States of America

12 11 10 09 08 07   5 4 3 2

Library of Congress Cataloging-in-Publication Data

Lamprecht, James L., 1947–
    Applied data analysis for process improvement : a practical guide to Six Sigma
      Black Belt statistics / James Lamprecht.
        p. cm.
    Includes index.
    ISBN 0-87389-648-3 (soft cover : alk. paper)
      1. Six sigma (Quality control standard).   2. Quality control—Statistical
methods.   I. Title.

    TS156.L3196 2005
    658.4'013—dc22   2004030721

ISBN 0-87389-648-3

Publisher: William A. Tony
Acquisitions Editor: Annemieke Hytinen
Project Editor: Paul O'Mara
Production Administrator: Randall Benson

ASQ Mission: The American Society for Quality advances individual, organizational, and community excellence worldwide through learning, quality improvement, and knowledge exchange.

Attention Bookstores, Wholesalers, Schools, and Corporations: ASQ Quality Press books, videotapes, audiotapes, and software are available at quantity discounts with bulk purchases for business, educational, or instructional use. For information, please contact ASQ Quality Press at 800-248-1946, or write to ASQ Quality Press, P.O. Box 3005, Milwaukee, WI 53201-3005.

To place orders or to request a free copy of the ASQ Quality Press Publications Catalog, including ASQ membership information, call 800-248-1946. Visit our Web site at www.asq.org or http://qualitypress.asq.org.

♾ Printed on acid-free paper

Quality Press
600 N. Plankinton Avenue
Milwaukee, Wisconsin 53203
Call toll free 800-248-1946
Fax 414-272-1734
www.asq.org
http://qualitypress.asq.org
http://standardsgroup.asq.org
E-mail: authors@asq.org

AMERICAN SOCIETY
FOR QUALITY

Contents

Figures and Tables

Preface

U sing statistical methodology to analyze and solve problems has a long tradition in manufacturing that dates back to at least the mid-1920s. With the rebirth of Six Sigma around 1998, the use of statistics to analyze and improve processes has once again regained a prominent place in an ever-growing number of corporations around the world. An increasing number of employees and managers, with the honorific title of Green Belt, Black Belt, or even Master Black Belt, are asked to apply statistical techniques to analyze and resolve industrial and nonindustrial (also known as transactional) problems. Because statistics is about collecting and analyzing data, these armies of certified individuals are faced continually with the daunting task of sorting out the vast number of sophisticated techniques placed at their disposal by an equally impressive array of statistical computer software packages.

This book is intended for the ever-growing number of certified Black Belts as well as the countless uncertified others who would like to understand how data can be analyzed. Many training programs, including those generally known as Six Sigma Black Belt courses, do a good job introducing participants to a large number of sophisticated statistical techniques in as little as 10 days. Most courses, as one brochure advertised, try to "keep it simple statistically," claiming the software (also labeled as the "easiest to use") will allow for easy interpretation of the results. Unfortunately, although it is true that statistical principles can be simplified, learning how to interpret results produced by any statistical software requires a basic understanding of the discipline known as statistics.

Using a linguistic analogy, although it is relatively simple to learn a few foreign words or even sentences in a short time, enough at least to ask simple questions at a restaurant or hotel, it is quite a different story to be able to understand the answers provided by native speakers, let alone maintain a conversation! Naturally acquiring fluency in a foreign language takes a little longer than a few days or weeks, often requiring many months or even a few years, depending on one's natural ability. It is also true that although most foreigners are able to understand and graciously overlook grammatical errors made by a novice speaker—and may even be willing to correct such errors patiently—statistical software packages are not so tolerant or understanding. If you ask a computer to do something statistically stupid, most of the time, unless it is really incomprehensible statistically, the software package will likely produce a meaningless (but very precise) answer that unfortunately will appear to the uninitiated as a most sensible answer that, if implemented, could result in costly consequences.

An additional difficulty faced by any certified or uncertified data analyst is that statistical computer software packages have become increasingly complex over the past decade. It is true that statistical software vendors have done a superb job expanding their Help menus. But trying to learn statistics by reading Help menus is like learning to send a rocket to the moon by reading a few books on calculus, physics, and chemistry: it requires an infinite amount of patience, perseverance, and resources. Finally, ever since its birth in the early 18th century, the discipline of statistics has become an enormously complicated subject consisting of many subdisciplines. This complexity is reflected in the fact that most statistical software packages consist of a great many statistical methods equally available to the novice and the expert. The popular statistical package used to generate all the tables and graphs in this book, for example, contains as many as 134 statistical routines and 18 different graph routines. In addition, each of these routines contains numerous options and other selections, which does not include the Data manipulation tab and the Calculation tab, each with over 30 additional options. Of all these routines, only eight statistical routines and six to seven different graphs are used in this book, essentially all that most data analysts need to analyze the majority of industrial problems. With the exception of Chapter 8, which focuses on problem definition and related methodologies, learning how to use the small subset of statistical routines in this book required less than 200 pages of explanation and numerous tables and figures. And yet most statistical books are generally at least two or three times as long. You may well ask how I could cover all the necessary topics. Simplification and condensation of information were required. Naturally, I could not write about every possible assumption underlying every statistical model (although I do mention the essential elements). Similarly, I could not discuss in detail all the possible tests regarding normality (or non-normality) of residuals, for example, and what to do about it, but I do talk about it. The fact is that in many cases an approximation of the assumptions will not lead to disastrous interpretations of the data. I also assume you do not want to become a professional statistician but rather be able to analyze data without committing some blatant errors. The book begins with the forgotten art of looking at data and the art of graphing data to see patterns. All too often, people rush into the analysis phase of data without taking the time (short as it is) to look at the data and see if anything particularly unusual can be found. Often looking at the data and asking questions about extreme data points (known as outliers) can be very insightful. This ability to call on intuition when looking at data is explored in Chapter 1 where various graph techniques are used to summarize data in order to reach conclusions. Unlike most textbooks, I also explain whenever possible the story behind the data. In other words, I describe what is *not* given by the data.

As databases increase in size or become otherwise more complicated, our ability to look at data intuitively is diminished, and we need to move up to the next step of analyzing data statistically and inferring conclusions. However, because the statistical analysis of data means the ability to interpret the statistical output generated by statistical software, it is necessary to have a basic statistical vocabulary. The classic method, favored by the Six Sigma training course, is a cookbook approach to statistics. The analogy to a cookbook is unfortunate because although it is true that almost anyone with an interest in cooking can use a recipe and produce, if not the first time then by the second or third time, an acceptable dish, the same is not true about cookbook statistics. The problem is not so much with the rules of statistical interpretation, for these can generally be packaged much as a recipe, but rather with when to use what ingredients. Stated differently, I would suggest that although so-called cookbook statistics can be efficient at telling you how much of what ingredient you need for a particular data recipe, it is not very good at telling you what to do after you have blended the ingredients, so to speak.

To avoid or at least minimize this problem, I realized that some fundamental principles of statistics covered in most introductory courses had to be mentioned. Deciding what was to be a minimum and how much explanation was required was not easy, but in all instances, no knowledge of algebra beyond the high school level is required to understand the elementary statistical principles introduced in Chapters 2 and 3. In Chapter 3 the examples analyzed intuitively in Chapter 1 are revisited and analyzed using formal statistical methods. Chapters 4 through 7 introduce the powerful methods of design of experiments, regression and correlation analyses, and response surface analysis.

Numerous examples illustrate how various techniques are applied. In the majority of cases, the examples also demonstrate how various statistics generated by statistical software packages are computed. Unlike most other authors, I have also explained what is usually not revealed in statistical textbooks or even expensive seminars. This is accomplished by discussing what is not explicitly stated in statistical exercises (the story behind the story), the very issues that countless experimenters face every day. Thus, instead of only explaining the mechanics of how a t-test or a two-way analysis of variance is performed, I also write about the assumptions generally ignored in cookbook and textbook examples. This methodology is emphasized in Chapter 1. Each example is reviewed from the perspective of what was *not* said in the example; in other words, the very information you will be faced with when you conduct your own analysis. In some cases, my explanation of a particular statistical technique is different from what is usually offered in most textbooks. Thus, for example, the well-known topic of control charts is briefly introduced in Chapter 4 and Chapter 9 within the context of the statistical risk associated with hypothesis testing. Some of the topics covered in this book (particularly in Chapter 7) could be considered advanced, but they are relatively easy to understand and also very useful. These topics include response surface analysis, finding the best factor(s) settings to optimize one or more response variables, and finding the best setting to minimize variability. These questions, which are of great importance to design and process engineers, typically are only found in specialized or advanced statistical textbooks.

The premise of the first seven chapters is that a problem has been defined and the necessary data have been collected, but what can be done when a problem has not yet been defined and the data have not been collected? Chapter 8 addresses those two important questions by offering a review of the essential elements of the define, measure, analyze, improve, and control (DMAIC) methodology. The final chapter, a case study, integrates some of the elements presented in Chapter 8 with some of the data analysis tools introduced in earlier chapters.

Titles of some sections in the book include the word *optional* or *advanced.* These sections cover more advanced but nonetheless useful topics, but skipping these sections will not affect the overall flow of the various subjects presented. I hope the information contained in this book will help you better formulate, analyze, and improve many interesting problems.

James Lamprecht
Hemet, California
December 2004
jimlamprecht@earthlink.net

PART I

Applied Data Analysis

1

Intuitive Statistics: The Values of Graphs for Decision Making

1.0 INTRODUCTION

When I first came up with the idea of intuitive statistics, I had no idea others had already written on the subject. However, as I was to discover, the term *intuitive statistics* has a variety of meanings. Gerd Gigerenzer and David J. Murray report the term was probably first used by the 19th-century German psychologist Ergon Brunwick when he described the intuitive perceptual and cognitive abilities of the mind.[1] This concept is different from the one used by statisticians, who have, over the years, used intuitive statistics to teach the subject more effectively. My use of the term is different from both statisticians' and psychologists'. Some years ago I noticed that in a majority of cases whenever one is asked to analyze a statistical problem of the type presented in statistical textbooks, one is usually able to guess correctly at the answer without any prior knowledge or application of sophisticated statistical tests. It is this ability to see the answer, as it were, by simply looking at the data or graphs of the data that I call *intuitive statistics*. The following series of examples not only introduce you to most of the fundamental issues that data analysts and experimenters face when analyzing data but also help illustrate what I mean by *seeing the data*.

1.1 THE USE OF GRAPHS

Example 1.1: In order to compare the mileage yield of two kinds of gasoline, several tests were run and the results shown in Table 1.1 were obtained.

   Question: Calculate a t value and use it to test the null hypothesis that there is no difference in the true average mileage yield of the two kinds

Table 1.1   Miles per gallon for Gasoline A and Gasoline B.

Gasoline A	Gasoline B
21	17
19	20
18	19
20	21
21	17
21	20

of gasoline against a two-sided alternative. Use alpha = 0.05. Translating the statistical jargon, the question asks, "Is there a difference in the mileage of Gasoline A versus Gasoline B?" The statistical test required to compare two populations is known as a t-test (hence the request to "calculate a t"; see section 3.6 in Chapter 3). If you are not in the business of gasoline performance, you can change the scenario to better fit your interest. Indeed, the two columns of numbers listed under the headings "Gasoline A" and "Gasoline B" could represent anything you wish: for example, number of customer complaints files by two departments (A vs. B) over a period of six weeks or in two different stores (A vs. B). Or, if you prefer, the numbers could represent the number of defective products produced by two assembly lines (A vs. B) over a period of six days or six weeks. Other scenarios could be imagined, and, in fact, the problem statement here is but a specific example of a type of problem that can be generalized to refer to the comparison of any two sets of numbers (usually measurements) coming from two *populations* (two types of gasoline, two departments, two assembly lines, two types of customers, and so on). You probably also noted that nothing was said about how the gasoline performance test was conducted. For example, we know nothing about the type of cars (age, weight, and other characteristics), type of tires, the driving conditions (for example, flat versus hilly terrain), the driving style of each driver, environmental conditions (that is, windy or rainy versus calm or dry day), and many other conditions. We do not know if six identical (or different) cars were used or if the same car was used for all tests. These are very important questions to ask because each of these *factors,* and perhaps even combination of factors (for example, type of car combined with driving conditions, or driving style and environmental conditions, tires combined with different drivers, or a car-and-tire interaction, and so on.) can influence mileage performance.

Because we are not told how the experiment was conducted, we can only assume all factors are equal or at least were equal during the length of the experiment. (Note: If you want to impress your colleagues, the Latin word for such an assumption is *ceteris paribus*.) In other words, we must assume that, if several cars were used, the cars were (ideally) of the same model and year. We also assume the terrain was the same (perhaps a closed race track) and the drivers were told to drive at a specified speed for so many miles; in other words, we assume *ceteris paribus* for all other known and unknown factors (a word not likely to be popular with engineers). Returning to the original question, I propose that without knowing anything about t-tests or alpha levels (in this example, alpha is set to 0.05), one can answer the question by simply looking at the data and, if need be, compute (with the aid of a pocket calculator) a couple of simple statistics, namely, the average and the range. My reliable pocket calculator assures me that, on the assumption my fingers and eye coordination are to be trusted, the following so-called statistics summarize the set of numbers previously described:

Average mileage for Gasoline A = 20

Range (that is, difference between the smallest and largest mileage) = 21 − 18 = 3 miles

Average mileage for Gasoline B = 19

Range = 21 − 17 = 4 miles

The range is an approximate measure of variation—the larger the range, the larger the variation. In this example we see that the 1-gallon difference in averages for gasoline performance is approximately equal to one-third to one-fourth of the range. Other, more precise, measures of variation such as the interquartile range and the standard deviation are introduced later.

Looking at the averages, we notice that Gasoline A is only 1 mile per gallon better than Gasoline B, whereas the range in performance for Gasoline A and B is 3 and 4 miles, respectively. What would you conclude? Would you say Gasoline A is unquestionably better than Gasoline B, or would you say there is essentially no difference in performance? Using statistical jargon, if you think Gasoline A is better than Gasoline B, you accept the *alternative hypothesis*. If you believe there is *no difference* in mileage between Gasoline A and Gasoline B, you accept the *null hypothesis* (null because it is the hypothesis of no difference; for a more detailed explanation, see sections 3.3 and 3.4 in Chapter 3).[2] What is your intuition vis-à-vis the performance of Gasoline A versus Gasoline B? If you still are not sure, perhaps the dot plots shown in Figure 1.1 will help you decide.

Numerous other graphical representations are available. For example, the radar graph shown in Figure 1.2 was produced using the Chart Wizard available in Microsoft's Excel (Note: The dot plot is not available in Excel

Gas type

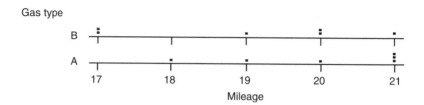

Figure 1.1   Dot plots for Gasoline A versus Gasoline B.

Table 1.2   Miles per gallon data.

Gas A	Gas B
21	17
19	20
18	19
20	21
21	17
21	20

and was produced using a popular statistical software.) The data needed to produce the radar chart (using a standard spreadsheet) were entered as shown in Table 1.2.

The radar graph shows a substantial amount of overlapping in the mileage performances of Gasoline A versus Gasoline B. Therefore, we would likely intuit no difference in performance between the two types of gasoline.

Example 1.2:   A methods engineer believes he has perfected a training program that can considerably shorten workers' assembly time for a certain mechanism. To verify the validity of his assumption, he plans to select 10 assemblers *at random* and conduct time and motion studies *before* and *after* the 10 workers have gone through the training program (see Table 1.3).This example is related to Example 1.1. This time, however, we are not comparing two different products or two different methods; rather we are assessing the impact of a new training program on the assembly time performance on 10 workers (the same 10 workers). Problems that compare before and after performance are analyzed using a statistical technique known as *paired,* or *matched, t-tests.* The technique computes the difference for each pair of measurements and analyzes whether or not the differences are statistically significant.

Question (stated without the statistical jargon): Does the training program improve the assembly time? What do the numbers tell you?

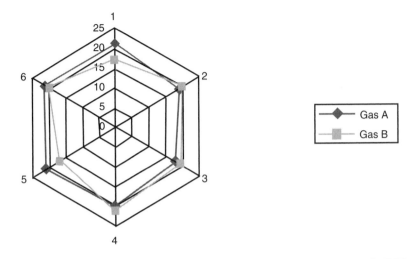

Figure 1.2   Radar graph for Gasoline A versus Gasoline B.

Table 1.3   Assembly time before and after training.

Worker	Assembly time before training	Assembly time after training
1	7	8
2	8	8
3	10	7
4	11	6
5	18	10
6	16	9
7	12	9
8	12	8
9	6	7
10	12	10
Average	11.2	8.2
Range	12	4

1.1.1 General Comments About the Study

You will notice that the methods engineer has selected 10 workers at *random*. Randomization is an important yet difficult statistical concept to explain. Within the context of this study, randomization means the engineer did not select all assemblers from one department, nor did he select only male or only female assemblers, only assemblers with three or more years of experience, and so on. In other words, the engineer did not *systematically* select assemblers with one, two, or three specific characteristics. Rather the engineer selected the assemblers at random, meaning that, from a population of assemblers who received the training (we are not told how large this population is), 10 assemblers were selected presumably from both sexes, perhaps 5 men and 5 women (assuming, of course, that both genders are equally represented on the assembly line), with a broad range of assembly experience and probably from the same department. Because we are not given any additional information besides the fact that 10 assemblers were randomly selected, we will not be able to analyze whether or not the new method has the same or a different impact (or *effect*) across the gender factor or across the experience factor.

Despite these restrictions, we can make some observations by simply looking at the numbers. Note, for example, how the range for the after-training assembly time (which is an approximate measure of variation) is substantially smaller (4 vs. 12). Note also that people who had a low assembly time *before* training (6, 7, or 8 minutes) did not benefit from the training; however, everyone else (7 out of 10) did improve. This observation could be of interest in that maybe these three individuals have unique skills that may be worth exploring further. It could also mean these three individuals have greater experience and have developed a technique that has allowed them to optimize their performance. Other causes could be postulated. The dot plots shown in Figure 1.3 help visualize the difference in performance. What is your conclusion? What do you see by looking at the dot plot and/or the radar chart (Figure 1.4)? What happened to the variability of the scores after training?

Note: The effectiveness of the radar chart decreases with the number of observations; 15 to 20 observations (and hence radial axes) is probably the limit.

Example 1.3:   The editors of an outdoor sporting magazine conducted a test to compare two oversize tire designs (A vs. B) of the type used

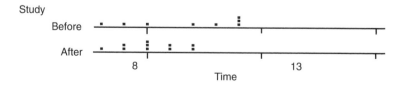

Figure 1.3   Dot plot for assembly time before and after training.

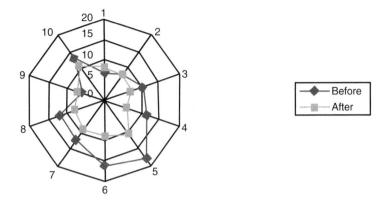

Figure 1.4   Radar graph for before and after training.

Table 1.4   Mileage per vehicle to reach minimal tread wear.

Vehicle	1	2	3	4
Tire A mileage	23,000	28,500	37,000	27,000
Tire B mileage	24,100	34,000	39,400	33,000

Average tire A mileage: 28,875
Range: 14,000
Average tire B mileage: 32,625
Range: 15,300
Difference in averages = 3,750 miles

on off-road vehicles. Four vehicles were fitted with both tires and driven in normal use until the tread reached a minimal level. The mileages achieved are shown in Table 1.4.

Question: The editors would like to know if tire B has a significant longer tread life than tire A.

You will notice that for each car, tire B outperforms tire A, on average by as much as 3750 miles. So, on this evidence alone, we would have to say tire B is better than tire A. But the average difference in performance of 3750 miles does not look all that impressive when we compare it to the ranges (14,000 and 15,300 miles for tires A and B, respectively.) Also, when I look at Figure 1.5, my intuition leads me to conclude that although there is certainly some difference in performance, it does not appear to be overwhelming. Still, I would say if the tires are priced equally, my preference

Tire

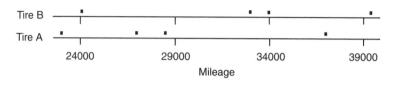

Figure 1.5   Dot plot for tire tread wear.

would be to buy tire B, and therefore my answer would be that tire B is better than tire A.

Note that in this example, we do not know anything about the vehicles, nor are we told about driving conditions; all we are told is that the tires were "driven in normal conditions," a rather vague statement. Yet it is known that tire wear is directly related to speed. For example, at 80 miles per hour (approximately 130 kph), a tire wears out 35% faster than at 60 miles per hour (100 kph). We can only assume the four vehicles are of a similar type (age, suspension, and so on.).This brings an interesting point about the comparison of averages versus the comparison of individual observations. Referring back to the original data, note that, as far as the owners of cars 2 and 4 are concerned, tire B is definitely better than A (5,500 and 5,000 miles, respectively, or about 17% to 19% better than tire A). Owners of cars 1 and 3 will not have the same strong opinion.

Example 1.4:   Suppose you conducted a customer satisfaction survey regarding the adequacy of your technical support service. Suppose further that your customer base can be broken down geographically into three regions. The nature and extent of these regions need not be considered for this example; in other words, the regions could represent three cities, three counties, three states, or three large geographical regions (for example, western states, central states, and eastern states). Table 1.5, known as a *contingency table*, summarizes the results from the survey. The total number of customers interviewed (N) is equal to 500.

Question: Is there a difference in customers' ranking (regarding the adequacy of technical service) across regions? Naturally, a statistical test known as a chi-square can be used to help us answer the question, but let us first see what can be learned from the data by simply looking at the numbers.

This example might be a little more difficult to resolve because the number of customers interviewed is not equal across all three regions. A total of 198 customers were interviewed from Region 2 (perhaps because it is the

Table 1.5 Customer satisfaction for technical support (N = 500).

	Adequacy of service			
	Inadequate	Barely adequate	Very adequate	Total
Region 1	75	54	12	141
Region 2	64	106	28	198
Region 3	28	82	51	161
Total	167	242	91	500

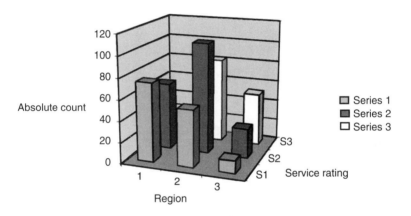

Figure 1.6 Three-dimensional frequency histogram by region and service rating.

largest region), whereas Region 1 only had 141 customers interviewed. Still, a pattern can be seen from the table. Hint: Look at the diagonal (75, 106, 51) or look at the three-dimensional chart (Figure 1.6). You may also want to compute row and column percentages. For example, 75 out of a total of 141 Region 1 customers, or 53%, said the service was inadequate. Similarly, out of the 167 customers who rated the service as inadequate, 75, or 45%, were from Region 1. You may want to compute the remaining row and column percentages; however, for this simple example, looking at the raw data should be sufficient to answer the question.

The three-dimensional chart shown in Figure 1.6 was produced using Excel Chart Wizard. Do the three regions rate adequacy of service the same? We revisit each one of these examples in Chapter 3.

1.2 OTHER GRAPHING TECHNIQUES: THE BOX PLOT DIAGRAM

The *box plot* diagram is another simple but yet informative diagram that can be used to summarize data. To explain how a box plot is prepared, let's first define the following terms:

> *Median* (q2): The median, also known as the second quartile, or q2, is a measure of central tendency. To find the median of n numbers, one must first rank the n number from low to high and apply the following simple formula:

$$\text{Median} = (n + 1)/2$$

If a fractional result is obtained, we make a linear interpolation between the two values corresponding to the two observations between which the fraction falls. Thus, referring back to Example 1, for the six numbers representing the mileage for Gasoline A (21, 19, 18, 20, 21, 21), we must first rank the values as follows:

$$18, 19, 20, 21, 21, 21$$

$$\text{Median} = (6 + 1)\ /2 = 3.5\text{th number}$$

This means the median is located at the 3.5th position. In other words, for this example, the median is the third value *plus* 50% of the difference between the third and the fourth values or $(20 - 21)/2 = 0.5$. Hence

$$\text{Median} = 20 + 0.5 = 20.5$$

> *First quartile* (q1): The first quartile (q1) is the $(n + 1)/4$ rank. Thus, for Gasoline A, $q1 = (6 + 1)/4 = 7/4 = 1.75$th position, meaning the first quartile is equal to $18 + 0.75(19 - 18) = 18.75$.

> *Third quartile* (q3): The third quartile (q3) is the $(3n + 3)/4$ rank. For this example, $q3 = (3 \times 6 + 3)/4 = 21/4 = 5.25$, which means the third quartile is the 5th (ranked) number plus 25% of the difference between the 5th and 6th numbers, or $21 + 0.25(21 - 21) = 21$.

Summarizing, we see that 50% of the values are below the median and 50% are above the median. A quarter of the values are below or equal to the first quartile and a quarter of the values are above the third quartile, which means at 50% the values must be within the interquartile range $= q3 - q1$. You may want to compute q1, q2, and q3 for Gasoline B. These results, along with other statistics, are shown in Table 1.6 of the descriptive statistics shown later. Finally, the vertical line extending from the box's hinge

Table 1.6 Descriptive statistics: mileage by gasoline.

Variable Gasoline	N	Mean	Median	StDev	SE Mean	Q1	Q3	Min	Max	Range
Mileage A	6	20.000	20.500	1.265	0.516	18.75	21.00	18	21	3
B	6	19.000	19.500	1.673	0.683	17.00	20.25	17	21	4

(that is, extending upward from the third quartile and downward from the first quartile) are known as whiskers. *Whiskers* extend to the lowest and highest observations that are inside the region defined by the following limits:

$$\text{Lower limit} = Q1 - 1.5\,(Q3 - Q1)$$

$$\text{Upper limit} = Q3 + 1.5\,(Q3 - Q1)$$

For this example we have for Gasoline A:

$$\text{Lower limit} = 18.75 - 1.5\,(21 - 18.75) =$$
$$18.75 - 1.5\,(2.25) = 15.375$$

$$\text{Upper limit} = 21 + 1.5\,(2.25) = 21 + 3.375 = 24.375$$

Because the lowest value for Gasoline A is 18, the lower whisker extends to 18 (which is well within the lower limit of 15.375). The highest value of 21 equals the third quartile and therefore there is no upper whisker. You may wish to compute the lower and upper limits for Gasoline B. Extreme values known as *outliers* (none for this example) are observations that fall outside the lower and upper limits. Outliers are represented with an asterisk (*). Although we do not yet know the meaning of "StDev" (standard deviation) and "SE Mean" (standard error of the mean; see section 3.1), we can make several observations:

1. For this example, the means are slightly lower than the medians. In fact, generally speaking, the mean is rarely equal to the median.

2. The standard deviation (1.265), standard error of mean (0.516), interquartile range (2.25), and range (3) for Gasoline A are lower than for Gasoline B (1.673, 0.683, 3.25, 4). All of these measures are measures of dispersion, and therefore it is reassuring to see that lower ranges imply lower interquartile ranges, lower standard deviations, and lower standard error of the means.

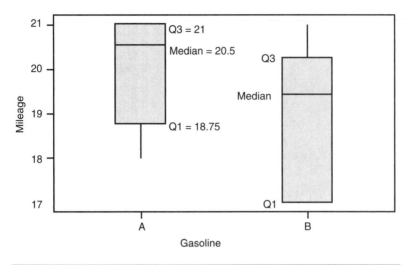

Figure 1.7   Box plot for Gasoline A versus Gasoline B.

We can now interpret the box plots shown in Figure 1.7. The box plot for Gasoline B is taller, as it were, than for Gasoline A because the interquartile range (or variation) is larger. Also, notice that the median for both box plots is toward the top of the graph and not in the middle. This indicates a certain amount of *skewness,* or lack of symmetry, in the data. This is particularly evident in the case for Gasoline A where three of the six values are 21s. When the median is *larger than* the mean (as it is in this example), the data are *negatively skewed* (that is, its tail is to the left). When the median is *less than* the mean, the data are said to *positively skewed* (that is, the tail is to the right). As we look at the two box plots, we can see a considerable amount of overlap between the two graphs, suggesting there is probably no difference in mileage performance. Using statistical jargon we would say we accept the *null hypothesis* of no difference.

Example 1.5:   One-way ANOVA. The set of numbers reproduced in Table 1.7 represent weekly sales (for a period of 10 weeks) in $1000 for four department stores.

Question: Is there a difference in sales between the stores?

To facilitate the analysis, the dot plots for each store (Figure 1.8), descriptive summary statistics (Table 1.8), and box plot diagrams are reproduced in Figure 1.9.

The box plots in Figure 1.9 reveal that Store 3 has the lowest interquartile range and Store 4 has the lowest median (and lowest mean) but the largest interquartile range (and hence the largest range, standard deviation, and standard error of the mean). If we compare the box for Store 3 with the box for

Table 1.7 Weekly sales ($1000) for four stores.

Store 1	Store 2	Store 3	Store 4
73	84	69	65
57	95	80	58
95	96	73	82
78	62	62	86
86	80	50	35
61	87	71	52
80	100	84	70
98	74	66	79
64	85	52	43
78	77	73	60
Average = 77	Average = 84	Average = 73	Average = 63

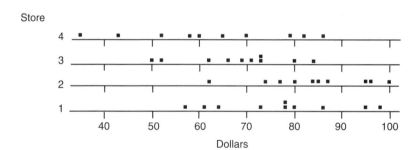

Figure 1.8 Dot plot of weekly sales by store.

Table 1.8 Descriptive statistics: weekly sales in dollars by store.

Variable	Store	N	Mean	Median	StDev	SE Mean	Minimum	Maximum	Q1	Q3
Dollar	1	10	77.00	78.00	13.74	4.34	57.00	98.00	63.25	88.25
	2	10	84.00	84.50	11.45	3.62	62.00	100.00	76.25	95.25
	3	10	68.00	70.00	10.95	3.46	50.00	84.00	59.50	74.75
	4	10	63.00	62.50	16.79	5.31	35.00	86.00	49.75	79.75

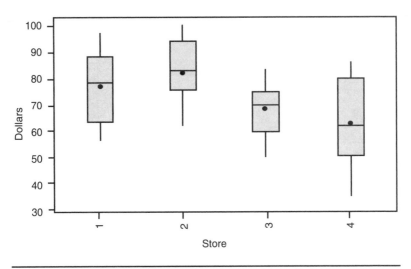

Figure 1.9 Box plot of weekly sales by stores.

Store 2, we notice the interquartile range for Box 3 is below the interquartile range for Box 2. In other words, the third quartile for Box 3 is less than the first quartile for Box 2. Or stated another way, 50% of the values for Store 2 are higher than 50% of the values for Store 3. A review of the dot plots will help you visualize how the data for Stores 2 and 3 are spread. Based on this observation, we might be tempted to conclude that the difference in sales between Store 2 and Store 3 is large enough to be considered different. A similar observation could be made for Box (Store) 4 and Box (Store) 2. In this case, however, the conclusion is perhaps not as clear cut because the interquartile ranges overlap slightly. Based on these observations, we could probably conclude that the data given here would indicate a difference in sales between some of the stores (between Store 3 and Store 2, for instance). Consequently, we would have to conclude that the sales amount between stores is not equal. Using statistical jargon. we would say we accept the *alternative hypothesis* of inequality (of sales).

Example 1.6: Two-way ANOVA (with and without replication). The numbers shown in Table 1.9 represent the number of defective pieces produced by four workmen *operating in turn* four different machines. Is there a difference in the performance of the workmen, and also, is there a difference in the performance of the machines? The statistical technique known as *two-way analysis of variance* can be used to answer these questions. However, because you presumably do not know how to perform a two-way analysis of variance, can you still answer the questions by looking at the data?

The best performance is by Workman D, who produced, on average, over the four machines, 21.75 defective pieces. The worse performance is

Table 1.9 Defective pieces by worker and machine.

	Worker A	Worker B	Worker C	Worker D	Average
Machine A	26	27	31	26	27.5
Machine B	19	21	27	18	21.25
Machine C	23	28	26	24	25.25
Machine D	22	26	25	19	23
Average Range	22.5 7	25.5 7	27.25 6	21.75 8	Grand average = 24.25

from Workman C, who produced 27.25 defective pieces. As for machines, the best machine is Machine B, with an average number of defective parts over the four workmen of 21.25 (vs. 27.5 for Machine A). To help visualize the problem, two dot plots are produced, one per workmen and the other per machines. The black dots on each graph represent the average number of defectives (see Figures 1.10 and 1.11). When we compare workers, it seems Workman 1 and Workman 4 form one group and Workman 2 and Workman 3 form another group. If we do a visual pairwise comparison of all four workmen, it would appear Workman 4 (the best on average) is better than Workman 3 (the worse on average) because his worse performance (26 defectives) is approximately equal to Workman 4's best performance (of 25 and 26 defective parts). Consequently, based on the comparison of Workmen 3 and 4, we could conclude that not all workers are equally competent.

When we look at the machine dot plot reproduced in Figure 1.11, we can see the best machine is A2. A pairwise comparison of all four machines indicates that the greatest difference (in the number of defective parts but also in the distance between the averages) is between Machine A2 and Machine A1. In fact, on closer inspection, we notice all workers produced their lowest number of defective parts when operating Machine A2 (19, 21, 27, and 18)! Consequently, based on these observations we could conclude something is different about Machine A2, and in fact it seems there is a worker-machine interaction because workers perform better on this machine.

The descriptive statistics (Tables 1.10 and 1.11) and box plots (Figures 1.12 and 1.13) reproduced here provide additional information that can facilitate the comparison in defective pieces between workmen and between machines. What do you observe and what are your conclusions regarding workmen to workmen performance and machine to machine performance? Are you more inclined to accept the null hypothesis of no difference in the number of defectives (per workmen and per machine), or the alternative hypothesis that states there is some difference among workers and/or among machines?

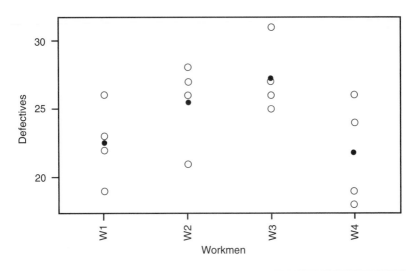

Figure 1.10   Dot plot of defective pieces by worker.

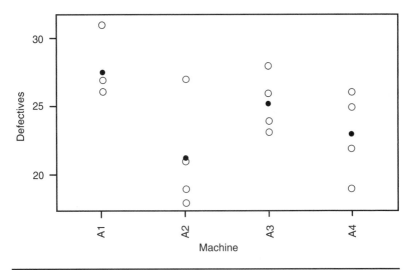

Figure 1.11   Dot plot of defective pieces by machine (A1-A4).

The contour plot diagram shown in Figure 1.14 represents yet another way to look at data. Contour plotting can be a useful mapping tool when we wish to visualize the variation of one variable (often called a *response variable*) across two other variables (in this example we are mapping the variation of defective pieces across worker and machine). The contour plot

Table 1.10 Descriptive statistics: defective pieces by workmen.

Variable	Workmen	N	Mean	Median	StDev	SE Mean	Minimum	Maximum	Q1	Q3
Defective	W1	4	22.50	22.50	2.89	1.44	19.00	26.00	19.75	25.25
	W2	4	25.50	26.50	3.11	1.55	21.00	28.00	22.25	27.75
	W3	4	27.25	26.50	2.63	1.31	25.00	31.00	25.25	30.00
	W4	4	21.75	21.50	3.86	1.93	18.00	26.00	18.25	25.50

Table 1.11 Descriptive statistics: defectives by machine.

Variable	Machine	N	Mean	Median	StDev	SE Mean	Minimum	Maximum	Q1	Q3
Defective	A1	4	27.50	26.50	2.38	1.19	26.00	31.00	26.00	30.00
	A2	4	21.25	20.00	4.03	2.02	18.00	27.00	18.25	25.50
	A3	4	25.25	25.00	2.22	1.11	23.00	28.00	23.25	27.50
	A4	4	23.00	23.50	3.16	1.58	19.00	26.00	19.75	25.75

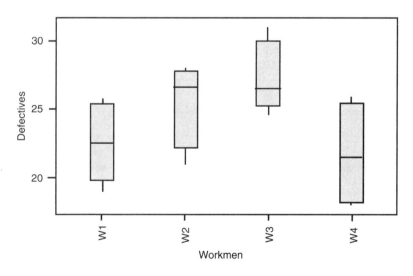

Figure 1.12 Box plots of defective pieces by workmen.

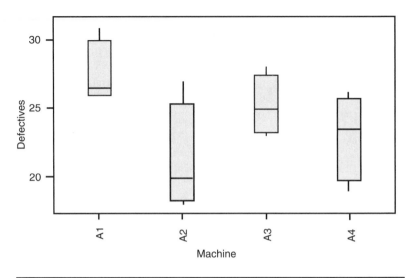

Figure 1.13   Box plots of defective pieces by machine.

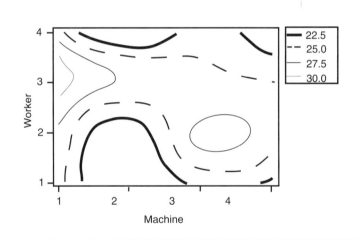

Figure 1.14   Contour plot for defective pieces.

should be read as a topographical sheet (assuming we know how to read such topographical sheets!). Although contour plotting should be used for continuous variables (that is, variables whose measurements are obtained via the use of an instrument), this example shows that contour plots can also be used (admittedly with some imagination), with discrete variables such as *workers* and *machines*.

represent lines of equal barometric pressure known as isobars. Similarly one can also use isotherms to prepare contour plots for surface temperature. Elevation, barometric pressure, temperature, and other measurements obtained on what is known as a continuous scale are ideally suited for contour plots. Because we are not looking at elevation (pressure or temperature) but rather number of defective pieces, the contour lines outline areas of equal defective pieces (that is, "isodefects"). As you can see from Figure 1.14, the "area" representing Worker 3 and Machine 1 has the highest number of defective pieces (30.0)—in topographical terms, this would represent a peak. Where are the valleys (of deficiencies)? It is clear from the contour plots that the best machine (with a "low" contour line of 22.5 defectives) is Machine 2. Even though the variable *Worker* is a discrete variable, the plot reveals that Worker 4 and Workers 2 and maybe Worker 1 are the best performers (you can confirm this by referring back to Table 1.9). Note: This example was shown to introduce the use of contour plots, and even though the surface variables are *not* continuous, the technique is robust enough to show it can be abused (as it was in this example) and still reveal meaningful results.

1.3 STANDARD DEVIATION AND STANDARD ERROR (OF THE MEAN)

It is now time to talk about two important statistical measures (actually one because the second is derived from the first), known as the *standard deviation*s and the *standard error* (of the mean). The standard deviations is a measure of spread or dispersion in a set of observations. Mathematically, the standard deviation is the square root of the average of the squared deviations from the mean (known as *variation*) or,

$$s = \sqrt{\frac{\sum_1^n (x_i - x\text{-}bar)^2}{n-1}} \text{ ; where x-bar } (\bar{X}) = \text{the average of n observations.}$$

The symbol $\sum_1^n$ means summation over n numbers. The x_i represents individual observations. This may sound complicated, but the following example will help clarify. If we return to our first example, we have the following set of numbers for Gasoline A and Gasoline B:

Gasoline A		Gasoline B
21	x_1	17
19		20

Continued

Continued

Gasoline A		Gasoline B
18	•	19
20	•	21
21		17
21	x_6	20
Average for A (Xbar$_A$) = 20		Average for B (Xbar$_B$) = 19

In this example we have six observations and thus n = 6. Each observation is symbolically represented by the letter x. Thus for Gasoline A, 21 represents x_1, 19 is x_2, and so on, up to 21 represented by x_6. You may wonder why the summation is divided by n − 1 instead of n. There are statistical reasons (relating to the lack of bias in the estimation) as to why this must be done. Note: One degree of freedom is used to compute the average from which the squared deviations are computed. That is why we divide by n − 1 instead of n. Suffice it to say, the division by n − 1 is required; however, notice that as the sample size n increases, the division by n − 1 instead of n becomes less and less significant. Table 1.12 summarizes the computations.

You should verify that the standard deviations for Gasoline A and Gasoline B are the same as the values reproduced in the descriptive statistics table (Table 1.6). The values 1.6 and 2.8 (the average of the squares of the deviations) is known as the *variance* (represented by the symbol s^2). One rarely refers to the variance of a variable simply because the unit of measurement is

Table 1.12   Computations for standard deviations for Gasoline A and Gasoline B.

$(x_i - \text{xbar}_A)$	$(x_i - \text{xbar}_A)^2$	$(x_i - \text{xbar}_B)$	$(x_i - \text{xbar}_B)^2$
21 − 20 = 1	1	17 − 19 = −2	4
19 − 20 = −1	1	20 − 19 = 1	1
18 − 20 = −2	4	19 − 19 = 0	0
20 − 20 = 0	0	21 − 19 = 2	4
21 − 20 − 1	1	17 − 19 = −2	4
21 − 20 = 1	1	20 − 19 = 1	1
n − 1 = 6 − 1 = 5	$\sum_{1}^{6}(x - xbar)^2 = 8$	n − 1 = 6 − 1 = 5	$\sum_{1}^{6}(x - xbar)^2 = 14$
	8/5 = 1.6 $s = \sqrt{1.6} = 1.2649$		14/5 = 2.8 $s = \sqrt{2.8} = 1.673$

(Table 1.6). The values 1.6 and 2.8 (the average of the squares of the deviations) is known as the *variance* (represented by the symbol s^2). One rarely refers to the variance of a variable simply because the unit of measurement is squared (not a convenient or intuitive value). For example, the variance for Gasoline A is 1.6 miles squared versus 2.8 miles squared for Gasoline B. It is more convenient and conventional to refer to the square root of the variance, which is, by definition, the *standard deviation*. Hence the standard deviation for the six mileages obtained with Gasoline A is 1.2649 miles (per gallon). The standard error of the mean is equal to the standard deviation divided by the square root of the number of observations (n):

$$\text{Standard error} = \frac{S}{\sqrt{n}}$$

From the table we can easily calculate the standard error for Gasoline A and Gasoline B. Because the square root of 6 = 2.449, we have standard error for A = 1.2649/2.449 = 0.516, which matches the value shown in Table 1.6. The standard error of the mean has a simple but revealing property. Notice that for a fixed value of the standard deviation S, the standard error of the mean decreases as the sample size n increases. Suppose, for example, that the standard deviation of 1.26 miles for Gasoline A was obtained for a sample of 25 cars (instead of the original sample of 6 cars). The standard error would decrease to $1.26/\sqrt{25} = 1.25/5 = 0.25$ instead of the 0.516 previously computed with a sample of 6 cars. If we increase the sample size to 100 cars (and assuming the same standard deviation of 1.26 would be obtained for these 100 cars), the standard error decreases to 1.26/10 = 0.126, and so on. Therefore, as the sample size increases, the standard error of the mean decreases; in other words, the estimate improves as the sample size increases.

1.4 EXPERIMENTAL ASSUMPTIONS

Until now, we have assumed *factors* such as drivers, type of car, type of terrain, and so on, were all equal or at least did not influence the variable being measured (for example, mileage, tire wear, and so forth). Suppose, however, we would like to be able to determine whether or not our assumption of "no influence" for each of these other factors is justified. How would we proceed? Ironically, to be able to assert that "other factors" are not important, we must design an experiment that will somehow measure or otherwise account for these factors. Let us return to our first example in which we contrasted the performance of Gasoline A versus Gasoline B. Suppose further that after some consultation with other experts it is decided the following six factors need to be investigated for their possible impact on the performance of gasoline:

1. Driving style

2. Type of car

3. Type of terrain

4. Type of tires

5. Tire pressure

6. Environmental conditions

Having identified the six factors, we next need to define how the factors will be defined; in other words, what is meant by "type of drivers," "type of cars," and so on. Notice also that the characteristic of each factor is itself different in that most factors are *qualitative,* whereas others are *quantitative.* For example, "driving style" is a qualitative characteristic. In contrast, "tire pressure" is a quantitative variable that can be measured. Finally, some factors such as "type of car" are too vague to be considered and may not even have an impact, particularly if the same model and year of car is used. Once a factor has been determined to be either qualitative or quantitative, we must next decide what characteristic (for qualitative factors) or values (for quantitative factors) we will assign to each factor. For example, for the qualitative factor "driving style," we must decide what type of driving styles to consider. For the quantitative factor "tire pressure," we must decide what tire pressure to select. One cannot select too many values, for as we will see, the more values selected, the more observations (that is, runs) need to be collected and the more expensive the experiment becomes. Let us see what happens if we only select two characteristics for each qualitative factor and two values for each quantitative factors:

1. Driving style (qualitative: aggressive vs. nonaggressive)

2. Type of car (qualitative but considered as unimportant, thus taken out)

3. Type of terrain (qualitative: flat vs. hilly)

4. Type of tire (quantitative: 15-inch diameter vs. 17-inch diameter)

5. Tire pressure (quantitative: 2 pounds below recommended pressure vs. 2 pounds above recommended pressure)

6. Environmental conditions (qualitative: rainy vs. dry)

These five factors (remember we have dropped factor 2, "type of car"), each at two *levels,* will generate 2^5, or 32, possible combinations, meaning we will need to collect 32 observations. If, as is often recommended, we also want to *replicate* the observations at least twice, we will need to collect another 32 observations for a total of 64 observations. If we increase the number of levels from two to three (for example, "flat," "hilly," and "mountain" for factor 3), the number of required observations jumps to $3^5 = 243$ times 2 for replication, or 486 runs—an expensive proposition! We return to these important issues in Chapter 4.

1.5 HOW TO COLLECT DATA

Now that we have selected our factors and the values (that is, levels) for each factor, how can we set up our experiment? Should we have the aggressive drivers drive on flat terrain using 15-inch tires set at low pressure on a rainy (or simulated rainy) condition and proceed systematically to all the other combination of settings, or should we select another approach? It turns out that statisticians came up decades ago with a methodology to optimize this type of experiment. We return to this topic in Chapters 3 and 4.

Example 1.6 elaborates further on a question first mentioned in Example 1.2 by introducing the concept of experimental design.

Example 1.6:   Suppose you work for the statistical department of a tire manufacturer. The research department has developed four kinds of rubber compounds used in the manufacturing of the tires. You have been asked to evaluate the possible effect of these four compounds on tire wear performance. How would you proceed?

Your first task should be to define how to measure performance. Performance will be measured as the thickness remaining on a tire after 1000 miles of driving; tread wear would be a logical measure of performance. You know that several factors (and combination of factors) may affect tire wear: weight of the car, type of surface, speed, type of suspension, tire position (such as front left, rear right), and so on. It is also true that one may control many of these factors by ensuring, for example, that all tires are inflated at the same pressure, the cars will be driven on the same surface (or terrain) during all tests, and the same type (model) of car will be used. You may wonder why the experimenter simply does not conduct the test using one car and one driver. Of course this may be possible, but then the results will only be valid for one car and one driver. Generalization would not be possible. It is therefore decided that because of limited budget (and also because I want to keep this example relatively simple), the test will be conducted using four cars and the tires will be mounted on four different wheel positions (a variation of this example often uses four cars and four drivers instead of four wheel positions.) Technically speaking, the cars and wheel position (or drivers, depending on the scenario) are not factors; rather they are often referred to as *nuisance variables*. For this experiment the dependent (or *response*) variable is thickness of tread, and the independent variable is the four kinds of rubber compound (that is, the four treatments) used in the construction of the tires. In addition, we have two nuisance variables: car and wheel position. Having defined the scenario, we can state the research question (the hypothesis) as follows:

Is tread thickness affected by the type of rubber compound?

The most efficient way to analyze this type of problem is the Latin-square design. Although the procedure for using Latin-square designs is a little cumbersome for designs greater than 4 x 4, these designs are efficient and pedagogically valuable to explain the importance of *randomization* when conducting experiments. However, because the topic of Latin squares is somewhat esoteric, it is relegated to Appendix A.

1.6 MEASUREMENT AND ENVIRONMENTAL CONDITIONS AS SOURCES OF ERROR

Besides controlling the nuisance variables of *cars* and *wheel position,* several other uncontrolled factors, or *noise,* can directly or indirectly affect tread wear. For example, if the front wheels are misaligned, tires will not wear evenly, which may in turn introduce an unknown bias to the measurement process. It is therefore important to ensure that all cars have their wheel alignment checked.

Tire pressure can also influence tire wear. All tires must therefore be properly inflated as per manufacturer recommendations. Because one or more gages can be used to measure tire pressure, this introduces yet another potential source of error. If only one gage is used, the accuracy and precision of the gage may introduce yet another source of error (random or systematic) and thus variation. If two or more persons are used to measure tire pressure, we have yet another source of variation: person-to-person variation.

Suppose that one of the cars, let us say Car a2, has a defective shock absorber at Wheel b3. This is likely to introduce a *systematic* source of error. The measurement of the tire wear is also subject to potentially several sources of errors and thus additional variation in the final measurement. As with the measurement of tire pressure, one could have a gage and or operator measurement error. For example, the gage used to measure tire wear may be faulty or the operator may not be using the gage properly, resulting in inaccurate and/or unreliable readings. All of these potential sources of errors are perhaps enough to discourage any amateur experimenter. If you are not discouraged by all these noise factors, you may well wonder how successful experiments are ever conducted. And yet, although all of the concerns just described regarding the various sources of errors are worth noting and minimizing as much as possible, they need not necessarily prevent us from conducting an experiment. Indeed, if we can ensure that all cars have a good wheel alignment, if only one (new) gage is used to measure all tire pressure, if the person using the gage has been trained to use the gages properly (that is, the pressure gage and the tread thickness gage), and if all shocks are checked before conducting the experiment, then we can assume the gage(s) will be accurate and precise—at least, accurate and precise enough for our (and most) needs and that all other noises have been controlled to the best of our ability.

The argument just presented could be challenged by some Six Sigma Black Belt purists who would suggest that prior to conducting any experiment one must first conduct a Gage Repeatability and Reproducibility study (or Gage R&R). These studies, which are reverently mentioned in most Six Sigma Black Belt courses, are particularly cumbersome and can often be costly to conduct. Gage R&R studies are aimed at determining whether or not the measurement process (which includes the instrument used and the operator(s) using the instrument to make the measurements) is capable of measuring an entity such as temperature, tire pressure, thickness of a parts, and so on, with enough precision (that is, precision that is not more than 20% to 25% of the magnitude of measurement). Because every measurement m consists of at least two components—the value being assessed plus an error component contributed in part by the instrument and the operator using the instrument—we could state that the purpose of a Gage R&R study is to allow an investigator to determine whether the noise (or error) in (or contributed by) the measurement system does not exceed approximately 20% to 25% of the actual measurement (see section 4.7.3 in Chapter 4 and the discussion in section 8.12.3 for further details).

1.7 CONCLUSION

The examples presented in this chapter consisted of small databases. The first example about gasoline performance consisted of only six measurements. Although other examples were introduced with slightly larger number of observations, these examples never exceeded more than 32 observations. Although it is true that with large data sets consisting of hundreds of observations it is difficult to visualize the database, it is nonetheless true that the use of simple graphs and data summarization tables are still very valuable to conduct a preliminary analysis of even large databases. Having introduced the importance and value of simple graphical techniques and data summarization statistics that are useful to not only see the data but also reach some preliminary, if not intuitive, conclusions regarding the validity of certain hypotheses, we now turn our attention to a more formal analysis known as statistical inference. In order to do so, it is necessary to first present some simple but fundamental notions of statistics; this is the subject of Chapter 2.

NOTES

1. Greg Gigerenzer and David J. Murray, *Cognition as Intuitive Statistics* (Hillsdale, NJ: Lawrence Erlbaum Associates, 1987), Chapter 3. The authors also make reference to Hermann von Helmholtz, who coined the term *unconscious inference,* a term associated with the concept of intuitive statistics. See also Gerd Gigerenzer, *Calculated Risks. How to Know When Numbers Deceive You* (New York: Simon & Schuster, 2002), and Gerd Gigerenzer et al., *The Empire of Chance. How Probability Changed Science and Everyday Life* (New York: Cambridge University Press, 1989).
2. I wrote "accept the null hypothesis" because some statisticians would state that one cannot "accept" a null hypothesis but can only "fail to reject it." Unfortunately, such an expression only confuses the novice, and also many authors routinely write about "accepting the null hypothesis."

2

Frequency Distributions

2.0 HISTOGRAMS AND THE NORMAL DISTRIBUTION

This chapter introduces a few of the fundamental principles of statistics, including some of important statistical theorems needed to understand many of the coefficients printed in statistical tables produced by statistical software packages. The following topics are discussed: frequency distributions and histograms, standardized Z transformation, the normal curve and its fundamental properties, as well as the chi-square and F distributions. The concepts introduced in this chapter are elaborated further in Chapter 3.

All data, be it political preferences, marketing studies to assess customer preferences, parts measurements to assess conformance to one or more specifications, anthropological measurements, pharmaceutical tests, or countless others, are known to follow certain types of frequency distribution. One of the traditional ways to represent the frequency distribution of a set of numbers graphically is the histogram.

The 80 measurements shown in Table 2.1 represent corrosion resistance for tin-plated steel. What is the frequency distribution of corrosion? The usual method to answer this question is to prepare a *histogram,* a pictorial representation of the frequency with which various values are distributed among chosen (or selected) intervals. The object of a histogram is to group a set of numbers into categories.

Histograms can easily be prepared using various statistical computer software packages or Microsoft's Excel. For example, the Data Analysis option found under the Tool tab in Excel allows one to create histograms. Even though histograms are easily drawn by computer software, it is important to know how they are prepared.

Table 2.1 Eighty corrosion resistance measurements.

0.72	0.92	0.92	**1.43**	0.83	0.48	0.65	0.78
0.48	0.96	0.72	0.48	0.83	0.49	0.78	0.96
0.88	1.03	0.78	1.12	0.83	0.78	0.83	1.06
1.23	0.18	0.96	1.18	0.48	0.55	0.97	1.21
0.94	0.38	0.73	0.65	1.36	0.47	0.72	0.77
0.79	1.26	1.06	0.90	0.77	0.35	0.78	0.77
0.88	1.20	0.71	0.95	0.91	0.64	0.73	1.09
0.83	0.78	1.04	1.33	0.47	**0.16**	0.57	0.65
0.64	0.65	**1.43**	0.63	0.79	1.00	0.92	0.45
0.48	0.79	0.97	0.57	0.95	1.12	0.70	1.05

Note: 1.43 is the maximum value and 0.16 is the minimum value.

For any data set, a histogram can be produced using the following five steps:

1. Compute the range of the data. The range is the difference between the maximum and minimum value. For our example, the range $= 1.43 - 0.16 = 1.27$.

2. Decide on how many *intervals,* or *classes* (k), the data needs to be grouped in. If you do not know how many intervals k to use, you can apply the following formula. (Note: Statistical software packages automatically determine the appropriate number of classes; however, they tend to overestimate the number of classes needed.)

   $k = 1 + 3.3 * \log_{10} n$, where n is the number of observations.

   For our example, we have n $= 80$ and k $= 1 + 3.3 * \log_{10}(80)$ $= 1 + 3.3 * 1.9 = 7.27$, or seven class intervals. The general guideline for the relationship between sample size and the number of intervals is as follows:

Sample size	Number of intervals
n	k
10	4
15	5
30	6

Continued

Continued

Sample size	Number of intervals
50	7
100	8
250	9
1000	11

3. Compute the range for each interval by dividing the range by the number of class intervals. For the example, we have $1.27/7 = 0.18$.

4. Compute the cell boundaries by adding 0.18 to the lowest value and continuing until you reach the highest value. The limits for the seven classes are as follows:

   a. $0.16 + 0.18 = 0.34$; hence the first interval ranges from 0.16 to 0.34; the midpoint for this interval is 0.25.

   b. $0.35 + 0.18 = 0.53$; for the second interval, the range is 0.35 to 0.53.

   c. $0.54 + 0.18 = 0.72$ (0.54–0.72)

   d. $0.73 + 0.18 = 0.91$ (0.73–0.91)

   e. $0.92 + 0.18 = 1.10$ (0.92–1.10)

   f. $1.11 + .0.18 = 1.29$ (1.11–1.29)

   g. $1.30 + 0.18 = 1.48$, (1.30–1.48)

   Summarizing, for each of the seven class intervals we have the following ranges:

   1 0.16–0.34

   2 0.35–0.53

   3 0.54–0.72

   4 0.73–0.91

   5 0.92–1.10

   6 1.11–1.29

   7 1.30–1.48

5. The final step is to count how many values fall within each of the intervals (hence the reference to frequency count).

Table 2.2 shows the frequency count, percentage, and cumulative percentage of the original 80 measurements. If we want to see what the histogram would look like for the seven categories defined in step 4, we need to recode the original 80 values. Table 2.3 shows the distribution of the recoded values (RecoCor) using the interval limits defined in step 4.

Table 2.2   Tally for discrete variables: corrosion.

Corrosion	Count	Percentage	CumPct
0.16	1	1.25	1.25
0.18	1	1.25	2.50
0.35	1	1.25	3.75
0.38	1	1.25	5.00
0.45	1	1.25	6.25
0.47	2	2.50	8.75
0.48	5	6.25	15.00
0.49	1	1.25	16.25
0.55	1	1.25	17.50
0.57	2	2.50	20.00
0.63	1	1.25	21.25
0.64	2	2.50	23.75
0.65	4	5.00	28.75
0.70	1	1.25	30.00
0.71	1	1.25	31.25
0.72	3	3.75	35.00
0.73	2	2.50	37.50
0.77	3	3.75	41.25
0.78	6	7.50	48.75
0.79	3	3.75	52.50
0.83	5	6.25	58.75
0.88	2	2.50	61.25
0.90	1	1.25	62.50
0.91	1	1.25	63.75
0.92	3	3.75	67.50
0.94	1	1.25	68.75
0.95	2	2.50	71.25
0.96	3	3.75	75.00
0.97	2	2.50	77.50
1.00	1	1.25	78.75
1.03	1	1.25	80.00
1.04	1	1.25	81.25
1.05	1	1.25	82.50
1.06	2	2.50	85.00
1.09	1	1.25	86.25
1.12	2	2.50	88.75
1.18	1	1.25	90.00
1.20	1	1.25	91.25
1.21	1	1.25	92.50
1.23	1	1.25	93.75
1.26	1	1.25	95.00
1.33	1	1.25	96.25
1.36	1	1.25	97.50
1.43	2	2.50	100.00
N = 80			

The histogram reproduced in Figure 2.1 represents the frequency distribution for the recoded corrosion variable. The diagram of Figure 2.2 represents the same histogram with a bell-shaped curve superimposed over it. The bar below the graph is a box plot of the data. The symmetric (bell) shape curve superimposed over the histogram is known as a *normal* (or *Gaussian*) *curve*; it is the most important distribution in statistics, and we return to it shortly.

This next set of data shown in Table 2.4 represents weekly orders received at a company over a period of 50 consecutive weeks. Notice how the histogram shown in Figure 2.3 is more skewed (with a tail to the right) than the previous histogram. Histograms skewed to the right are called *positively skewed.*

Table 2.3   Tally for discrete variables: RecoCor = recoded corrosion.

RecoCor	Count	Percentage	CumPct
1	2	2.50	2.50
2	11	13.75	16.25
3	15	18.75	35.00
4	23	28.75	63.75
5	18	22.50	86.25
6	7	8.75	95.00
7	4	5.00	100.00
N = 80			

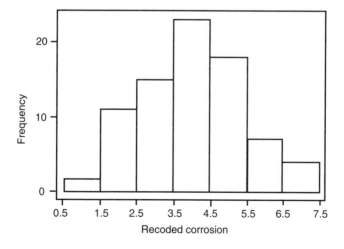

Figure 2.1   Histogram of 80 recoded corrosion measurements.

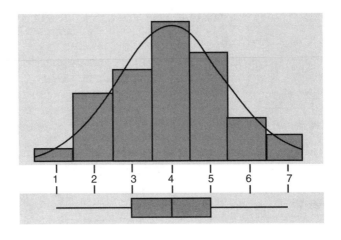

Figure 2.2 Histogram of 80 corrosion-resistant measurements with fitted normal curve.

Table 2.4 Weekly orders for 50 consecutive weeks.

41	52	46	42	46	36	44	68	58	44
49	48	48	65	52	50	45	72	45	43
47	49	57	44	48	49	45	47	48	43
45	56	61	54	51	47	42	53	41	45
58	55	43	63	38	42	43	46	49	47

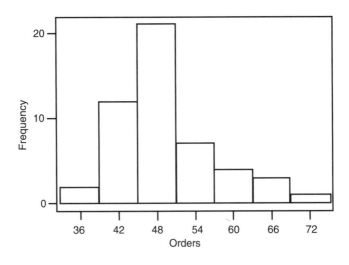

Figure 2.3 Histogram for orders.

2.1 PROPERTIES OF THE NORMAL DISTRIBUTION

Over the past 250 to 300 years, scientists in various fields of inquiry have noticed certain recurring shapes of frequency distributions. Some of these distributions have become so prevalent that they have acquired their own name: normal curve, negative exponential, Poisson, chi-square, and a host of others. Although each one of these distributions plays an important role in statistical theory, the normal curve, whose properties were investigated as early as the 17th century, is the cornerstone of statistical theory.

The two distributions shown in Figure 2.4 and Figure 2.5 were generated using a random number generator. Random number generators are provided by most statistical software and are also available with the statistical option of Excel. The two histograms reproduced here were generated by asking the software to generate two sets of 1000 normally distributed random numbers having the following characteristics:

Variable "Normal" has an average = 20 and a standard deviation = 1.26.

Variable "FatNorm" has an average = 20 and a standard deviation = 5.0.

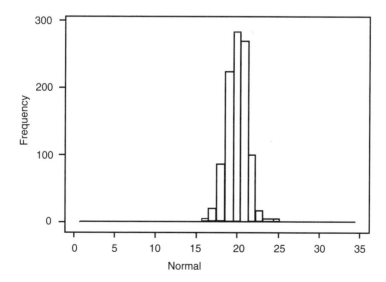

Figure 2.4 Normal distribution for average (X-bar) = 20 and standard deviation = 1.26.

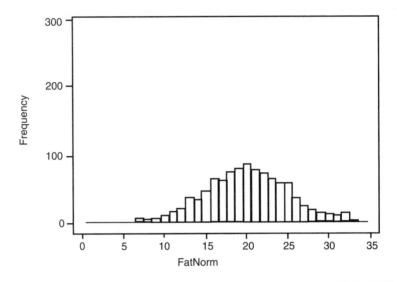

Figure 2.5   Normal distribution for average = 20 and standard deviation = 5.0. The number of categories was determined by the statistical software package, which uses a different formula than the $k = 1 + 3.3 * \log_{10} n$ formula introduced in section 2.0.

To facilitate the comparison, the two histograms are overlapped in Figure 2.6. Figure 2.7 represents an approximation of the normal curve fitted over the histograms (not shown). (Note: For all of the following histograms, the number of frequency intervals was computed by the statistical software using a formula that is different from the $k = 1 + 3.3 * \log_{10} n$ formula introduced in section 2.0.)

Notice that the graph (and histogram) for the variable FatNorm is wider than the graph for the variable Normal. This is to be expected because the standard deviation for FatNorm is four times the standard deviation for Normal. We can conclude from this simple observation that the shape of a normal distribution is affected by the standard deviation; the larger the standard deviation, the wider (fatter) the normal curve. The normal curve has the following interesting properties (see Figure 2.8).

1. Fifty percent of its area is spread between plus and minus 0.67 standard deviation.

2. Sixty-eight percent of its area is spread between plus and minus 1.0 standard deviation.

3. Ninety-five percent of its area is spread between plus and minus 1.96 standard deviations.

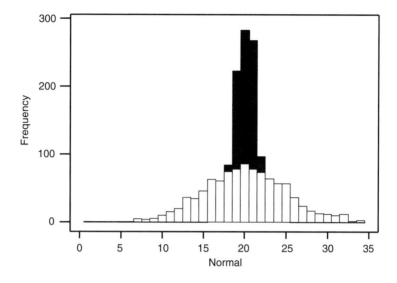

Figure 2.6   Overlap of Figures 2.4 and 2.5.

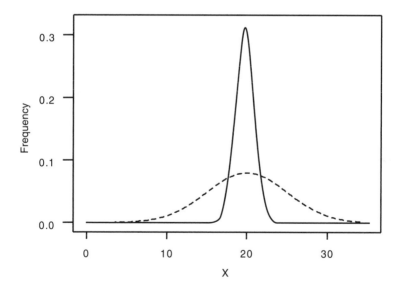

Figure 2.7   Smooth normal curves fitted over the two histograms of Figure 2.5 (histograms not shown).

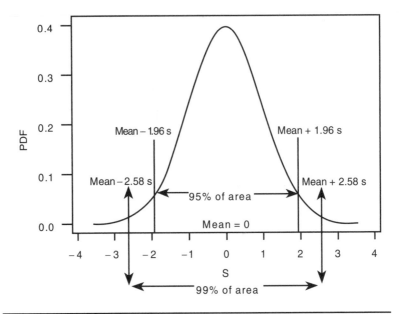

Figure 2.8   Properties of the standard normal distribution.

4. Ninety-nine percent of its area is spread between plus and minus 2.58 standard deviations.

To verify the properties just listed, the histogram of Figure 2.9 was produced by generating 500 normally distributed random numbers with a mean of 0 and a standard deviation of 1, a normal distribution centered at 0 and with a standard deviation of 1, known as the *standard normal distribution.*

The 500 random numbers were then recoded as follows (the five-digit significance is necessary because the random numbers were generated with five decimal points):

-4.00000 to $-2.58001 = -4$

-2.58000 to $-1.96001 = -3$

-1.96000 to $-1.00001 = -2$

-1.00000 to $0.00000 = -1$

0.00001 to $1.00000 = 1$

1.00001 to $1.96000 = 2$

1.96001 to $2.58000 = 3$

2.58001 to $4.00000 = 4$

A frequency tabulation of the recoded values is shown in Table 2.5. You will verify that 67.80% of the numbers fall between $+/- 1$ (standard

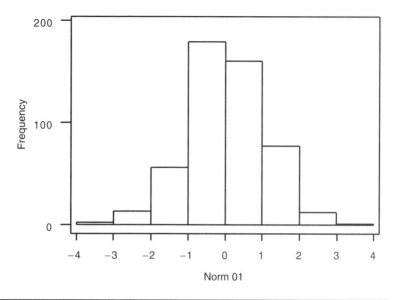

Figure 2.9   Histogram of 500 randomly generated numbers using a normal distribution centered at 0 and with a standard deviation of 1.

Table 2.5   Tally for discrete variables: recoded random variable.

Recoded	Count	Percentage
−4	4	0.80
−3	11	2.20
−2	56	11.20
−1	179	35.80
1	160	32.00
2	77	15.40
3	9	1.80
4	4	0.80
N = 500		

deviation), 94.4% are between +/− 1.96 standard deviations, and 98.4 are between +/− 2.58 standard deviations. One can also state that *for a normal distribution:*

1. Five percent of the values will fall *beyond* +/− 1.96 standard deviations.

2. One percent of the values will fall *beyond* +/− 2.58 standard deviations.

When testing hypotheses, the 5% and 1% values are referred to as alpha (α) values. These alpha values (that is, 5%, or 0.05, and 1%, or 0.01) are known as *level of significance,* whereas the associated Z-values (that is, 1.96 and 2.58) are known as *critical values* (see also Chapter 3).

An obvious question to ask is this: "Does the same property apply for a set of observations that is normally or (approximately normally) distributed but whose standard deviation is not equal to 1?" The answer is yes. In fact, the magnitude of the standard deviation and the value of the mean is of no consequence when one realizes that any set of normally distributed numbers X_i can be *standardized* to a standard normal distribution with mean = 0 and a standard deviation = 1. To standardize any set of numbers, one needs to:

1. Compute the average $\overline{X}$ (X-bar) and the standard deviation of the numbers.

2. Apply the following linear transformation: $Z_i = \dfrac{X_i - \overline{X}}{s}$ for each observation X_i.

The Z-values are equivalent to the standard deviations of the standard normal distribution; a Z-value of +1.96 is the same as a deviation of +1.96 standard deviation above the average (see Figure 2.10).

To standardize the 80 corrosion values, one needs to:

1. Compute the average (X-bar) = 0.816; the standard deviation (s) = 0.2679.

2. Transform each of the 80 values listed in Table 2.1 to a Z-value. For the first value we have

$$Z_1 = [0.72-0.816]/0.2679 = -0.3583$$

For the last value we have

$$Z_{80} = [1.05-0.816]/0.2679 = 0.8734$$

The complete set of Z-values is reproduced in Table 2.6. As you might expect, I did not compute the 80 Z-values (only the first and 80th values are shown here); rather the task was assigned to my faithful computer software. The standardized Z-values for the weekly orders listed in Table 2.4 are listed in Table 2.7.

If you were to compute the mean and standard deviation for the Z-values (Table 2.6 and 2.7), you will find out that for both tables the means are equal to 0 and the standard deviations are equal to 1. You will also recall that for a normal distribution, values greater than + or −1.96 (or approximately 2.0) only occur 5% of the time, whereas values greater than + or −2.58

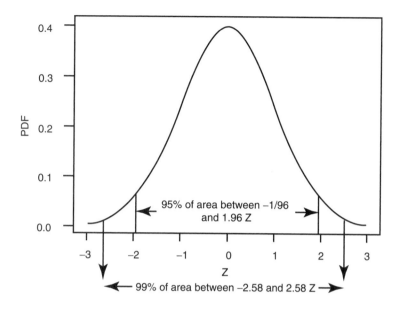

Figure 2.10   Normal distribution for Z-values (PDF = probability density function).

Table 2.6   Standardized Z-values for the 80 corrosion-resistant measurements of Table 2.1.

−0.35840	0.38827	0.38827	2.29229	0.05227	−1.25441	−0.61974	−0.13440
−1.25441	0.53761	−0.35840	−1.25441	0.05227	−1.21708	−0.13440	0.53761
0.23894	0.79894	−0.13440	1.13495	0.05227	−0.13440	0.05227	0.91094
1.54562	−2.37443	0.53761	1.35895	−1.25441	−0.99308	0.57494	1.47095
0.46294	−1.62775	−0.32107	−0.61974	2.03096	−1.29175	−0.35840	−0.17174
−0.09707	1.65762	0.91094	0.31360	−0.17174	−1.73975	−0.13440	−0.17174
0.23894	1.43362	−0.39574	0.50027	0.35094	−0.65707	−0.32107	1.02294
0.05227	−0.13440	0.83628	1.91896	−1.29175	−2.44909	−0.91841	−0.61974
−0.65707	−0.61974	2.29229	−0.69441	−0.09707	0.68694	0.38827	−1.36642
−1.25441	−0.09707	0.57494	−0.91841	0.50027	1.13495	−0.43307	0.87361

Note: For Z1 and Z80, the computed values using a pocket calculator are not identical to the Z values computed by the software: −0.3583 versus −0.3584, 0.8734 versus 0.87361.

Table 2.7   Standardized weekly order values.

−1.0636	0.39886	−0.3988	−0.9306	−0.3988	−1.7284	−0.6647	2.52613	1.19659	−0.6647
0.00000	−0.1329	−0.1329	2.12726	0.39886	0.13295	−0.5318	3.05794	−0.5318	−0.7977
−0.2659	0.00000	1.06363	−0.6647	−0.1329	0.00000	−0.5318	−0.2659	−0.1329	−0.7977
−0.5318	0.93068	1.59545	0.66477	0.26591	−0.2659	−0.9306	0.53182	−1.0636	−0.5318
1.19659	0.79772	−0.7977	1.86136	−1.4624	−0.9306	−0.7977	−0.3988	0.00000	−0.2659

only occur 1% of the time. Stated differently (and remembering that the normal distribution is symmetrical), we should expect approximately 2.5% of the values for each table to be greater than 2.00 and 2.5% of the values to be less than −2.00. For Table 2.6 we would therefore expect 2.5% of the 80 Z-values, or two Z-values, to be larger than 2.00. Scanning Table 2.6 we find that the following three values are greater than + 2.00: 2.29229 (twice), and 2.03096, which is very close to the expected number. For Table 2.7 we would expect 2.5% of the 50 Z-values or one Z-value to exceed + 2.00. Scanning Table 2.7 we find that three (and not one) values (2.12726, 2.52613, and 3.05794) exceed +2.00. Not quite what we expected. Let us see if we can verify the frequency for other intervals. For example, based on the properties of the normal curve, we know that 68% of the values should fall between +/− 1 standard deviation. We would therefore assume (because of symmetry) that approximately 34% of the 50 Z-values should fall between 0 and 1 standard deviation. Thirty-four percent of 50 Z-values = 17 values. If we count the number of Z-values that are in the range 0 to +1, we count only 12 Z-values and not 17. The prediction does not seem very good. What could have gone wrong? If we refer back to the histogram for the variable Orders, we will notice that it is skewed to the right (positive skew); the distribution does not appear to be normally distributed. Consequently, because the distribution for Orders is not likely to be normally distributed, the percentages above or below a specified standard deviation cannot be expected to match exactly those predicted for a normal distribution. The more skewed the distribution, the less accurate the estimated percentages will be.

2.2 FREQUENCY DISTRIBUTION OF AVERAGES

The symmetrical properties of the normal frequency distribution and of percentages associated with specific Z-values (for example, 1.64, 1.96, and 2.58) are, as we see in Chapter 3, extremely useful when estimating parameter and/or testing hypotheses. And yet, what can one do when the frequency distribution of the collected data is *not* normal? Does this mean the process of statistical inference must be abandoned? Of course not, for although it is true the assumption of normality is important when conducting statistical tests, not all statistical tests are based on the assumption that the data comes from a normal distribution, and, more importantly, some statistical tests are more tolerant of deviation from normality. In addition, statisticians have demonstrated that when the sample size (n) increases, the mean of nonnormal frequency distributions begin to approximate a normal distribution (see Chapter 3). Moreover, a very useful theorem known as the central limit theorem states the following:

> For a large sample size (n), the sampling distribution of the mean approximates that of a normal distribution.

Although there is not a formal definition of what constitute a large sample size, most statisticians agree a sample size of at least 30 is adequate. Thus if we have a large set of data from which we could take several samples of approximately 30 observations each and compute the average for each sample, we would observe that irrespective of the distribution of the original data, the distribution of the averages would approximate (or tend toward) a normal distribution. Because we only have 50 data points for Orders (see Table 2.4), we cannot easily obtain samples of 25 to 30 observations and compute the means for each sample. We could, however, randomize the 50 data points, sample 30 data points, compute an average, randomize the 50 points once again and sample another 30 points, compute the average, and repeat this process until we have enough averages to produce an histogram. If we were to do this repeated sampling (each time replacing and randomizing the original 50 data points), the central limit theorem tells us that, even though the distribution of the order data shown in Figure 2.3 is positively skewed and, therefore, not normal, the distribution of the averages obtained from a sample of size n (where n should be around 30) will be approximately normal. If we use sample sizes smaller than 30, a modified version of the normal distribution known as a *t-distribution* must be used (see Chapter 3).

This property of the averages is very valuable and the foundation of statistical inferences concerning the estimation of a population average (μ) that is derived from the computation of a sample average (X-bar). Because the Z transformation can be applied to any set of data, it can also be applied to averages, and consequently we can state that for sample size larger than 30, the Z-values

$$Z = (\text{X-bar} - \mu)/S_{\text{X-bar}}$$

are normally distributed. Note that in the equation we divide by the standard error ($S_{\text{x-bar}}$) of the mean and *not* by the standard deviation of the observations, where $S_{x\text{-bar}}$ is the *standard error* of the average and equal to the standard deviation divided by the square root of n (the number of observations).

Example 2.1:   Suppose 80 corrosion measurements reveal that the average corrosion is equal to 0.816 and the standard deviation is equal to 0.26. What would be the equivalent Z score?

Applying the preceding formula, we have Z= (0.81 − 0.85)/0.26/$\sqrt{80}$ = −0.034/0.029 = −1.17 (see Figure 2.11), which is within the +/− 1.96 range of values. Note: Remember that less than 5% of the values of a normal distribution fall beyond +/− 1.96 standard deviation, which means 2.5% of the values are greater than +1.96 and 2.5% of the values are smaller than −1.96.

2.3 DEGREES OF FREEDOM

Mathematically speaking, the *degrees of freedom* is the name given to the number of linearly independent observations occurring in a sum of squares (such as, for example, the sum of squares used to compute a standard deviation). Stated differently, one can define the number of degrees of freedom as the number of elements that can be chosen freely. Let us look at a simple

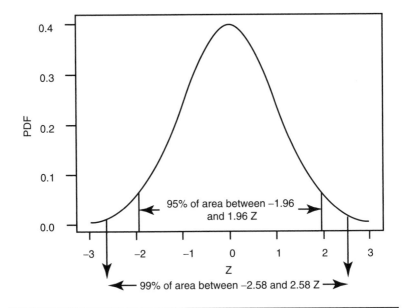

Figure 2.11   Computed Z-value assuming the average equals 0.85.

example. Suppose you are told to guess the color of a traffic light without looking at it. Traffic lights have three colors: red, yellow, and green. If you are told the light is not green and not red, you can conclude the light is yellow. We say a three-color traffic light has two degrees of freedom because once we are told two colors, we can deduce the third one. By extension, any variable that has n measurements is said to have n−1 degrees of freedom. Similarly, in order to compute the standard deviation (see Chapter 1), one must first compute the average and thereby consume one degree of freedom and then compute the squared deviation from the mean. This is why the squared deviation from the mean is divided by n−1 instead of 1.

2.4 CHI-SQUARE (χ^2) AND F DISTRIBUTIONS

Chi-square (denoted by the Greek letter χ^2) and F distributions are two distributions used when performing statistical tests on variances. The chi-square distribution is a positively skewed distribution, but, as you can see from the graphs in Figures 2.12 through 2.15, the skewness decreases as the number of degrees of freedom (df) increases. Figure 2.15 shows that for degrees of freedom greater than 30, the chi-square distribution approximates a normal distribution. One can also observe that the (critical)

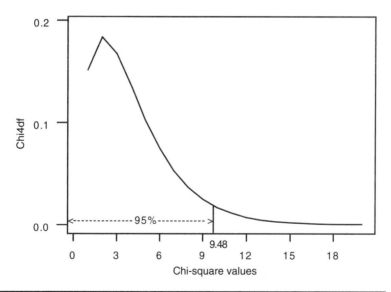

Figure 2.12 Chi-square distribution with 4 degrees of freedom (df) and the associated χ^2 value (9.48) corresponding to the 95th percentile.

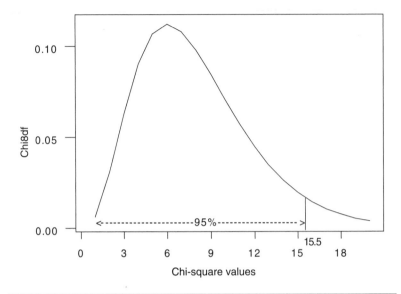

Figure 2.13 Chi-square distribution with 8 degrees of freedom (df) and the associated χ^2 value (15.5) corresponding to the 95th percentile.

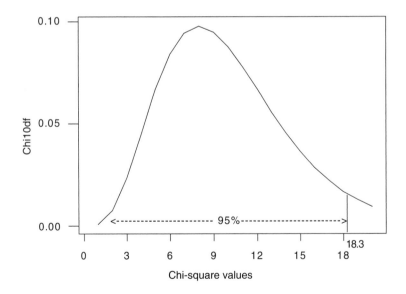

Figure 2.14 Chi-square distribution with 10 degrees of freedom (df) and the associated χ^2 value (18.3) corresponding to the 95th percentile.

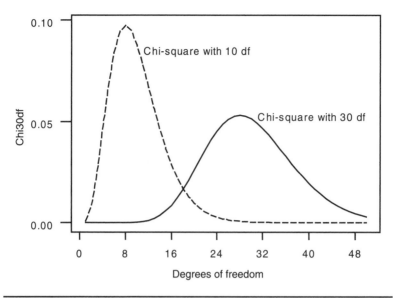

Figure 2.15   Chi-square distributions with 10 and 30 degrees of freedom.

chi-square value corresponding to the 95 percentile (that is, the chi-square value below which 95% of the values can be found) varies as the degrees of freedom increases (see Figures 2.12–2.14). Because it is not practical to produce a graph for every possible number of degrees of freedom, chi-square tables (not reproduced in this text but available in any statistical textbook) are available for reference. Naturally, statistical software can also compute the appropriate chi-square values for any percentage (90, 95, 99, and so on).

Statisticians have demonstrated that if a set of measurements X_i comes from a normal distribution, the square of these measurements X_i^2 as well as the sum of squares of these measurements is distributed as a chi-square distribution. If we recall (see Chapter 1) that the sample variance (S^2) is equal to the sum of squared deviations from the average (divided by $n-1$), it follows that the variance of a set of measurements that are normally distributed is itself chi-square distributed. One important test of statistical inference known as the analysis of variance (ANOVA) involves assessing and comparing the magnitude of the ratio of two variances to a critical value known as an F-value. F-values are derived from chi-square distributions. A well-known statistical theorem states that the ratio of two variables that are chi-square distributed with v_1 and v_2 degrees of freedom has an F distribution with v_1 and v_2 degrees of freedom.

Theorem: If X_1 and X_2 are independent variables having chi-square distributions with v_1 and v_2 degrees of freedom, then

$$Y = \frac{X_1/v_1}{X_2/v_2}$$

has an F distribution with v_1 and v_2 degrees of freedom. An important consequence of this theorem is that because variances (S^2) are chi-square distributed, the ratio of two variances (S_1^2/S_2^2) with v_1 and v_2 degrees of freedom, respectively, is distributed as an F distribution with v_1 and v_2 degrees of freedom. The proof of these theorems can be found in most statistical textbooks. The theorem will be demonstrated graphically with the use of computer-generated histograms. The histograms shown in Figures 2.16 and 2.17 (Chi4 and Chi5) were produced with the aid of statistical software by generating 250 random numbers with chi-square distributions with 4 and 5 degrees of freedom, respectively. Figure 2.18 (Chi4-5) is the ratio of Chi4 to Chi5 (Chi4-5 = Chi4/Chi5). Figure 2.19 (F4-5) was generated using 250 random numbers with an F distribution with 4 and 5 degrees of freedom. As can be seen, the Chi4-5 histogram closely resembles the F4-5 histogram.

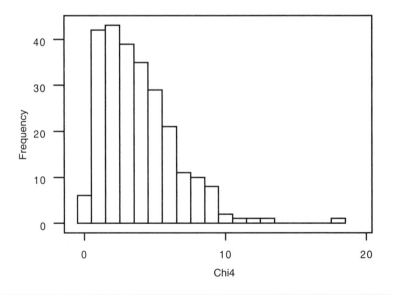

Figure 2.16   Chi-square distribution with 4 degrees of freedom.

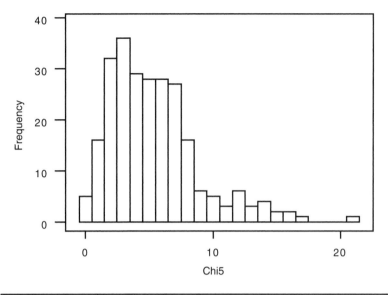

Figure 2.17 Chi-square distribution with 5 degrees of freedom.

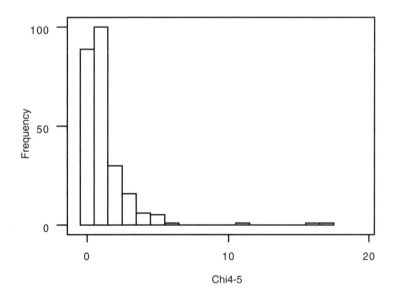

Figure 2.18 Ratio of two chi-square distributions (chi-square 4/chi-square 5).

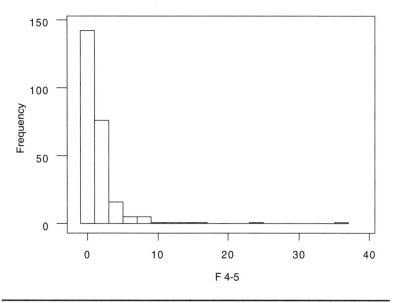

Figure 2.19   F distribution with (4, 5) degrees of freedom.

2.5 CONCLUSION

The distribution of data comes in various shapes and forms. The most important distribution, from which are derived many of the principles of statistical inference discussed in Chapter 3, is the bell-shape distribution, also known as the normal or Gaussian curve. The assumption of normality is the cornerstone of statistical inference. Other important distributions derived from the normal curve are the chi-square and F distributions. These distributions are important when testing for the homogeneity of variance among samples. The F distribution, used to perform variance ratio tests, is an integral part of any analysis of variance table produced by all statistical software packages whenever one performs analysis of variance experimentation. But before introducing the subject of analysis of variance, we must first understand the principles of statistical inference, the subject of Chapter 3.

3

Statistical Inference

3.0 INTRODUCTION

As is the case with learning a foreign language, before learning how to read statistical output table produced by computer software we must have some knowledge of the vocabulary as well as some understanding of the fundamental rules of statistical inference. *Statistical inference* is the process of arriving at conclusions or decisions concerning the *parameters* of *populations* based on information contained in samples.

3.1 POPULATION VERSUS SAMPLE

Before conducting any statistical analysis we must collect data. Once the data are collected we can either look at the raw data and attempt to detect patterns or, as shown in Chapter 1, analyze the data graphically. However, this practice of letting the data speak for themselves, as it were, becomes increasingly difficult as larger sets of observations and/or variables are collected. Although it is true that a graphical summary, such as a box plot for example, of 50 or even 500 or more observations for two, three, or even four variables is as equally effective as a box plot for 10 observations, the detection of patterns becomes more tedious if not impossible when the number of variables to analyze increases to five or more variables. Moreover, irrespective of the number of observations, the complexity of analysis increases exponentially as the number of pairwise combinations (between variables) increases. Consequently, although it is relatively easy to use graphs and data summarization techniques to detect patterns or perhaps differences among four or fewer variables, this technique becomes rapidly more tedious with six, seven, or more variables—hence the need to use other more powerful techniques of formal statistical inference that are better suited to analyze and summarize data.

Traditionally, when large sets of numbers (that is, large databases) are collected, most people find it more convenient to summarize the information contained in a set of numbers by computing well-known measures of central tendency such as the average and measures of variation such as the standard deviation. However, data analysts are faced with yet another dilemma. Suppose you are an explorer from the planet X27B and your superiors have asked you to calculate the average height of humanoids on the planet Gaia, more commonly known as Earth. The powerful computers have already counted the *population* and announced, much to your dismay, that 6.523 billion humans are on the planet. Your assistant has confirmed that your sophisticated lasers can measure each human in 1 second. Once the data are collected, the average height can be computed in one nanosecond or less. Although you have plenty of time (after all, you are a space traveler), you hesitate to invest the 6.523 billion seconds necessary to collect the data. That is about 207 earth years and you don't really want to stick around for that long. Besides, you have other solar systems to investigate before the end of the year. What can you do? Fortunately, your faithful computer reminds you that an appropriate *sample* of the earth's population could be used to *estimate* the height of the earth's population. This sounds like a great idea, and you immediately ask your computer to sample the population. Your computer replies, "How large should the sample be?" Because you are an explorer and not a statistician, you have no idea what the correct sample size should be: 6 million humans, 6,000, 600, or some other number. Fortunately, you have a powerful and all knowing computer, so you nonchalantly ask, "How large should the sample be?" to which the computer answers, "How precise do you want your estimate to be?" This is getting annoying. What is this estimate all about? You ask for some clarification. The computer explains that if you want to be 100% sure of the actual average height of humanoids, you would have to measure the whole population and compute the *mean* height of all 6.523 billion people. If you were to do so, you would have obtained what is known as the *population mean,* represented by the Greek letter μ (pronounced mu). However, because, in your infinite wisdom, you decided *not* to measure the whole population but rather to take a sample from the population, the best you can do is to *estimate* the *population mean* by computing a *sample average,* usually denoted by the letter X-bar. Naturally, or perhaps intuitively, you sense that the *larger the sample size,* the better the estimate, that is, the closer the estimated value for the sample average will be to the population mean (mathematically, the smaller the distance X-bar $- \mu$ will be).

Naturally, if you calculate an average to estimate the population mean (in this case, mean height) you cannot be 100% sure the average will be equal to the mean; you can only be a fraction of 100% sure, perhaps 90% or 95% sure. Stated differently, we can say that every time we take a sample to estimate a population mean (that is, the parameter μ), *or any other parameter,* we automatically introduce an *error* (e). Suppose, for example, that we are 95% sure of our estimate. That would mean there is a 5% chance the population mean will be outside our estimated range (in other words, that we have erred in our estimation). Graphically, we would have:

```
   X-bar – e              X-bar + e

   |– – – –  X-bar  – – – – – –|

   2.5%<------------- 95% -------------- >2.5%

              (1 – α)
```

This probability of committing an error, which for this example has been arbitrarily set at 5%, is referred to by statisticians as a *decision risk.* Statisticians have traditionally labeled this risk with the Greek letter alpha (α). Statistical inference is therefore the process of arriving at conclusions or decisions concerning the *parameters* of *populations* based on information contained in samples. This is interesting, but it still does not tell you how large a sample should be. The answer to this question will have to be postponed for a few more pages. The distinction between sample data or population data is not always as clear cut as depicted in our extraterrestrial example. Suppose you receive a lot of 1000 bricks and before accepting the lot you would like to measure the breaking strength of the bricks to ensure they meet some national standard. You could select at random 10 or 15 bricks and conduct your test. In this case the lot of 1000 bricks could be viewed as the population of bricks delivered to your facility. However, as far as the manufacturer of bricks is concerned, the lot of 1000 bricks is but a fraction (a sample) of the population of bricks produced in a week or in a month.

Suppose you are in charge of marketing research for a multinational corporation. You recently discovered a database that contains all of the sales records (say, eight years of data) for a particular store in California. If you wish to analyze the data, the California database represents the population of data. However, if you wish to generalize your study to all stores across every region, the database is only a sample of all records. Problems of statistical

inference are traditionally divided into two major subclasses: (1) problems of
point estimation and (2) problems of *testing hypotheses.*

3.2 POINT ESTIMATION

In sports, where statistics reigns, averages are routinely quoted or cited by
the press and the media in general. On any given day we can learn that the
average number of points scored by the star of a local basketball team is
24.2 or 18.4 (or any other number) points per game. We can also learn that
the same player averages 2.5 rebounds and 5.2 assists per game. And yet,
despite these impressive statistics, we can also read that the same player had
"an off night" and scored only 14 points in a recent game. Is such a relatively poor statistic (14 points) within the player's acceptable performance,
and moreover, what would be the player's "acceptable performance"? In
other words, how accurate or valuable are averages in predicting performance? Statistically speaking, statistics such as average score, average number of rebounds, or average number of assists are not very valuable unless
we also know the variation (or variance) for each of these statistics. In other
words, a player scoring on average 24.2 points per game may appear to be
better than a player scoring 18.4 points, but an astute coach would also like
to know how consistent or predictable each player is. Indeed, over a span of
30 games, for example, the player averaging 24.2 points may have had one
or more very bad games scoring below 10 points and one or two very good
games scoring over 40 points. In contrast, for the player averaging 18.4
points over 30 games, his worst game may have been 15 points and his best
game may have been 21 points (his range of 6 points is much smaller than
the first player whose range is 30 points). We would say the second player
is more predictable (reliable) than the first player. The predictability or reliability of an average (such as the scoring average for a basketball player)
can be estimated by computing a *confidence interval* around the average.
We could state, for example, that we are 95% confident the average score
for a player ranges between 14 to 34 points. How are *confidence intervals*
computed?

3.2.1 General Commentary

Whenever an average ($\overline{X}$, or X-bar) is calculated from a sample to estimate
a *population parameter* such as the population *mean* μ, X-bar is said to be
a *point estimate* of the parameter mu (μ). Think of a point estimate as
something like a vibrating or oscillating point whose exact location cannot
be estimated but only approximated. Although we cannot calculate the
exact value of a parameter, we can establish an upper and lower boundary

within which we are reasonably confident the value will be located. This boundary is known as a *confidence interval* of the mean. Returning to our basketball players, we see that the average score per player was based on a sample size of 30 games. The population of games would be equal to the total number of games played by a player in a season, for example. However, the population could also be defined to be the total number of games played over a player's career. In such a case it is unlikely the player would achieve the same scoring performance level over a period of 10 or 15 years, for example.

3.2.2 How Is the Confidence Interval for a Mean Computed?

Two formulas are used to compute the confidence interval for a population mean:

1. If the sample size (n) used to estimate the mean is greater than 30, the point estimation for the population mean μ is calculated as follows:

$$- Z_{\alpha/2} < \frac{\overline{X} - \mu}{s / \sqrt{n}} < Z_{\alpha/2} \tag{3.1}$$

or

$$\overline{X} - Z_{\alpha/2} \frac{s}{\sqrt{n}} < \mu < \overline{X} + Z_{\alpha/2} \frac{s}{\sqrt{n}} \tag{3.2}$$

In these equations, $\overline{X}$ (X-bar) is the average obtained from a sample size of size n. The $Z_{\alpha/2}$ values depend on the *level of confidence* we want to achieve (that is, 90%, 95%, 99%). The level of confidence is defined as $1 - $ alpha or $1 - \alpha$; α is referred to as the *significance level*. Thus, for example, when we said we want to be 95% confident of our estimate, this means that $1 - \alpha = 0.95$ or that the significance level $\alpha = 0.05$ (the two statements are identical). This also means we are 95% confident that $(\overline{X} - \mu) \sqrt{n}$ /s will be within -1.96 and 1.96. We therefore assume a 2.5% chance (0.025) that $(\overline{X} - \mu) \sqrt{n}$ /s will be greater than 1.96 and a 2.5% chance (0.025) that $(\overline{X} - \mu) \sqrt{n}$ /s will be less than -1.96.

Inequality (2) indicates that the standard error (SE) of the mean $\frac{s}{\sqrt{n}}$ is multiplied by a constant $Z_{\alpha/2}$. The most common values used for $Z_{\alpha/2}$ are 1.96 (for alpha (α) = 0.05 or $\alpha/2$ = 0.025, that is, 95% confidence) and 2.58 (for alpha (α) = 0.01 or $\alpha/2$ = 0.005, that is, 99% confidence).

The most frequently used $Z_{\alpha/2}$ values are:

for 90% confident or α = 0.10, $Z_{.05}$ = 1.64

for 95% confident or α = 0.05, $Z_{.025}$ = 1.96

for 98% confident or α = 0.02 , $Z_{.01}$ = 2.33

for 99% confident or α = 0.01, $Z_{.005}$ = 2.58

2. If the sample size (n) used to estimate the mean is less than 30, the standard error of the mean is multiplied by a different constant known as a t value:

$$\bar{X} - t_{\alpha/2,\,n-1}\, \frac{s}{\sqrt{n}} < \mu < \bar{X} + t_{\alpha/2,\,n-1}\, \frac{s}{\sqrt{n}} \qquad (3.3)$$

We cannot as easily suggest values for $t_{\alpha/2,\,n-1}$ because, unlike the constant $Z_{\alpha/2}$, the $t_{\alpha/2,\,n-1}$ values varies according to the degrees of freedom (df), which is equal to the sample size (n) minus 1 (or n − 1) (see Table 3.1 for a list of some T-values). Fortunately, statistical software selects the appropriate T- (or Z) value based on the sample size and the alpha level.

Example 3.1: Suppose that over a period of 30 games, the average and standard deviation for the two basketball players are:

Player 1: Average (X-bar$_1$) = 24.1, standard deviation (s$_1$) = 10

Player 2: Average (X-bar$_2$) = 18.4, standard deviation (s$_2$) = 2.5
Sample size n = 30 (games). Square root of 30 = 5.47.

What is the 95% confidence interval of the mean for Player 1 and Player 2? Because the sample size n is equal to 30, we can use the $Z_{0.025}$ value of 1.96 for the 95% confidence interval.

Confidence interval for the mean score for
Player 1: 24.1 − 1.96 * (10/5.47) = 20.5

24.1 + 1.96 * (10/5.47) = 27.6

20.5 < μ < 27.6

Based on our sample of 30 games, we can be 95% confident that the mean score for Player 1 will vary between 20.5 and 27.6 (essentially between 21 and 28) points per game. Verify that for Player 2 the 95% confidence interval is 17.5 < μ < 19.1. What would be the 99% confidence

Table 3.1   Sample of T-values of $t_{\alpha/2}$ for α = 0.10, 0.05 and 0.01 significance levels.

Degrees of freedom (n − 1) where n = sample size	$t_{0.05}$ for 90% confidence	$t_{0.025}$ for 95% confidence	$t_{0.005}$ for 99% confidence
4	2.132	2.776	4.604d
5	2.015	2.571	4.032
9	1.833	2.262	3.250
10	1.812	2.228	3.169
14	1.761	2.145	2.977
15	1.753	2.131	2.947
19	1.729	2.093	2.861
20	1.725	2.086	2.845
25	1.708	2.060	2.787
Infinity	1.645	1.960	2.576

Note that as the sample size increases to infinity, the T-values for the 90%, 95%, and 99% confidence converge to 1.64, 1.9,6 and 2.58, which are equal to the Z-values. In other words, for sample sizes larger than 30, the t distribution approximates the normal distribution from which the Z- values are derived.

interval? Notice that the interval will be wider if you want to be 99% sure the Z-value is 2.58 versus 1.96 for the 95% interval. Increased certainty must be exchanged for a wider confidence interval.

Summary: The sample average ($\overline{X}$) and the sample standard deviation (s) are used to obtain a point estimate of the population mean (mu = μ). The point estimate is bounded by the upper and lower limits of the confidence interval. These limits vary depending on the level of confidence desired.

Exercise: If the preceding averages and standard deviations were obtained for 15 (instead of 30) games, we would have to use the tabulated t values listed for 15 − 1 = 14 degrees of freedom ($t_{0.025}$ = 2.145 for the 95% confidence interval). The 95% confidence interval would be slightly wider, which is logical because the statistics were obtained from a smaller sample size; the smaller the sample size, the greater the uncertainty.

3.3 HYPOTHESIS TESTING

Hypothesis testing is concerned with decisions or conclusions concerning assumed values of (population) parameters. Suppose, for example, that you wanted to know if a new training method was effective in reducing the number of assembly errors. Historical data shows that prior to training the weekly average for the number of errors is 87.5 errors/week. After training, the weekly average dropped to 73.8. You would like to know if this drop in the average can be attributed to the new training method or if it is only attributed to chance, that is, random events. In the case of the basketball players cited earlier, we might be interested in knowing whether the superstar who averages 24.1 points per game is truly (statistically) better than the player averaging 18.4 points per game.

Every data analysis and hence statistical problem can be stated in terms of hypotheses. There are two types of statistical hypotheses: *null hypotheses* (H_o) and *alternative hypotheses* (H_a). The null hypothesis (H_o) is the hypothesis of "no difference." Examples of null hypotheses would be:

1. There is no difference in the assembly rate between Operator A and Operator B.

2. The production process is in control; in other words, there has been no change in the process. This statement could be quantified by stating that the process (still) operates at some preestablished but stable value, for example, 15.6.

3. The number of weekly errors has not changed since a new procedure was implemented.

4. There is no customer preference between Product A and Product B.

5. There is no difference in the precision between two measuring instruments.

For each of the preceding five null hypotheses (H_o), we can formulate the following alternative hypotheses (H_a):

1. There is a difference in the assembly rate between Operator A and Operator B.

2. The process is not in control, or the process no longer operates at 15.6 (that is, the process has shifted).

3. The number of weekly errors has changed since the new procedure was implemented.

4. Customers prefer Product A over Product B (or vice versa).

5. There is a difference in precision between the two measuring instruments.

Notice that each of the preceding statements could be stated with more precision as follows:

1. The assembly rate for Operator A *is better* than the assembly rate for Operator B (or vice versa).

2. The process operates at a value *greater than* 15.6, or the process operates at less than 15.6.

3. If you suspect the new procedure is an improvement, you could state that the number of weekly errors has decreased.

4. You could state that customers prefer Product A by as much as 30% (or vice versa).

5. Instrument A is *more precise* than Instrument B (or vice versa).

There are two types of null and alternative hypotheses: *simple or exact* and *composite or inexact*. A simple hypothesis, whether it is a null or an alternative hypothesis, states exactly what the value of a statistic might be. For example,

1. The assembly rate is equal to 15 units per hour.

2. The process operates at 15.6.

3. The number of weekly errors is equal to 23 per week.

4. Fifty percent of customers prefer Product A.

5. The difference in precision between the two instruments is equal to 0 (there is no difference).

Any hypothesis that is not a simple hypothesis is a *composite* hypothesis. For example,

1. The assembly rate is less than 15 units per hour (or is greater than 15 units per hour).

2. The process operates at a value that is greater than 15.6 (or less than 15.6).

3. The number of weekly errors is less than 23 (or greater than 23).

4. More than 50% of customers prefer Product A (or vice versa).

5. Instrument A is 1.5 times more precise than Instrument B (or vice versa).

Whenever an alternative hypothesis is formulated to state that a statistics is either greater than (>) or less than (<) some value, the hypothesis is said to be *one sided*. More specifically, for hypotheses stated as "greater than," we say it is an *upper* or *right-tailed test*. For "less than," we say it is a *lower* or *left-tailed test*. If the alternative hypothesis states that a statistic is "not equal to" (≠) some value, we say it is a *two-tailed* test.

Here are some examples:

1. H_0: Assembly rate = 15 units

    H_a: Assembly rate ≠ 15 units (two-tailed test) (there is a difference in the assembly rate)

    Or H_a: Assembly rate is greater than (>) 15 units (upper or right-tailed test)

2. H_0: Process = 15.6 (the process is in control)

    H_a: Process ≠ 15.6 (two-tailed test—the process is out of control and correction action should be taken)

    Or H_a: Process < 15.6 (left-tailed test—the process is below target value and is also out of control).

Other examples:

3. You wish to test the strength of a rope (or of a cable). You want the rope to have a mean breaking strength of at least 1000 pounds. A supplier sends you a roll to test its strength. You formulate the following hypotheses:

    H_0: Mean strength < 1000 pounds; don't buy the make.

    H_a: Mean strength > 1000 pounds; buy the make.

3.4 HOW TO TEST A HYPOTHESIS: STATISTICAL INFERENCE

1. State the null hypothesis H_0 and the alternative hypothesis H_a.

2. Select the appropriate statistics (that is, mean or variance-standard deviation) that needs to be tested and select the appropriate *test statistics* (for instance, Z- or T-values, chi-square value, F-value, and so on; see later for clarification). With each test statistic comes a series of assumptions associated with the test (that is, normality, independence of error terms and linearity assumptions of the error term for ANOVA, and so on, for other tests). In most everyday applications we can usually assume these assumptions are valid, and even if they are not valid most statistical tests are robust

and thus can tolerate some deviations. We must recognize, however, that in some cases certain assumptions are violated by the data and in such instances the assistance of a statistician may be required to see if the data may be mathematically transformed to better fit the underlying assumptions of a particular test.

3. Decide on the *level of significance* alpha (α) and the sample size N. The traditional values for alpha are 0.05 or 0.01. The sample size will vary depending on a host of conditions associated with the nature of the experiment and the need for precisely estimating the parameters in question. Invariably, the sample size is usually associated with cost-related issues such as sampling cost (that is, cost of obtaining data), time, available resources, confidence in a supplier, past performance of a supplier, and so on. Statistical software can be used to compute a sample size; however, in most applications, the experimenter is either given a set of numbers or, because of budgetary or other practical constraints often relating to scheduling, can only select a smaller than desired sample size; in other words, you "get what you can."

4. Collect your sample data and compute the sample statistic(s).

5. Compute the appropriate test statistics as defined from number 2 (T-value(s), Z-value(s), chi-square value(s), and F-value(s), for instance). We can either compare the value of the test statistics to a critical value as shown is section 4.2 or use step 6.

6. Look up the probability value (P) for the test statistics. Before the age of computers (and still today), the probability was determined by simply looking up probability values in the appropriate statistical tables (for example, normal distribution, T-values, chi-square values, binomial values, F-values, or Poisson values). Today, these probability values are computed automatically by statistical software.

7. Once the probability has been computed, apply the following decision rule:

   a. If the (computed) probability is *less than* the significance level alpha, reject the null hypothesis H_o (in other words, accept H_a).

   b. If the (computed) probability is greater than the significance level alpha, accept H_o. Note: In all of the examples presented in this chapter, the level of significance alpha is arbitrarily set to the traditional value of 0.05.

3.4.1 Types of Statistical Hypothesis Tests (Test Statistics)

Although dozens of statistical tests are available, only a few tests are reviewed in this section. These tests cover approximately 75% to 80% of all situations encountered by most data analysts. If you understand these few tests, you can apply the principles to any other statistical test. Most applications of data analysis are concerned with:

1. Tests concerning means (t-test for sample size less than approximately 30 or z-test for sample size > 30)

2. Tests concerning the difference between means (z-test for n > 30 or t-test and paired t-test for n < 30)

3. Tests concerning variances (F-test)

4. Tests concerning proportions (binomial test for n < 100 or z transformation for n > 100)

5. Tests concerning differences among k proportions (chi-square)

6. Tests concerning contingency tables (chi-square)

7. Tests of goodness of fit (chi-square)

8a. Tests between one or more response (or dependent) variable(s) and one or more independent variables (regression analysis) or more generally, use of:

8b. Design of experiments or use of the general linear model:

   • One-way ANOVA

   • Two-way or N-way ANOVA

   • Factorial designs and fractional factorial designs

   • Central composite designs

These eight conditions are summarized as follows:

What you need to test	Type of statistical test
The value of a mean.	t-test if n < 30; z-test if n > 30.
The difference between two means.	If n < 30, t-test for independent samples and paired t-test for paired samples (see examples). Z-test is n > 30.
Equality of variances.	F-test.
The value of a proportion.	If n > 100, use a z transformation from smaller sample sizes; use binomial distribution.
The difference among k proportions.	Chi-square.

Continued

Continued

What you need to test	Type of statistical test
Contingency tables.	Chi-square.
The difference between more than two means.	One-way analysis of variance.
Whether two variables have an effect on a mean. Can be extended to N variables.	Two-way analysis of variance. N-way analysis of variance.

3.4.1 Errors and Risks in Hypothesis Testing

Whenever a null hypothesis is accepted or rejected on the basis of a sample, there is always a risk of making a wrong decision. Although some statisticians would remind us that one cannot technically accept a null hypothesis but only fail to reject it, I have found that this expression tends to confuse people. Consequently, I retain the expression *accept the null hypothesis*. In fact, whenever hypotheses are tested for statistical significance, we are always exposed to two possible types of errors: (1) the sampling data could lead an experimenter to reject the null hypothesis when in fact it should have been accepted (Type I error), and similarly (2), one could accept the null hypothesis when in fact it should have been rejected (Type II error). These two types of errors are summarized in Table 3.2.

Committing a Type I error, or alpha risk (in other words, rejecting H_o when it should be accepted), is also known as the *significance level* and is denoted with the letter alpha (α). Committing a Type II error has no specific name and is simply known as the beta (β) risk. For a fixed sample size α and β vary inversely, that is, as alpha increases, beta decreases. It may be helpful to know that committing a Type I error is also known as the *producer's risk,* whereas a Type II error is known as the *consumer* (or *customer*) *risk.* Consequently, whenever a supplier (manufacturing or service) wants to test a null hypothesis (for example, that a process is in control), the producer

Table 3.2   Type I and Type II errors in decisions.

	H_o is true	H_a is true
Accept H_o	Correct decision	Type II error (β)
Accept H_a	Type I error (α)	Correct decision

runs the risk of concluding that the process is out of control when in fact the process is in control. Similarly, from the point of view of the consumer or customer purchasing parts or components from the same process, the customer risk is that the supplier wrongly states the process is in control when in fact it is out of control. The fact that the supplier wrongly states the process is in control does not mean the supplier is lying about the capability of the process; rather it simply confirms that any decision based on sampling data is subject to some form of risks. When only the α risk is specified, it is usually set at some conventional value such as 0.05 or 0.01. When H_o is rejected at $\alpha = 0.05$, we say the result is statistically significant, and when H_o is rejected at $\alpha = 0.01$, we says the result is "highly significant." Moreover, when a null hypothesis (H_o) is rejected at a significance level of $\alpha = 0.05$, it only means that based on the sample data we could expect rejection of a *true null hypothesis* only 5% of the time *in the long run*. In other words, if we were to conduct several identical experiments over a certain period of time, we would be expected to *wrongly reject* the null hypothesis 5% of the time (that is, reject the hull hypothesis when in fact it should have been accepted). There is no answer as to what is the correct or ideal value for alpha (α). One can only suggest that if an erroneous rejection of H_o is deemed costly or subject to serious consequences, one should set α to a small value (usually 0.05 or even 0.01 or smaller). If, however, an erroneous acceptance of H_o can be costly or serious, the α risk should be set higher and β should be set at a lower value (lower than α, that is). Unfortunately, cost estimates are often subjective in that a producer and a consumer will rarely, if ever, agree on their assessment or perception (real or imaginary) of a risk—hence the difficulty associated with determining the so-called correct alpha and beta risks.

3.4.2 Alpha and Beta Risks and Sample Size: An Example (Advanced Section)

After several days of monitoring a drilling process using the well-known technique of control charts, a process engineer has established that the process is in control if the average diameter (measured in millimeters) is within the range 74 +/− 0.03. The standard deviation of the process has been established to be 0.01. The process engineer would like to know how large a sample he should take if management is willing to assume an alpha risk of 0.002 of mistakenly stopping the process and a beta risk of 0.005 of mistakenly leaving the process when the process average is off by 0.03 mm. Formulating the problem in terms of statistical hypotheses we have:

H_o: Process is in control when the mean diameter is equal to 74 (that is, $\mu_0 = 74$).

H_a: Process is not in control if the mean diameter is less than 73.97 or greater than 74.03.

Having stated the alpha (Type I) and beta (Type II) risk, the process engineer would like to know the minimum number of parts that would need to be sampled to determine the process status (that is, in control vs. out of control). You will have noticed that for this example, the alpha risk (α) is set at 0.002, which is substantially smaller than previously selected values of 0.05. Why such a small value was selected is explained at the end of this section. Also, the beta risk (set at 0.005) is two and a half times the alpha risk. This simply means that, as far as the supplier is concerned, wrongly rejecting the null hypothesis (process in control) is more important (or costly) than wrongly rejecting the alternative hypothesis (process in out of control)—naturally, the customer of the parts would probably want to restate these risks, but we cannot go into these arguments. Figure 3.1 is a graphical representation of the problem. Interpreting Figure 3.1: Because the null hypothesis states the process is in control when the mean diameter is equal to 74 mm and is *not* in control when the mean diameter is greater than $74 + 0.03 = 74.03$ (μ_2) or less than $74 - 0.03 = 73.97$ (μ_1), we have a two-sided condition, which means the alpha level of 0.002 must be divided by 2, or $0.002/2 = 0.001$, as shown at both extremities of the central normal curve of Figure 3.1 [see also Equation (3.4)]. Similarly, because the process can be out of control either at the upper end or lower end, a Type II error can be committed if the average mean falls within the lower end beta region of the right curve or the upper beta region of the left curve [see Figure 3.1 and Equation (3.5)]. However, this error of the second kind is only committed if H_o is accepted when H_a is true, and therefore the beta value of 0.005 need not be divided by two. In order to be able to compute the sample size, we need to recall from Equations (3.1) and (3.2) in section 3.2.2 that the confidence interval for a mean is:

$$\mu_0 - Z_{alpha/2} * \frac{\sigma}{\sqrt{n}} \leq \bar{X} \leq \mu_0 + Z_{alpha/2} * \frac{\sigma}{\sqrt{n}} \qquad (3.4a)$$

where μ_0 is the assumed population mean under the null hypothesis. If the null hypothesis is true it can be wrongly rejected (hence committing a Type I error equal to α), if $\bar{X}$ is greater than or less than a critical value defined by the following inequalities (in other words, if $\bar{X}$ falls within the alpha region defined to the left and right side of the central curve):

$$\bar{X} \geq \mu_0 + Z_{alpha/2} * \frac{\sigma}{\sqrt{n}} \text{ or if } \bar{X} \leq \mu_0 - Z_{alpha/2} * \frac{\sigma}{\sqrt{n}} \qquad (3.4b)$$

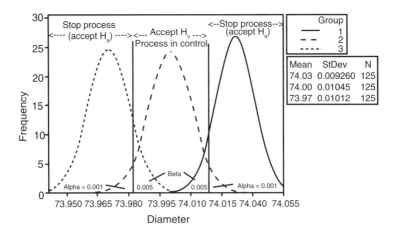

Figure 3.1 Testing of the null hypothesis $\mu_0 = 74$ (central normal curve) versus the alternative hypothesis represented by the left and right curves $\mu_1 = 73.97$ and $\mu_2 = 74.03$.

Under the alternative hypothesis (and referring to Figure 3.1), a similar argument can be presented, and we see that if the alternative hypothesis is true (that is, if the mean diameter is represented by either the left or right curve of Figure 3.1), it can be wrongly rejected (hence committing a Type II error) when

$$\bar{X} \geq \mu_1 + Z_{1-\text{beta}} * \frac{\sigma}{\sqrt{n}} \text{ or if } \bar{X} \leq \mu_2 - Z_{\text{beta}} * \frac{\sigma}{\sqrt{n}} \qquad (3.5)$$

where μ_1 and μ_2 are the hypothesized lower and upper means under the alternative hypothesis. From Equations (3.4) and (3.5), we can select any appropriate pairs of equations to solve for the sample size n.

Using a statistical software program or a Table of Areas under the Normal Distribution (found in any statistics textbook), we know that for $\alpha/2 = 0.001$, $Z_{0.001} = 3.09$. Similarly, for $\beta = 0.005$, $Z_{0.005} = 2.58$.

The null hypothesis states that $\mu_0 = 74$.

The alternative hypothesis states that $\mu_1 = 73.97$ or $\mu_2 = 74.03$ (or more generally that $\mu_0 \neq 74$).

Standard deviation $\sigma = 0.01$.

To calculate the sample size n and calculate the critical values, we only need to equate the appropriate set of inequalities defined by Equations (3.4) and (3.5). If we select the left side of the Figure 3.1, identified in bold letters in Equations (3.4) and (3.5), we have

$$74 - 3.09 * \frac{0.010}{\sqrt{n}} = 73.94 + 2.58 * \frac{0.010}{\sqrt{n}}$$

Solving for the square root of n, we have $\sqrt{n} = 1.89$ or n = 4. The critical values are

$$74 - 3.09 * (0.010/2) \leq \bar{X} \leq 74 + 3.09 * (0.010/2) \text{ or } 73.985 \leq \bar{X} \leq 74.015$$

using Equation (3.4). You could also use Equation (3.5).

Therefore the decision rule would be as follows: take a sample of 4 parts and compute the average diameter. If the average diameter is between 73.98 and 74.015, the process is in control; if the average diameter is less than or equal to 73.98 or if the average diameter is greater than or equal to 74.015, the process is out of control and will need to be adjusted. Remember that this decision is subject to the risk that alpha = 0.002 and that beta = 0.005. Why was the alpha level set at 0.001? As we have seen, an alpha level of 0.001 is equivalent to a Z-value of 3.09, which is essentially equal to the well-known plus or minus three sigma upper and lower control limit values used in control charts. The three sigma control limits are therefore (nearly) equivalent to a one-sided alpha value (or Type I error) of 0.001. Consequently, the standard control limits generated for most control charts are very conservative vis-à-vis the Type I error; in other words, the odds of stating the process is out of control when in fact *it is in control* is set to a very low probability. If the control limits are brought closer to the mean, that is, if we were to use 2.5 or 2.6 sigma values, the Type I error would increase but the Type II error would decrease. If the economic consequences of allowing a process to operate in an out-of-control condition is significantly larger than the cost of investigating and eliminating so-called special causes that are responsible for out-of control conditions, then we should consider setting control limits at less than the traditional three sigma limits.

3.4.3 Computation of the Z Statistics for n > 30

Null Hypothesis H_o: μ = some value usually referred to in statistical books as μ_o

You have three options for the alternative hypothesis:

Alternative H_a: $\mu > \mu_o$

Alternative H_a: $\mu < \mu_o$

Alternative H_a: $\mu \neq \mu_o$

Compute $Z = \dfrac{(X\text{-}bar - \mu_0)\sqrt{n}}{s}$ or, because $s/\sqrt{n}$ is the standard

error of the mean, this is equivalent to dividing $(X\text{-}bar - \mu_0)$ by the standard error of the mean. Note: The formula to compute Z for large

population is usually written $Z = \dfrac{(X\text{-}bar - \mu_0)\sqrt{n}}{\sigma}$ where σ is the stan-

dard deviation for the population. However, because in most cases of data analysis the standard deviation of the population is not known (unless one has a substantial amount of historical data, as may be the case with control charts, for instance), one must estimate the population standard deviation σ with the sample standard deviation s as shown in the first equation.

1. For alternative H_a: $\mu > \mu_0$, if $Z \geq Z_\alpha$ accept H_a (where $\geq$ means "greater than or equal to"). Thus for α (alpha) equal to 0.05 (a typical value), $Z_{0.05}$ is equal to 1.64. Consequently if $Z \geq 1.64$, reject H_o and accept H_a; otherwise accept H_o.

2. For alternative H_a: $\mu < \mu_0$ if $Z \leq -Z_\alpha$ accept H_a (where $\leq$ means "less than or equal to"). Thus if $Z \leq -1.64$, accept H_a; otherwise accept H_o.

3. For alternative H_a: $\mu \neq \mu_0$ if $Z > Z_{\alpha/2}$ or $Z < -Z_{\alpha/2}$, accept H_a; otherwise accept H_o. Remember that in this case (two-sided hypothesis), for $\alpha = 0.05$, $Z_{\alpha/2} = 1.96$.

All of this may look complicated, but the following example demonstrates how easy it is.

3.5 TESTS CONCERNING MEANS (Z-TEST FOR SAMPLE SIZE > 30)

Example 3.1:   In one of our earlier examples you were asked to decide whether or not a supplier supplied parts that were within a corrosion specification of no more than 0.75. To verify the supplier's claim, the quality engineer tested (or looked at) the test reports for the last 80 deliveries (see Table 2.1). The following hypotheses are formulated:

H_o: Mean corrosion (μ) = 0.75 (μ_0)

H_a: Mean corrosion > 0.75 (that is, we suspect the corrosion values to be larger than the specifications)

The alpha (significance) level is set at 0.05. Because the sample size n = 80, a one-tailed Z-test can be used. The alternative hypothesis H_a is a one-sided upper-(right) tailed test; thus according to paragraph 1 of section 3.4.3, if the calculated Z is $\geq Z_{0.05} = 1.64$, we must reject the null hypothesis H_o. Table 3.3 was generated using statistical software. The mean = 0.816; the constant we wish to compare the mean to is $(\mu_o) = 0.75$. The standard error of the mean equals the standard deviation (s) 0.2679 divided by the square root of 80 (which is equal to 8.94), or $0.2679/8.94 = 0.0300$.

$$Z = (0.816 - 0.75)/0.030 = 2.2$$

Because $Z = 2.2$ is greater than $Z_{0.05} = 1.64$, we must reject H_o and accept H_a. The same conclusion can be reached by reading the P (probability) value (see step 7 in section 3.4). The value of 0.014 listed under the heading P(robability) is the probability of obtaining a Z-value as large as 2.2. Because the probability (0.014) is less than alpha = 0.05, we must reject the null hypothesis H_o and accept the alternative hypothesis H_a. The mean corrosion value, estimated by the average computed from a sample of 80 tests, exceeds the specification.

How is the 95% lower confidence bound computed? Remember that in this case the hypothesis test for the mean is one sided (upper tailed). H_a states that the mean is greater than 0.75, so we do not need to divide alpha (α) by 2. We only need to know if the lower confidence bound of the mean contains the value 0.75. If it does, we must accept H_o (however, we already know H_o is rejected). Because alpha was set to 0.05, we know from section 3.2.2 that $Z_{0.05} = 1.64$. And therefore using the left half of the inequality in Equation (3.2) from section 3.2.2 we have:

$$\bar{X} - Z_{0.05} * (s/\sqrt{n})$$

$0.816 - 1.64 * 0.03 = 0.816 - 0.0492 = 0.7668$ (which is
equal to the 95% lower bound value listed in Table 3.3)

Table 3.3   One-sample Z: corrosion.

Test of mu $(\mu) = 0.75$ vs. mu $(\mu) < 0.75$
The assumed sigma = 0.2679

Variable	N	Mean	StDev	SE Mean
Corrosion	80	0.8160	0.2679	0.0300

Variable	95.0% Lower Bound	Z	P(robability)
Corrosion	0.7667	2.20	0.014

Table 3.4   One-sample Z: corrosion.

Test of mu (μ) = 0.75 vs. mu (μ) not = 0.75						
The assumed sigma = 0.2679						
Variable	N	Mean	StDev		SE Mean	
Corrosion	80	0.8160	0.2679		0.0300	
Variable			95.0% Confidence Interval		Z	P(robability)
Corrosion			(0.7573, 0.8747)		2.20	0.028

If we were not sure of the direction of the alternative hypothesis (in this case higher), we could have formulated the hypothesis as H_a: Mean corrosion ≠ 0.75. Table 3.4 shows how the probability (P) would be affected by this reformulation of the alternative hypothesis.

The null hypothesis would still be rejected, but notice how the Probability has now doubled to 0.028 instead of 0.014. Why? (Hint: two-tailed test versus one-tailed test.) Notice that the 95% confidence interval (CI) for Corrosion (0.7573, 0.8747) does not include the null hypothesized value 0.75, which is why the null hypothesis is rejected.

Exercise: Verify that the 95% confidence interval is indeed (0.7573, 0.8747) (use Equation (3.2) in section 3.2.2). What would be the 99% confidence interval?

3.5.1 More Examples

1. A marketing research study claims that the average commute to work for a resident of Riverside County is 22,500 miles per year. A recent survey of 100 Riverside County drivers showed that the average commute was 20,750, with a standard deviation of 3250 miles. You wish to test the hypothesis that the average commute as stated by the research study is indeed 22,500 versus the alternative hypothesis that the average commute is not equal to 22,500.

   H_o: Mean commute = 22,500 (exact or simple null hypothesis)

   H_a: Mean commute ≠ 22,500 (inexact or composite alternative hypothesis)

2. The Quality Assurance Department sampled eight steel beams and found the average compressive strength to be 54,312 psi with a standard deviation of 486 psi. How would you test the hypothesis that the true compressive

strength from which the sample was obtained is 55,000 psi against the alternative hypothesis that it is less?

H_o: Mean compressive strength $= 55,000$ psi

H_a: Mean compressive strength $< 55,000$ psi

3. A production process is considered to be under control if the parts it makes have a mean length of 35.50 mm with a standard deviation of 0.45 mm. To determine whether or not the process is under control, each morning a process engineer takes a sample of 40 parts. Should the process be adjusted if on a particular morning the process engineer obtains a mean of 35.62 mm and a standard deviation of 0.49 mm?

H_o: Mean part length $= 35.50$mm

H_a: Mean part length $\neq 35.50$mm or H_a: Mean part length > 35.50

4. A food buyer for a restaurant chain invites suppliers of canned vegetables to submit samples for testing. One of the quality characteristics investigated by the buyer is accuracy of the weight (as stated on the label). If a submitted sample of six cans from one supplier has a drained weight of 250.3, 249.6, 248.4, 247.9, and 250.3 grams, can the buyer assume the average weight is at least 250 grams per can?

3.6 TEST CONCERNING DIFFERENCES BETWEEN MEANS (Z-TEST OR T-TEST AND PAIRED T-TEST)

Example 3.2: In Chapter 1 two types of gasoline were compared using a variety of graphs. Because we would like to compare whether or not there is a difference in mileage performance between two independent samples (Gasoline A vs. Gasoline B) and the sample size is only six, the appropriate test is a t-test.

1. H_o: Mean mileage for Gasoline A $=$ Mean mileage for Gasoline B

or

H_o: $\mu_A = \mu_B$

H_a: Mean mileage for Gasoline A $\neq$ Mean mileage for Gasoline B or

$H_a: \mu_A \neq \mu_B$

2. The appropriate statistics will be the means. The test statistics will be a t-test.

3. The *level of significance* alpha (α) is set at 0.05. Because the sample size is N = 6, we must use a t-test. We assume for now there is no difference in the variances between the two types of gasoline.

The data are collected and entered into the statistical software. Steps 5 and 6 outlined in section 3.4 are performed by the statistical software and reproduced in Table 3.5.

Because the P-value = 0.270 is greater than 0.05, we must accept the null hypothesis; there is no difference in the performance between A and B (just as we had suspected from our intuitive approach). You will have noticed that the degrees of freedom (df) is equal to 10 and yet only six observations were obtained (for each gasoline). There are 5 degrees of freedom for Gasoline A and 5 degrees of freedom for Gasoline B for a total of 10 degrees of freedom (see section 3.6.1).

Comment: Notice that because standard deviations for Gasoline A and Gasoline B are almost equal, 1.26 versus 1.67, we can assume the square of the standard deviations, namely the variances, are equal. Our assumption of equality of the variances between the two samples seems justified (for further details, see Example 3.6).

Example 3.3:   The marketing research department of a computer store that provides services over the Internet claims the weekly expenditure of Californians exceeds the weekly expenditure of Washingtonians by at least $25 per week. To test this claim a random sample of 25 purchasing orders from California and 25 purchasing orders from Washington is selected for the last five days. The results from the survey are shown in Table 3.6. Formulate your hypothesis and verify the claim (see section 3.6.1 for an explanation of pooled standard deviation [StDev]).

Table 3.5   Two-sample t-test and CI: Gasoline A, Gasoline B.

	N	Mean	StDev	SE Mean
Gas A	6	20.00	1.26	0.52
Gas B	6	19.00	1.67	0.68

Difference = mu (μ) Gas A − mu (μ) Gas B
Estimate for difference: 1.000
95% CI for difference: (−0.908, 2.908)
T-test of difference = 0 (vs. not =): T-value = 1.17, P-value = 0.270, DF = 10
Both use pooled StDev = 1.48

Table 3.6 Expenditure for the week of March 8, 2004: California versus Washington.

California	Washington
380	319
288	324
475	333
367	339
330	302
406	347
445	331
284	323
370	375
345	359
346	344
342	304
389	338
449	319
405	317
360	255
426	329
337	319
362	297
439	310
434	358
435	376
425	347
459	355
383	303

H_o: California Expenditure − Washington Expenditure = \$25
H_a: California Expenditure − Washington Expenditure > \$25

We still set our alpha level = 0.05. The alternative hypothesis is a one-sided (left) test. Because the sample size (n) is only 25, we will need a t-test. Because the two populations are independent (that is, Californians vs.

Washingtonians), we will need to conduct a two-sample t-test (and not a paired t-test). Table 3.7 assumes the variances for Californian and Washingtonian expenditures were equal. However, upon reviewing the standard deviations for California and Washington (51.9 vs. 26.8) (see Table 3.7), it was decided this assumption of equality of variance was perhaps not justified. A second set of computations was performed based on the assumption that the variances are not equal (see results in Table 3.8). Comparing the results from both tables, we can see that the results are almost identical and the conclusion remains the same. What can you conclude? What do the P-values of 0.003 in Table 3.7 and 0.004 in Table 3.8 tell you? Do you accept the null hypothesis (H_o) that states the difference in expenditure is equal to $25, or do you accept the alternative hypothesis (proposed by the Marketing Department) that suggests Californians spend on average more than $25 per week than Washingtonians?

Table 3.7   Two-sample t-test and CI: California, Washington (assuming equal variance).

	N	Mean	StDev	SE Mean
California	25	387.2	51.9	10
Washington	25	328.9	26.8	5.4

Difference = mu (μ) California − mu (μ) Washington
Estimate for difference: 58.3 (difference between 387.2 and 328.9)
95% lower bound for difference: 38.7 (see section 3.6.1)
T-test of difference = 25 (vs. >): T-value = 2.85, P-value = 0.003, DF = 48
Both use pooled StDev = 41.3 (see section 3.6.1)

Table 3.8   Two-sample t-test and CI: California, Washington (assuming unequal variance).

	N	Mean	StDev	SE Mean
California	25	387.2	51.9	10
Washington	25	328.9	26.8	5.4

Difference = mu (μ) California − mu (μ) Washington
Estimate for difference: 58.3
95% lower bound for difference: 38.6
T-test of difference = 25 (vs. >): T-value = 2.85, P-value = 0.004, DF = 35

3.6.1 How Are the Values Presented in Table 3.7 Computed?

The pooled standard deviation is equal to

$$Sp = \sqrt{\frac{(n_1 - 1)s_1^2 + (n_2 - 1)s_1^2}{n_1 + n_2 - 2}} \qquad (3.6)$$

The T-value is computed as follows:

$$t = \frac{X\text{-}bar_1 - X\text{-}bar_2 - \delta}{\sqrt{\frac{(n_1 - 1)s_1^2 + (n_2 - 1)s_1^2}{n_1 + n_2 - 2}}\sqrt{\frac{1}{n_1} + \frac{1}{n_2}}} \qquad (3.7)$$

where n_1 and n_2 are the sample sizes for each sample here and both values are equal to 25; s_1^2 and s_2^2 are the variances (that is, square of the standard deviations) for each sample, and δ is equal to the difference we wish to test—this is usually equal to 0, but in this example $\delta = \$25$ and the X-bars are the averages for each samples (here equal to 387.2 and 328.9, respectively).

Variance for California is equal to the square of 51.9, or 2693.61

Variance for Washington = 718.24

Replacing these values in Equations (3.4) and (3.5) we have

$$Sp = \sqrt{\frac{24(2693.61) + 24(718.24)}{25 + 25 - 2}} = \sqrt{\frac{81884.4}{48}} = 41.3.$$

Notice that 48 is the number of degrees of freedom printed in Table 3.7.

$$t = \frac{387.2 - 328.9 - 25}{\sqrt{\frac{24(2693.61) + 24(718.24)}{25 + 25 - 2}}\sqrt{\frac{1}{25} + \frac{1}{25}}}$$

or

$$t = \frac{33.3}{41.3\sqrt{\frac{2}{25}}} = 33.3/11.68 = 2.85$$

You will notice that the number of degrees of freedom shown in Table 3.8 is different from the number reported in Table 3.7 (35 vs. 48). If the assumption of equality of variance between the two populations cannot be made, a complex formula (not reproduced here) must be used to compute the degrees of freedom. Fortunately, the t-test is robust to inequality of variance. In other words, even if the variances are not equal and a t-test is performed under the assumption of equality of variance, the difference in results (as evidenced in this example) is minimal and does not affect the conclusion.

Example 3.4 (Paired t-test): A doctor at a hospital wants to know if there is a systematic difference in the blood pressure readings obtained with two different instruments. He selects 10 patients and measures their blood pressure using two different instruments (A and B) (see Table 3.9). Note: If you cannot relate to this example, you can modify the scenario. For example, you could say a quality engineer wants to know if the same measurement is obtained with two calipers (or scales). Instead of 10 patients the quality engineer would select 10 parts and measure, for example, the length of each one with Caliper A and Caliper B. The readings could represent length in millimeters (instead of blood pressure).

H_o: The difference (D) in readings obtained from each instrument is equal to 0.

H_a: The difference (D) in readings obtained from each instrument is different from 0.

More specifically we would have:

H_o: $\mu_D = 0$ or $\mu_A - \mu_B = 0$ (that is, the difference in readings is equal to 0)

H_a: $\mu_D \neq 0$ or $\mu_A - \mu_B \neq 0$ (two-sided alternative hypothesis, the difference is $\neq 0$)

Notice that this example is slightly different from the marketing research example of Example 3.3. Here the *same* patient is measured with

Table 3.9 Blood pressure data for 10 patients.

	Instrument A	Instrument B	Difference
Patient 1	144	147	−3
Patient 2	165	167	−2
Patient 3	125	124	1
Patient 4	149	152	−3
Patient 5	141	146	−5
Patient 6	118	120	−2
Patient 7	131	135	−4
Patient 8	126	126	0
Patient 9	147	149	−2
Patient 10	154	157	−3

two different instruments. In such cases, the measurement is obtained for a pair or units (here patients), hence the name paired t-test (see also example for testing in Chapter 1). In Example 3.3 we wanted to know if the spending expenditure of two *different populations* was the same (Californians vs. Washingtonians). Results for the paired t-test are shown in Table 3.10.

The average difference for the means is equaled to -2.3 with a 95% confidence interval of $(-3.564, -1.036)$. Because the confidence interval *does not* contain the value 0, the null hypothesis H_o must be rejected. The same conclusion can be reached by reading the (probability) P-value of 0.003; because this value is much less than the significance level of 0.05 (alpha value), the null hypothesis must be rejected. If we had formulated the alternative hypothesis as H_a: $\mu_A < \mu_B$ or $\mu_A - \mu_B < 0$, the result would have been as shown in Table 3.11.

We would still reject the null hypothesis in preference of the one-sided (lower-tailed, alternative hypothesis) and conclude that Instrument A reads, on average, lower than Instrument B. Note that the 95% upper bound for the mean difference (-1.276) does not contain 0. This conclusion is a little more informative than simply stating that Instrument A does not read the same as Instrument B.

Example 3.5: Paired t-test from Chapter 1. In Example 2 (Chapter 1) you were asked to decide intuitively whether or not training had helped

Table 3.10 Paired t-test and CI: instrument A, instrument B for H_a: $\mu_A \neq \mu_B$.

	N	Mean	StDev	SE Mean
Instrument A	10	140.00	14.73	4.66
Instrument B	10	142.30	15.46	4.89
Difference	10	−2.300	1.767	0.559

95% CI for mean difference: $(-3.564, -1.036)$
T-test of mean difference = 0 (vs. not = 0): T-value = -4.12, P-value = 0.003

Table 3.11 Paired t-test and CI: instrument A, instrument B for H_a: $\mu_A < \mu_B$.

	N	Mean	StDev	SE Mean
Instrument A	10	140.00	14.73	4.66
Instrument B	10	142.30	15.46	4.89
Difference	10	−2.300	1.767	0.559

95% upper bound for mean difference: −1.276
T-test of mean difference = 0 (vs. < 0): T-value = -4.12, P-value = 0.001

improve assembly time. Let us see how the same problem would be analyzed using a formal hypothesis testing process. Because you need to compare two means and the sample size is less than 30 (only 10 workers were tested), the appropriate test is a t-test, but which type of t-test, the t-test for *independent* population or for a *paired* population? Because the *same* 10 workers are tested before and after training, the correct t-test is the paired t-test.

1. H_o: Average assembly time before training = Assembly time after training

    or H_o: Average time before − Average time after = 0 (that is, mean difference in assembly time μ_D = 0)

    H_a: Average assembly time before training > Assembly time after training

    or H_a: The mean difference in assembly time is > 0 (μ_D > 0. Note: The alternative hypothesis is stated in the greater than format because the comparison is between before and after training. If we had entered the data for *after training* first, we would then compare the after training to the before training and, using this format, we would then expect the difference would be less than (that is, training after is [expected to be] less than training time before).

2. The appropriate statistics will be the mean difference (μ_D = 0). The statistical test will be the paired t-test.

3. Alpha = 0.05; sample size N = 10.

4. The data (from Example 2, Chapter 1) is reproduced in Table 3.12. The statistical analysis is shown in Table 3.13.

Conclusion: Because the P-value = 0.007 is < 0.05, we must reject the null hypothesis H_o and accept H_a; the assembly time before training is significantly longer than after training.

3.7 TESTS CONCERNING VARIANCES (F-TEST)

In some cases we might be interested in knowing if the standard deviation of a sample is equal to some predetermined value. For example, a supplier of some expensive chemical liquid compound may claim the standard deviation does not vary by more than 5 milliliters (ml). If we take a volumetric sample of 15 containers and calculate the standard deviation, we would like to know if the standard deviation of the population is equal to 5 ml (H_o) or if it is greater than 5 ml (H_a). If the standard deviation is less than five, that

Table 3.12 Assembly time before and after training.

Worker	Assembly time before training	Assembly time after training	Difference d_i
1	7	8	−1
2	8	8	0
3	10	7	3
4	11	6	5
5	18	10	8
6	16	9	7
7	12	9	3
8	12	8	4
9	6	7	−1
10	12	10	2

Table 3.13 Paired T-test and CI: before and after training.

	N	Mean	StDev	SE Mean
Before	10	11.20	3.77	1.19
After	10	8.20	1.32	0.42
Difference	10	3.000	3.127	0.989

95% lower bound for mean difference: 1.187
T-test of mean difference = 0 (vs. > 0): T-value = 3.03, P-value = 0.007

would be even better. In fact, as far as the supplier is concerned, the smaller the standard deviation the better (that is, the more precise is filling machines), but this is another problem.

To assess the equality or inequality of two standard deviations we need to conduct a variance ratio test known as a F-test. In section 2.4 of Chapter 2 we learned that variances from normal populations have a chi-square distribution. We also saw that the ratio of two chi-square distributions has an F-distribution. To test the null hypothesis,

$$H_o: \sigma^2_1 = \sigma^2_2$$

against the one-sided alternative $\sigma^2_1 > \sigma^2_2$ or $\sigma^2_1 < \sigma^2_2$ we need to compute the following ratios:

$$s^2_1/s^2_2 \geq F_{\alpha,\, n1-1,\, n2-1} \text{ or } s^2_2/s^2_1 \geq F_{\alpha,\, n2-1,\, n1-1}$$

where s_1^2 and s_2^2 are estimates of the population variances (σ_1^2 and σ_2^2), estimates obtained from a sample. For the two-sided alternative $\sigma_1^2 \neq \sigma_2^2$ compute $s_1^2/s_2^2 \geq F_{\alpha/2,\ n1-1,\ n2-1}$ if $s_1^2 \geq s_2^2$ or

$$s_2^2/s_1^2 \geq F_{\alpha/2,\ n2-1,\ n1-1} \text{ if } s_1^2 < s_2^2$$

The F values can either be obtained from F tables printed in the appendix section of most introductory books on statistics or they can be computed using statistical software. However, if you have access to a statistical software (an option I recommend highly), there is no need to compute F-values because the software will have an option to perform an equality of variance test.

Example 3.6: Are the variances for the two instruments in Example 3.4 the same?

$$H_o: \sigma^2_A = \sigma^2_B$$
$$H_a: \sigma^2_A \neq \sigma^2_B$$

Alpha is set at 0.05. The population variances are estimated by taking a sample of 10 patients and computing the sample variances s^2_A and s^2_B. Figure 3.2 shows the results for the equality of variance test. The computed P-value for the F-test is 0.888, which is greater than the significance value of 0.05; therefore we must accept the null hypothesis (H_o) of equality of variance.

What is the difference between the Levene's test and the F-test? The F-test assumes the data comes from a normal distribution; Levene's test is less restrictive in that it applies for *any* continuous distribution. Could you

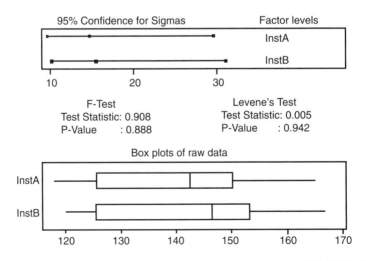

Figure 3.2   Equality of variances for instruments.

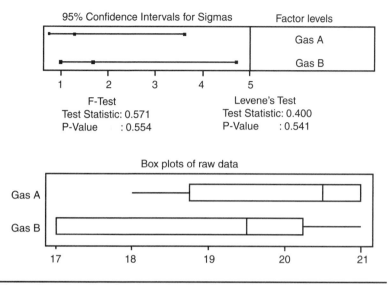

Figure 3.3 Equality of variance for Gasoline A versus Gasoline B.

have reached the same conclusion by simply looking at the two box plots or perhaps the two 95% confidence intervals? (Hint: Notice that the two box plots for Instrument A and Instrument B almost completely overlap each other.)

Example 3.7: Is the assumption of equality of variance justified in the gasoline example (Example 3.2)? The statement of the hypotheses would be similar to the statements found in Example 3.6. Referring to Figure 3.3, what would be your conclusion?

Comment: Because the P-value for the F-test is 0.554, what must you conclude? Notice how the 95% confidence intervals for each sigma overlap. The box plots for the raw data are the same as those produced in Chapter 1 except they are rotated 90° to the right. Notice that for this example, the two box plots do not overlap as much as the two box plots shown in Figure 3.2. You will also notice that the P-values reproduced in Figure 3.3 are not as large as the P-values reproduced in Figure 3.2; in other words, the more overlap between the box plots, the greater the P-value (or the more likely we are to accept the null hypothesis), and the less overlap we have, the less likely will be the probability that we accept the null hypothesis.

Example 3.8: In Exercise 3.3 (section 3.6) we assumed the variances in spending between California and Washington were equal. The F-test shown in Figure 3.4 indicates this assumption was incorrect (that is, reject H_o). How would you formulate the hypothesis?

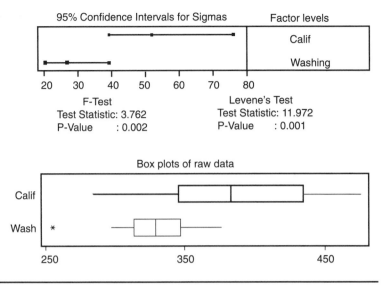

Figure 3.4   Equality of variance for California versus Washington.

3.8 TESTS BASED ON COUNT DATA

Count data are data obtained without the help of an instrument such as, a scale, a pressure gage, a thermometer, a pH meter, a speedometer, and a host of other sophisticated instruments. Count data, as the name suggests, are obtained by counting occurrences of events: 15 defective parts, 18 patients with high blood pressure, 3 scratches per part, 8 nonconformances per audits, and so on. Most often, count data are converted into percentages. Thus, for example, we may have 15 defective parts out of 230 parts received, or 6.52%, defective; 18 out of 52 patients, or 28.8%, may have high blood pressure; 3.5% of parts may have some sort of scratches (which is different than saying there are 3 scratches per part on average); 34.8% of customers may rate a product "Very High" on a satisfaction scale, and so on. Count data and their derivatives, proportion data, can be analyzed using the following sample of statistical methods.

3.8.1 Test Concerning Proportions (Binomial Test for n < 100 or z Transformation for n > 100)

Example 3.9: A quality inspector claims that at least 25% of all parts received from a vendor do not meet one or more requirements. In order to test the inspector's claim, the quality director decides to look at 100 receiving inspection reports from the specified vendor. The inspection reports were selected at random and covered a period of four months. His inspection reveals that 18 inspection reports specified a type of nonconformance. Is the inspector's claim justified?

In this example, the nature of the data is different from previous examples. In each of the previous examples a quantitative measure was obtained. For example, we wanted to know about the value of a corrosion measure, the mileage performance of two types of gasoline, the reduction in assembly time, and so on. The quality inspector described in Example 3.9 does not measure any product characteristics. He merely claims that 25% of the parts received do not meet the requirement. The part either meets or does not meet the requirement. Because there are only two values, there can only be two probabilities: either the part meets specification with probability p or it does not meet the specification with probability q = 1 − p. These binary (yes-no) values, which occur with probabilities p and q, are known as a Bernoulli model. The repeated sequence of n Bernoulli events (defined as *trials*) is known as a *binomial process* and characterized by a frequency distribution known as a *binomial distribution*.

Problems that are concerned with proportions (or percentages) can, under certain conditions, be analyzed using a *binomial test*.[1] If the repeated sequence n is greater than 100 trials, the binomial distribution can be approximated by a normal distribution using the following Z transformation:

$$Z = \frac{X - np}{\sqrt{np(1 - p)}}$$

Returning to Example 3.9, we have the following hypotheses:

$$H_o: p = 0.25; \text{ (that is, } p = p_0)$$

$$H_a: p > 0.25; \text{ (that is, } p > p_0)$$

The same decision rules defined in (3.4) apply except that we now test $p > p_o$, $p < p_o$ or $p \neq p_o$. For alpha = 0.05, $Z_{0.05}$ = 1.64. If the computed Z-value is greater than 1.64, reject H_o; otherwise, accept H_o. Sample size = 100, X = 18, np = 100 * 0.25 = 25, np(1 − p) = 25 * 0.75 = 18.75.

$$Z = \frac{18 - 25}{\sqrt{18.75}} = \frac{-7}{4.33} = -1.61$$

The Z-value is negative, which indicates that (over the four months from which the samples of inspection records were selected), the proportion p of reports with nonconformance is likely to be *less than* 0.25 (25%) and not greater than 25% as the quality engineer claimed. However, based on the way we stated the hypothesis, we must accept the null hypothesis H_o, which states that the proportion p = 0.25. If we were to reverse the alternative hypothesis to state H_a: p < 0.25, the computation would be the same but now the Z-value would have to be less than $-Z_{0.05} = -1.64$ (see section 2.2). As we can see the computed Z-values is equal to -1.61, which is not quite large enough to reject the null hypothesis (but very close); consequently, we can only conclude that P = 0.25. The computer-generated Table 3.14 shows how close we are to rejecting the null hypothesis. The P-value of 0.063 is barely 0.013 larger than the significance level of 0.05. Still, unless the probability value is less than 0.05 we cannot reject the null hypothesis. If we had a priori stated that the significance level alpha was equal to 0.10, we would then have rejected H_o. However we cannot arbitrarily change the significance to fit the conclusion; to do so defeats the whole purpose of objective (statistically driven) data analysis.

The 95% upper and lower bounds are computed in a manner similar to the calculations shown in section 3.2.2, Equations (3.1) and (3.2).

$$\text{Upper bound} = \frac{X}{n} + Z_{\alpha/2}\sqrt{\frac{\frac{X}{n}(1-\frac{X}{n})}{n}}$$

For alpha = 0.05 we have: $Z_{0.025} = 1.96$. X = 18, X/100 = 0.18;

$$\sqrt{\frac{0.18 * 0.82}{100}} = 0.0384.$$

The upper bound = 0.18 + 1.96 * 0.0384 = 0.2553.

The lower bound would be equal to 0.18 − 1.96 * 0.0384 = 0.1047.

The 95% confidence interval for the estimated proportion p is therefore:

$$0.1047 < p < 0.2553.$$

Table 3.14   Test and CI for one proportion.

Test of p = 0.25 vs. p < 0.25

Sample	X	N	Sample p	95.0% upper bound	Exact P-value
1	18	100	0.180000	0.255145	0.063

3.8.2 Test Concerning Differences Among K Proportions (Chi-Square Test Denoted by the Greek Letter χ^2)

Example 3.10: A process engineer would like to test the efficiency of two manufacturing processes. He samples 400 parts from Process 1 and finds out that the process yielded 28 defective parts. A sample of 300 parts from Process 2 yields 15 defective parts. Are the two process yields identical?

   Example 3.11 (extension of 3.10): A manager wants to know if the proportion of defective parts produced by a machine remains constant from day to day. Over a period of three days he collects the numbers shown in Table 3.15.

   Is the process stable? In other words, is the same proportion of defective parts produced each day? (Note: The question of how to improve this process is another issue.)

   The null hypothesis is: proportion defective for 1st day = proportion defective 2nd day = proportion defective for 3rd day.

$$H_o: p_1 = p_2 = p_3$$

$$H_a: \text{one of the } p_i\text{s is different}$$

$$\text{Set alpha} = 0.05.$$

   The statistical test used to compare K proportions is known as a chi-square test. Even though the chi-square test has not yet been described, enough hypotheses have been tested in previous examples to reach a conclusion. Because the P-value printed at the bottom of Table 3.16 is equal to 0.502 (which is greater than alpha = 0.05), we must accept the null hypothesis of equality of proportions; in other words, the process is in control because there is no statistical difference in the proportion of defective parts produced over the last three days.

3.8.3 Chi-Square (χ^2) Test Calculations

The data represented in Table 3.15 are generalized in Table 3.17.

Table 3.15   Proportion of defective parts over a period of three days.

	1st day	2nd day	3rd day
Number of defectives	12	15	6
Number of good parts	88	105	74
Total number of parts	100	120	80

Table 3.16 Chi-square test: defective, nondefectives.

	Defectives	Nondefectives	Total
1	12	88	100
	11.00	89.00	
2	15	105	120
	13.20	106.80	
3	6	74	80
	8.80	71.20	
Total	33	267	300

Chi-square = 0.091 + 0.011 + 0.245 + 0.030 + 0.891 + 0.110 = 1.379

DF = 2, P-value = 0.502

Table 3.17 Generalized proportion table for K samples.

	Sample 1	Sample 2 . . .	Sample k
Successes	x_1	x_2	x_k
Failures	$n_1 - x_1$	$n_2 - x_2$	$n_k - x_k$

1. For k samples, calculate the pooled estimate

$$P = \frac{x_1 + x_2 + \ldots + x_k}{n_1 + n_2 + \ldots + n_k}$$

From Table 3.15 we have $p = \dfrac{12 + 15 + 6}{100 + 120 + 80} = 0.11$.

2. Calculate the expected cell frequencies $e_{1j} = n_j p$ and $e_{2j} = n_j(1 - p)$. Thus for cell$_{12}$ and cell$_{22}$ we have $e_{12} = 120 * 0.11 = 13.2$ and $e_{22} = 120 * (1 - 0.11) = 106.8$.

The six expected values are

11	13.2	8.8
89	106.8	71.2

3. Compute the following chi-square (χ^2) statistics:

$$\chi^2 = \sum_{i=1}^{2}\sum_{j=1}^{k} \frac{(f_{ij} - e_{ij})^2}{e_{ij}} \text{ or,}$$

$$\chi^2 = \frac{(12 - 11.0)^2}{11.0} + \frac{(15 - 13.2)^2}{13.2} + \frac{(6 - 8.8)^2}{8.8} +$$

$$\frac{(88 - 89.0)^2}{89.0} + \frac{(105 - 106.8)^2}{106.8} + \frac{(74 - 71.2)^2}{71.2}$$

$\chi^2 = 0.091 + 0.245 + 0.891 + 0.011 + 0.030 + 0.110 = $ 1.379 (which equals the value listed in Table 3.17).

4. The chi-square value varies depending on the significance level alpha and the number of degrees of freedom that is equal to the number of samples $-$ 1 (or k $-$ 1). The computer software calculates that given the 3 x 2 table of Table 3.16 the probability of obtaining a chi-square value equal to 1.379 is equal to 0.502, which means that we must accept the null hypothesis.

Alternative explanation: Most statistical software packages allow the user to compute what are known as *critical values* from various distributions. These critical values are the maximum values that can be obtained by a test statistic in order to accept a null hypothesis. If the computed test statistics is larger than the critical value, the null hypothesis is rejected. The chi-square value for alpha = 0.05 and with 2 degrees of freedom $(\chi^2_{0.05, 2}) = $ 5.991 (this value was computed using a statistical software). Because the computed chi-square of 1.379 is *less than* 5.991, we must accept the null hypothesis.

3.8.4 Test Concerning Contingency Tables (Chi-Square)

Example 3.12 (continuation of Example 4, Chapter 1): The analysis of contingency tables is useful when we want to analyze the relationship between two variables measured on a categorical or ordinal scale. By a categorical scale, I mean a scale devoid of any distance metric between the values of the scale. This example illustrates the use of categorical and ordinal variables. The variable Region consists of three regions. For each region, we could assign a value, for example, Region 1 = 1, Region 2 = 2, and Region 3 = 3. Naturally, the fact that Region 3 is (arbitrarily) assigned the value 3 does not mean Region 3 is three times larger or better or whatever else than Region 1; there is no distance between among three categories of values. Note: Mathematicians would say there is no metrics.

The variable Adequacy is slightly different from the variable Region because Adequacy can be perceived as being measure on some rudimentary *ordinal scale*. Indeed, a rating of Very Adequate is better than a rating of Moderately Adequate, which in turn is better than a rating of Below Average. In such a situation, we can say there is a *rank ordering* of the variable Adequacy: Very Adequate is better than Moderately Adequate, which is better than Below Average or,

Very Adequate > Moderately Adequate > Below Average

However, although we know there is a rank order, we do not know the distance between the ranks. Thus, for example, if we were to assign the values 1, 2, and 3 to Below Average, Moderately Adequate, and Very Adequate, we could *not* say a rating of Very Adequate is three times better than a rating of Below Average; however, unlike the categorical variable Region, we know such a rating is slightly more informative. When analyzing 3 x 3, 4 x 4, or N x N contingency tables, the null hypothesis we want to test is that two variables are *independent*. More specifically, if P_{ij} is the probability that an item will fall in the ith row and jth cell, then the null hypothesis of independence states that:

$$H_o: p_{ij} = (p_{i.}) (p_{.j})$$

$$H_a: p_{ij} \neq (p_i) (p_j)$$

Within the context of this example, we would like to know if the Adequacy rating is independent of the Region; that is, are all regions rating Adequacy with the same proportions of Below Average, Moderately Adequate, and Very Adequate, or is there some difference among regions? Table 3.18 summarizes the results. How to read Table 3.18? Each cell of Table 3.18 contains four values: Count, % of Row, % of Column, and % of Table. If we look at Row 1, Column 1 (that is, cell 11 for Region 1 and Below Average), we see that out of 141 responses from Region 1, 75, or 53.19%, of the responses rated Adequacy as Below Average. However, looking down the Below Average column we see that out of the 167 persons who rated

Table 3.18 Tabulated statistics: district, adequacy.

Cell contents—			
Count			
% of Row			
% of Column			
% of Table			
Count			

Rows: District	Columns: Adequacy Below Average	Moderate	Very	All
Region 1	75	54	12	$141 = f_{1.}$
	53.19	38.30	8.51	100.00
	44.91	22.31	8.51	25.64
	13.64	9.82	2.18	25.64
	75	54	12	141
Region 2	64	106	78	$248 = f_{2.}$
	25.81	42.74	31.45	100.00
	38.32	43.80	55.32	45.09
	11.64	19.27	14.18	45.09
	64	106	78	248

Continued

Continued

Table 3.18 Tabulated statistics: district, adequacy.

Region 3	28	82	51	$161 = f_{3.}$
	17.39	50.93	31.68	100.00
	16.77	33.88	36.17	29.27
	5.09	14.91	9.27	29.27
	28	82	51	161
All	167	24	141	550
	30.36	44.00	25.64	100.00
	100.00	100.00	100.00	100.00
	30.36	44.00	25.64	100.00
	167	242	141	550
	$f_{.1}$	$f_{.2}$	$f_{.3}$	f

Chi-square = 59.401, DF = 4, P-value = 0.000

Adequacy as Below Average, 75, or 44.91%, were from Region 1. Finally, the 75 respondents of Row 1, Column 1, represent 13.64% of all 550 respondents.

The computation for the chi-square value are similar to those outlined in section 8.2 except the expected cell frequencies are computed as follows:

$$E_{ij} = [(f_{i.}) * (f_{.j})] / f$$

Thus, for example, $e_{23} = [248 * 141]/550 = 34968/550 = 63.57$; $e_{12} = [141 * 242]/550 = 34122/550 = 62.04$, and so on. The chi-square value of 59.401 is computed using the same equation as shown in step 3 of section 3.8.3. Because the P-value (0.000) is less than 0.05, we reject H_o and accept H_a. This means there is some sort of dependency between the Adequacy rating and the Region. Looking more closely at the numbers shown in Table 3.18, we can see that Region 1 does *not* rate Adequacy as high as the other two regions. For example, of all the people that rated the service as Very Adequate (141), only 8.51% are from Region 1, whereas 55.32% and 36.17% are for Regions 2 and 3, respectively. This difference in satisfaction would need to be investigated.

3.8.5 Test of Goodness of Fit (Chi-Square): Advanced Section (Optional)

Whenever we want to know if a set of numbers follows a particular (frequency) distribution, we need to perform a "goodness of fit" test. Although there are many distributions to choose from (normal, chi-square, F, Poisson, and others), one of the most important statistical distributions is the normal distribution. Because the assumption of normality is one of the fundamental assumptions of statistical inference, the normality test is probably the most frequent test. One of the easiest ways to test if a set of numbers follows a particular distribution is to perform a chi-square test on the data. The principles of the chi-square test have already been explained in Examples 3.11 and 3.12. The test consists of comparing observing frequencies to predict frequencies of the assumed distribution. The following examples will help illustrate how to conduct a goodness of fit test.

Example 3.13: The supervisor of a call center recently attended a Six Sigma seminar. One of the things she remembers from the seminar is that the number of phone calls coming to a call center follow what is known as a Poisson distribution. The frequency of occurrence of the following events have been known to follow a Poisson distribution:

A. Queuing type events

    a. Number of cars arriving at a tollbooth every 15 seconds or every 30, 60, or any other number of seconds

    b. Number of customers queuing at check out stands per unit of time

    c. Number of phone calls arriving at a call center

B. Accidents, errors, breakdowns

    a. Number of accidents in a given period of time

    b. Number of typing errors on a page or the number of errors per month

    c. Number of (machine) breakdowns per day, week, month, or any other unit of time or space

    d. Number of scratches or other types of quality flaws per part unit or per surface area (for example, number of scratches per part, number of scratches per square foot or square inch, or, more generally, number of defects per unit of time or per unit or per units of surface area)

The general assumption governing the types of events listed under A and B is that the events occur independently of each other for certain time (or space) intervals (for example, per second, per minute, per hour, per feet, per square inch, per square foot, or per square mile). Mathematically, the frequency distribution of a Poisson event is represented by the following equation:

$$f(x) = \frac{\lambda^x e^{-\lambda}}{x!} \text{ for } x = 0, 1, 2, 3 \ldots \qquad (3.8)$$

where e is approximately equal to 2.71828 and "x!" signifies "x factorial." The factorial of any number N is that number multiplied by all of the numbers preceding N. For example, for X = 4, 4! = 4 * 3 * 2 * 1 = 24. An interesting property of the Poisson distribution is that the standard deviation is equal to the mean lambda (λ). Thus as the mean increases so does the standard deviation. One of the characteristics of the Poisson distribution is that it a positively skewed distribution but the skewness decreases as the mean lambda increases. Figure 3.5 shows a Poisson distribution for Wait Time with an average wait time lambda = 1.5. Figure 3.6 shows how the Poisson distribution becomes more symmetrical when the average wait time increases to 5 minutes.

If the average number of calls per minute is 1.5, the probability of receiving 4 calls in the next minute is:

$$f(4) = \frac{1.5^4 e^{-1.5}}{4!} = 0.04706$$

One does not usually calculate probability values using Equation (3.8); instead one either refers to a statistical table or simply relies on statistical software to perform all of the necessary computations. (Return to Example 3.13.) Curious as to whether or not the Poisson distribution applies to the number of calls received at her center, the supervisor decides to look at wait time (that is, the number of minutes customers had to wait before an operator answered incoming calls) for the last 400 calls received at the center. The

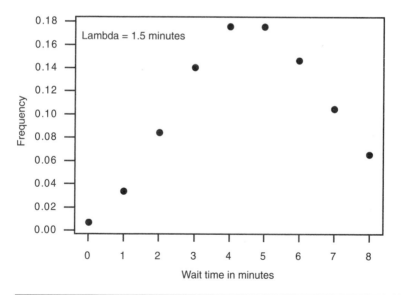

Figure 3.5   Poisson distribution of customer waiting time at a call center. Average waiting time (λ) = 1.5 minutes.

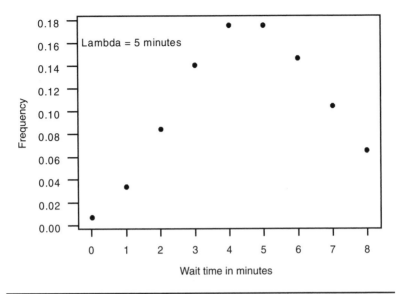

Figure 3.6   Poisson distribution of customer waiting time distribution at call center. Average waiting time (λ) = 5 minutes.

data and associated calculations are shown in Table 3.19. The null and alternative hypotheses are as follows:

H_o: Wait times come from a Poisson distribution

H_a: Wait times do not come from a Poisson distribution

Significance level alpha = 0.05

One of the assumptions of the chi-square test (which also applies to contingency tables) is that the frequency of occurrence of an event must equal at least five. Referring to Table 3.19, we notice that the frequency counts for a wait time of 6, 7, and 8 minutes are all less than 5. To ensure the count is at least equal to 5, we must combine the frequency count of the last four rows (that is, wait time equal to 5, 6, 7, and 8), thereby reducing the number of rows in Table 3.19 to six.

A chi-square value is computed using Equation (3.9). This equation compares the squared deviation between observed and expected frequencies (similar to step 3, section 3.8.3).

$$\chi^2 = \sum_{i=1}^{m} \frac{(f_i - e_i)^2}{e_i} \tag{3.9}$$

where m = the number of frequency categories. The number of degrees of freedom is equal to the number of frequency categories minus 2. Allowing

Table 3.19   Tabulated statistics: district, adequacy.

Wait in minutes (1)	Observed frequencies f_i and observed minutes (2)	Poisson probabilities with $\lambda = 1.5$ minute (3)	Expected frequencies e_i (4)
0	89	.2231 × 400 =	89.2
1	143 (1 × 143 = 143 mn)	.3347 × 400 =	133.9
2	94 (2 × 94 = 188 mn)	.2510 × 400 =	100.4
3	42 (3 × 42 = 126 mn)	.1255 × 400 =	50.2
4	20 (4 × 20 = 80 mn)	.0471 × 400 =	18.8
5 5 × 8 = 40mn	8 Combining rows 5–8 we have 8 + 3 + 1 + 0 = 12	.0141 × 400 =	5.6 Combining rows 5–8, we have 5.6 + 1.4 + 0.3 + 0.0 = 7.3
6	3 (6 × 3 = 18 mn)	.0035 × 400 =	1.4
7	1 (7 × 1 = 7 mn)	.0008 × 400 =	0.3
8	0	.0001 × 400 =	0.0
Total minutes = 602 Lambda = 602/400 = 1.5			

for the fact that we combined the last four categories (rows 5-8) into one, we have $6 - 2 = 4$ degrees of freedom. Inserting the appropriate values from column (3) and (4) of Table 3.19 (and using equation 3.9) we have:

Chi-square (χ^2) = 0.000448 + 0.618446 + 0.407968 + 1.3394442 + 0.076595 + 3.026027 = 5.468 or, rounding up, 5.47. The last step is to determine whether a chi-square value of 5.47 is large enough to reject H_o. Two methods are available.

Refer to a chi-square table (or use a statistical software program to look up the chi-square value for $\chi^2_{0.05, 4}$. If the computed chi-square value (5.47) is *greater* than the $\chi^2_{0.05, 4}$ value, we must reject the hypothesis H_o; if the computed chi-square value is *less* than the $\chi^2_{0.05, 4}$ value, then accept H_o. Table 3.20 and Figure 3.7 show that for alpha = 0.05, the chi-square value with 4 degrees of freedom is equal to 9.48. Because the computed value of 5.47 is less than 9.48, we must accept the null hypothesis.

Alternatively, we could also calculate the probability of occurrence of the computed value (that is, 5.47) to determine if it falls within the 95% region of acceptance (of H_o) or if it falls within the 5% rejection region of alpha.

Using statistical software we can determine that the probability that a chi-square value (with four degrees of freedom) is *less than or equal* to 5.48 is equal to 0.7585 (Table 3.20 and Figure 3.7). This means that alpha = 1.0000 − 0.7585 = 0.2415, which is larger than the significance level of 0.05; therefore we must accept H_o.

Table 3.20   Inverse cumulative distribution function.

Chi-Square with 4 DF

P(X <= x)	x
0.0500	9.4877

Table 3.21   Cumulative distribution function.

Chi-Square with 4 DF

x	P(X <= x)
5.4700	0.7585

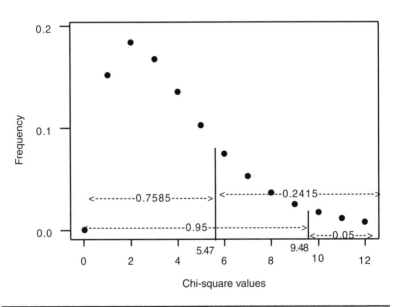

Figure 3.7   Chi-square values and probabilities.

There is, in fact, a third method that is simpler yet: use statistical software to test whether of not a set of numbers follow a particular distribution (in this case, a Poisson distribution). The software would perform the preceding calculation and print a probability value.

3.9 HOW TO DETERMINE SAMPLE SIZE

When we last left our space explorer, he was still trying to have his computer tell him what would be an adequate sample size to estimate the average height of earthlings. After some additional inquiries the computer finally admitted that, in order to determine the size of the sample, two additional pieces of information are needed: (1) something about the variability (that is, the *variance*) of the estimated measurement (in this example height) and (2) how close the sample estimate X-bar ($\bar{X}$) needs to be to the population mean μ. In other words, our space explorer needs to state how much error he is willing to accept (mathematically, X-bar $- \mu <\, = E$). For example, our extraterrestrial statistician may decide the estimated average height should be within a centimeter of the population mean (that is, the error should be no more than 1 centimeter or, X-bar $- \mu <\, = 1$ centimeter). Deciding on how much error is desired is easy, but how do we calculate variability of something we have not yet measured? If we have not yet collected any data, how is it possible to know what the variance is? Of course, from the spaceship the explorer has had many opportunities to observe these humans, and during the course of his observations he noticed that for some inexplicable reason, humans were not all the same height. He simply assumed this failure to achieve uniformity in height was probably caused by some imperfection in the reproductive process (something his civilization had resolved about 500,000 years ago). Still, how can we quantify this entity known as variability or variation? When asked to resolve this dilemma, the computer nonchalantly suggested that the variability of a data set whose mean we are trying to estimate via a sample must be estimated by taking a sample! If this sounds like a circular argument that is because *it is*!

Summary: To estimate a population mean, we must take a sample. The size of the sample will depend on how precise we would want the estimate X-bar ($\bar{X}$) to be (that is, how close X-bar should be to the population mean), and this in turn will depend on how much variability (or variance) there is in the population. The variance or variability of the population can only be *estimated* by computing a statistic known as the *standard deviation,* but paradoxically, the standard deviation can only be calculated by taking a sample from the population! In essence, we must take two samples; the first estimates the variance of the population. Once the estimated variance is calculated, we can calculate the sample size needed to estimate the population mean by using the following formula:

$$n = \left[\frac{Z_{\alpha/2} \times S}{Error} \right]^2 \qquad (3.9)$$

where $Z_{\alpha/2}$ is the same standardized Z used to assess the degree of confidence (or probability). As already explained in section 2.2, the two most common values for $Z_{\alpha/2}$ are 1.96 (for 95% confidence) and 2.58 for 99% confidence. To obtain an estimate (S^2) of the population variation (σ^2), the space explorer selects a small sample of 30 humans. The number 30 is purely arbitrary (but safe); 20 or 25 could have been chosen. However, having noticed the many ethnic groups spread over several continents (with different population density), our amateur statistician decides to select 30 individuals randomly, ensuring that at least two individuals are taken from each continent. Suppose the standard deviation (SD) of these 30 height measurements is approximately 41 centimeters (16 inches); you must next decide on the acceptable amount of error (that is, the precision of the measurement). After some deliberation and a few communication exchanges with headquarters, it is decided that, just to be safe, it is necessary to be 95% certain the estimated average will not exceed the population mean by more than 1 centimeter (that is, 95% certain that the error in estimation will not exceed 1 centimeter (about 0.4 inch). Using Equation (3.10) and remembering that $Z_{0.05/2}$ is equal to 1.96, we have

$$n = \left[\frac{1.96 * 41 \text{ cm}}{1 \text{ cm}} \right]^2 = (880.63)^2 = 6475$$

Our extraterrestrial statistician can be 95% confident that a sample of 6475 humans will generate an average height that will be within 1 centimeter of the (true) population height (μ). Happy that the job will be done in less than two hours (instead of 207 years), our amateur anthropologist/statistician tells his assistant to start collecting data.

3.9.1 Sampling for Count Data

Most of us have seen the tabulated results of marketing or political surveys published in newspapers. Often a footnote indicating the margin of error is printed with the survey. These margins of error are usually stated as +/− 3%. How are these margins computed?

Suppose you need to conduct a customer survey. After some deliberation you produced a carefully phrased short questionnaire whose purpose will be to assess customer satisfaction for a particular set of products. The opinions assessed by the series of questions will be measured using a simple binary (Yes-No) satisfaction scale. (Note: One could use a 5-point Likert scale and later recode the data into a 2-point binary scale.) Aware of the fact that mailing questionnaires is an inefficient process (returning at best 1%), you decide you will call your customers, but because you have over 3750 customers, calling every one of them is not cost effective and you must now decide how many customers will have to be called. You will note that in this example we are assessing the *proportion* of customers (p) that are satisfied (and not satisfied, $1 - p$) with a line of products. These types of problems are slightly different for the problem faced by the space explorer because we are not *measuring* a height but rather assessing a percentage (see binomial distribution examples). The formula used to estimate the sample size n is similar to Equation (3.10) (of section 3.9) except that we must insert the standard deviation for proportion.

$$n = p(1-p)\left(\frac{Z_{\alpha/2}}{Error}\right)^2 \tag{3.10}$$

Because in most cases we do not know a priori what the proportion (that is, percentage) p will be, we assume $p = 0.5$. Suppose we want to be 95% sure that our estimate for p will be within 3% (that is, Error $= 0.03$), we have, using Equation (3.11):

$$n = 0.5 * 0.5\left(\frac{1.96}{0.03}\right)^2 = 0.25(64.33)^2 = 1067$$

After interviewing 1067 customers, you will be able to report that you are 95% sure the proportion of customers that like (or do not like) your products is within $+/- 3\%$. If the sample size is not economically feasible, it can be reduced by either increasing the error (perhaps to 5%) or diminishing the confidence level (perhaps to 90%), or both. (Note: The sample of 1067 is typical of most national surveys.) But what if you only have a small sample size of let's say approximately 300 customers; how would you proceed? You can still use Equation (3.11) to compute the "Error." After rearranging Equation (3.11) we have:

$$Error = \sqrt{\frac{p(1-p)}{n}} * Z_{\alpha/2}$$

Thus if we have a sample size n of 300 customers and if we further assume we still wanted to be 95% certain of our estimate, we could compute the error to be $\sqrt{\frac{0.5*0.5}{300}} * 1.96 = 0.056$. This estimate tells us that if we only have 300 customers to interview, our error would be 5.6%, which is not too bad when you consider that a sample of 1067 customers only guarantees an error rate of 3.0%!

3.10 CONCLUSION

Having reviewed some of the most frequently used statistical tests and explained how various statistics routinely printed by statistical software packages are computed, we now proceed to an explanation of a statistical technique introduced as early as the 1950s in the chemical industry and popularized more recently by Six Sigma methodology, namely, design of experiments.

NOTE

1. The two assumptions are that (1) the probability of a success is the same for each trial (this assumption may not always be satisfied in a manufacturing or service world) and (2) the trails are independent. In other words, the result of one trial does not influence the next result. The classic example is the flip of a coin—for each flip the probability of obtaining heads (or tails) is equal, and the result from one flip does not influence the probability of the next flip (which is assumed to be 0.5).

4

Design of Experiments

4.0 INTRODUCTION

Although Francis Isidor Edgeworth in 1885 was the first to apply the fundamental principles of analysis of variance used in experimental designs, R. A. Fisher is generally recognized as the first statistician to have developed the technique of modern experimental design during the early 1920s when he worked at the famous Rothamsted agricultural station in England. Linguistic remnants of this early association with agricultural research is still evident to this day when we refer to experimental *treatment, plots,* or *blocks.* By the mid-1930s, the success of the experimental approach in agricultural research was noted by scientists including social scientists and it was not long before the technique began to spread to other disciplines. The use of statistical control chart developed by Shewhart in the late 1920s was well-known and applied throughout many industrial sectors by the 1940s. The application of experimental designs in industry first evolved in the early 1950s in the chemical industry. By the mid-1980s, when Six Sigma methodology began to acquire some notoriety, the use of experimental designs in a broad range of industries began to increase exponentially. Today, experimental designs and other statistical techniques are routinely taught by a host of Six Sigma consulting firms.

The expression *experimental design* refers to a series of activities conducted during an investigation that is designed to test or verify hypotheses. This series of activities consists of the following steps:

1. Formulation of the null and alternative statistical hypotheses concerning one or more parameters

2. Specification of the significance level (that is, confidence level) that will be used to decide which hypothesis is likely to be true

3. Formulation of *a plan* that will specify how the data will be collected

4. Collection of the data according to the stated plan

5. Computation of the appropriate statistics and inferring, based on the appropriate test, the probable truth or falsity of the null hypothesis

There are several types of experimental designs. To most people who have attended Six Sigma Black Belt courses, an experimental design or a design of experiment (DoE) consists of a set of planned experiments whereby the experimenter varies under controlled conditions a set of factors (these designs are discussed in Chapter 5). And yet, the field of experimental designs is much broader than so-called DoEs. As we see in this chapter, planned experiments can be designed either with qualitative variables, quantitative variables, or qualitative and quantitative variables, and they need not always include the use of design matrices. In fact, as shown in Figure 4.1, the subject of experimental designs and consequently of the analysis of experimental data is so vast that we can only cover a few of the most important methods, notably the analysis of variance.

As its name implies, the analysis of variance (or ANOVA) is a method based on the analysis and partitioning of the total variability of a set of observations or measurements. Although there are many types of ANOVAs, each with their own set of assumptions, this chapter focuses on those most commonly used: ANOVAs found in industrial applications, the one-way ANOVA used to analyze the effect of one factor or variable (X) on a response variable (Y), and the two-way ANOVA, which is used to analyze the effects of two factors or variables on a response variable Y. The two-way ANOVA can easily be generalized to N variables (or factors), or N-way ANOVA.

4.0.1 General Mathematical Comments Regarding Analysis of Variance (Optional)

Analysis of variance problems belongs to a class of mathematical models known as the general linear model. Suppose we have collected n observations $y_1, \ldots, y_n$ on a variable Y. The variable Y could represent any measurement or characteristic of your choice: height of an individual, number of errors on a purchasing order, percentage of some chemical, number of department stores, number of customer complaints filed per week, or an infinite number of other possibilities.

I. Randomized designs

   A. Complete block designs

      1. Completely randomized design

      2. Randomized block design

      3. Latin-square design

      4. Greco-Latin square design

      5. Hyper-Greco-Latin square design

   B. Incomplete block designs

      1. Balanced incomplete block design

      2. Youden square balance incomplete block design

      3. Partially balanced incomplete block design

   C. Factorial designs

      1. Completely randomized factorial design

      2. Randomized block factorial design

      3. Hierarchical randomized design

      4. Split-plot design

      5. Fractional factorial design (many varieties)

      6. Taguchi design (a variation of fractional factorial designs)

   D. Others

      1. Extreme-vertices design (often used in chemistry)

      2. Scheffe Simplex design (also used in chemistry or chemical engineering)

Figure 4.1 Types of experimental designs (partial list).

The general linear model postulates that if we can assume the average value of each $\bar{Y}_i$ is a linear function of p unknown parameters $a_1, \ldots, a_p$, that is,

$$\bar{Y}_i = a_1 X_{1i} + \ldots + a_p X_{pi} \text{ for } i = 1, \ldots, \text{n observations and where}$$

$X_1, \ldots, X_p$ are known constants, then each observation y_i can be written as:

$$y_i = a_1 X_{1i} + \ldots + a_p X_{pi} + e_i \text{ for } i = 1, \ldots, \text{n observations,}$$

and where $e_1, \ldots, e_n$ are error variables.

The general linear model assumes the following:

1. The average for the errors (e_i) is equal to 0.

2. The errors are uncorrelated or independent of each other (that is, no relationship exists between the errors).

3. The errors have a common variance sigma (σ^2).

4.1 ONE-WAY ANOVA

4.1.1 General Principles

Associated with every experimental design is a mathematical model that describes the various sources of variability that influence or have an effect on individual measurements. These "various sources of variability" are often referred to as *factors*. If we can assume the mathematical model represents an accurate description of the various sources of variability, we can then state that the purpose of any experiment is to allow the experimenter to evaluate the effects of one or more factors on a set of measurements or observations.

The simplest model, known as the one-way ANOVA, allows an experimenter to analyze the effect of one factor (set at various levels) on a set of observations or measurements. The one-way ANOVA allows us to compare the average of a variable for several categories (or populations). For example, suppose you are the quality manager in a plant where three inspectors (A, B, and C) are responsible for product inspection. You suspect that each inspector interprets the inspection procedure for product 1021AB differently. To test your theory you collect information on the number of product defects found by each inspector over a period of a week. Your design plan is simple: collect the corrective action reports for each inspector for the previous week and write down the number of nonconformances associated with product 1021AB for each inspector. A generalized version of the data is presented in Table 4.1. Where X_{ij} is the number of product defects found by the ith inspector by the jth day and $\bar{X}_i$ (X-bar i) is the average for inspector i. For this simple example, the variable (or factor) Inspector is represented by three qualitative levels: Inspector A, Inspector B, and Inspector C.

The mathematical model associated with the one-way analysis of variance, or ANOVA, is as follows:

$$i = 1, 2, 3, \ldots, k \text{ groups (or treatments or levels)}$$

$$X_{ij} = \bar{X}_i + e_{ij} \quad \text{for} \tag{4.1}$$

$$j = 1, 2, 3, \ldots, n \text{ observations}$$

Table 4.1 A generalized array of numbers for one-way ANOVA.

A	B	C	
X_{11}	X_{12}	X_{13}	
	•	•	
	X_{ij}		
	•	•	
X_{15}	X_{25}	X_{35}	
------	------	------	
$\bar{X}_1$	$\bar{X}_2$	$\bar{X}_3$	$\bar{\bar{X}}$ (Grand mean)

where e_{ij} is the *experimental error* or *residual* representing all uncontrolled and/or unknown sources of variation affecting a particular measurement. From the example of Table 4.1 we would have:

$$i = 1, 2, 3 \text{ (3 inspectors)}$$
$$X_{ij} = \bar{X}_i + e_{ij} \quad \text{for}$$
$$j = 1, 2, 3, 4, 5 \text{ (5 days)}$$

This equation tells us that the value of each observation is equal to the factor average, which can also be viewed as a column average, plus an error term (e). Because each column average will deviate from the grand average by a constant (say β), we can make the following substitution: if we let $\bar{X}_i = \bar{\bar{X}} + \beta_i$ (where $\bar{\bar{X}}$ is known as the *grand mean*), Equation (4.1) can be rewritten as:

$$i = 1, 2, 3, \ldots, k \text{ groups (or treatments or levels)} \quad (4.2)$$
$$X_{ij} = \bar{\bar{X}} + \beta_i + e_{ij} \text{ for}$$
$$j = 1, 2, 3, \ldots, n \text{ observations}$$

where the betas (β_i) representing the factor level of the ith population are subject to the condition:

$$\sum_{i=1}^{k} \beta_i = 0$$ (this condition simply means the mean of the $\bar{X}_i$ equals $\bar{\bar{X}}$)

and where e_{ij} is the same *experimental error, or residual,* as shown in Equation (4.2).

Equation (4.2) states that an individual observation X_{ij} is equal to the grand (overall) mean $\bar{\bar{X}}$ plus a treatment effect β_i, plus an error effect e_{ij} that is unique for each individual observation. Using simple algebraic manipulation it can be shown that the effects $\beta_i = (\bar{X}_i - \bar{\bar{X}})$ represent the deviation of the average of the ith treatment from the grand mean and [from (4.1)] we see that the errors $e_{ij} = (X_{ij} - \bar{X}_i)$. The implicit assumptions of the mathematical model depicted by Equation (4.2) are:

1. The error terms e_{ij} are independent within treatment and across all factor levels; in other words, the measurements or observations do not influence each other. This condition is satisfied in the example depicted in Table 4.2 in that the number of nonconformances reported by an inspector does not influence the number of nonconformances reported by the other inspectors (assuming, of course, the evaluations are done independently). Thus, for example, if an inspector was to report her number of nonconformances to the other inspector in the hope of influencing their findings, then obviously the condition of independence would be violated.

2. The experimental errors (or residuals) are assumed to be normally distributed.

3. The variance due to experimental error for each factor level is homogeneous; in other words, $S_1^2 = S_2^2 = S_k^2$.

Under these general conditions, the null hypothesis we want to test is that for k levels, the k population means are all equal, or, in another words,

$$H_o: \beta_i = 0 \text{ for } i = 1, 2, 3, \ldots, k$$

or, stated differently,

$$H_o: \bar{X}_1 = \bar{X}_2 = \bar{X}_3 = \ldots \bar{X}_k$$

The alternative hypothesis is that the means are not all equal,

$H_a: \beta_1 \neq 0$ for at least one value of i; or one or more $\bar{X}_k$ is (are) different.

To test these hypotheses, the method of analysis of variance analyzes the total variability of the data. Before proceeding any further, we must first introduce a few definitions. If we generalize the data matrix presented in Table 4.1 (representing the number of nonconformances reported by each inspector), we have for any factor with k levels the following data matrix (see Table 4.2).

The *total sum of squares* (SST) for the preceding X_{ik} observations is defined as

$$\sum_{i=1}^{k} \sum_{j=1}^{n} (x_{ij} - \bar{\bar{x}})^2 .$$

Table 4.2   Generalized table for a one-factor data matrix.

	Factor level 1	Factor level 2	...	Factor level k	
First observation or measurement	X_{11}	X_{12}	X_{1j}	X_{1k}	
Second observation					
			X_{ik}		
Nth observation	X_{N1}	X_{N2}		X_{Nk}	
Averages	$\bar{X}_1$	$\bar{X}_2$		$\bar{X}_k$	$\bar{\bar{X}}$

The *between levels* (or between groups) sum of squares SSB is defined as $n\sum_{i=1}^{k}(\bar{x}_i - \bar{\bar{x}})^2$ and the *within level* (or within group) sum of squares, which is more commonly known as the *error sum of squares,* or SSE, is defined as $\sum_{i=1}^{k}\sum_{j=1}^{n}(x_{ij} - \bar{x}_i)^2$.

If the null hypothesis is true, we can conclude that the total sum of squares $\sum_{i=1}^{k}\sum_{j=1}^{n}(x_{ij} - \bar{\bar{x}})^2$ of all the data is *due entirely to chance.* If the null hypothesis is not true, then part of the total sum of squares can be attributed to differences among the k means.

4.1.2 Overview of One-Way ANOVA Computations

The foundation of analysis of variance rests on the calculation of various sums of squares and comparing ratios of sums of squares. For Table 4.3, for example, these sums of squares consist of three components known as (1) *total sum of squares* (SST), (2) *within group sum of squares,* also known as *error sum of squares* (SSE), and (3) *between group sum of squares* (SSB). If we divide these sums of squares by their respective degrees of freedom, we obtain what is known as the *mean squares.* One of the properties of mean squares is that they are distributed as chi-squares and therefore (as explained in Chapter 2, section 2.4), the ratio of two mean squares will be distributed as an F-distribution.

$$\text{Mean Square of Error (MSE)} = \text{SSE}/k(n-1)$$

$$\text{Mean Square Between Group (MSB)} = \text{SSB}/k$$

A word of clarification is in order. When explaining the analysis of variance, the term *group* is often used in statistical textbooks when referring to sum of squares. Thus we speak of sum of square between or within groups. However, when we talk about factors such as inspectors, we refer to the *levels* of the factor. To add to the confusion, some textbooks refer to levels as *treatments* (in reference to the days when the first experimental designs were conducted in agricultural research stations). The term *treatment* is common in biostatistical textbooks or textbooks with an emphasis on medical research. In this context, the word *treatment* is appropriate because the purpose of the experiment is to investigate whether or not a set of treatments on a set of patients, for example, has (or does not have) a particular effect.

Although the words *group, level,* and *treatment* are used synonymously, my preference is to refer to factor levels. Thus, in the case of the preceding example, the inspector factor has three (in this case, qualitative) levels. We could also say that the three inspectors represent three groups. The use of the term *treatment* would not be applicable in this case. When, as in the inspector example, a set of n measurements (or observations) are obtained over three levels, we obtain three groups of measurements. The purpose of conducting an ANOVA is to investigate whether there is a difference among (the means) of these groups or, stated differently, we wish to know whether there is a factor effect caused by one or more of the factor levels. Without proof we will state that the total sum of squares can be partitioned or decomposed, into two components as follows:

$$SST = SSE + SSB$$

or

$$\sum_{i=1}^{k}\sum_{j=1}^{n}(x_{ij} - \overline{\overline{x}})^2 = \sum_{i=1}^{k}\sum_{j=1}^{n}(x_{ij} - \overline{x_i})^2 + n\sum_{i=1}^{k}(\overline{x_i} - \overline{\overline{x}})^2$$

It turns out that if the null hypothesis is true, the mean square error (MSE) and mean square between group (MSB) are independent estimates of the variance of the error (e). If, however, the alternative hypothesis is true (that is, if there is a treatment effect), then MSB provides an estimate of the treatment effects plus the error variance and therefore MSB will be larger than MSE. To test the null hypothesis we compute the following F-ratio (remember that the ratio of two chi-square distributions follows an F-distribution):

$$F = \frac{SSB/k-1}{SSE/k(n-1)} = \frac{MSB}{MSE}$$

If the F-ratio is greater than a critical $F_{\alpha,\,k-1,\,k(n-1)}$ we reject the null hypothesis; if it is smaller than the critical $F_{\alpha,\,k-1,\,k(n-1)}$ we accept H_o. In other words, when the mean square between groups is significantly larger than the mean square error (mean square within group), we reject the null hypothesis (H$_o$) that there is no treatment effect, which is the same as saying that some treatment effects (β_i) are not equal to zero. If we accept the null hypothesis Ho, we must conclude that the means ($\overline{X}_i$) for each level of the factor (that is, each group or, for the preceding example, each inspector) are statistically equal. In contrast, if we reject the null hypothesis (and consequently accept the alternative hypothesis H$_a$), we must conclude that at least one mean is significantly different from the others.

Most statistical software packages do not print the critical F-value but rather an F-ratio and its associated probability value (P). One must then compare the probability to the significance level alpha and apply the decision rule described in Chapter 3.

Statistical software packages summarize the results of an ANOVA in the form of a table known as the analysis of variance table. A generic version of an ANOVA table is presented in Table 4.3.

Example 4.1: One-Way Analysis of Variance. Three inspectors (A, B, and C) work on the same assembly line. The number of product defects found by each inspector over a period of five days are shown in number 3 below. We would like to know if the number of defects (or nonconformances) is the same for the three inspectors.

After replacing the generic factor level β_i [from Equation (4.2)] with the Inspector factor, the mathematical representation of this model is:

$$\text{Number of nonconformances}_{ij} = \overline{\overline{X}} + \text{Inspector}_i + e_{ij}$$

1. Hypotheses

    H$_o$: $\overline{X}_A = \overline{X}_B = \overline{X}_C$ or, H$_o$: Inspector$_i$ = 0 for i = 1, 2, 3

    H$_a$: Inspector$_i \neq 0$ for at least one value of i; or one or more $\overline{X}_i$ is (are) different

2. Significance level alpha (α) = 0.05

3. The experimental plan is as follows: Collect the nonconformance data for each inspector for a period of five

Table 4.3 Generalized one-way analysis of variance table.

Source of variation	Degrees of freedom	Sum of squares	Mean square	F
Between groups	k − 1	SSB	$MSB = \dfrac{SSB}{k-1}$	$\dfrac{MSB}{MSE}$
Within groups or *Error*	k(n − 1)	SSE	$MSE = \dfrac{SSE}{k(n-1)}$	
Total	kn − 1	SST		

days. The data matrix with associated means for each inspector (that is, level) and the grand mean are:

A	B	C
73	84	69
57	95	80
95	96	73
78	62	62
86	80	50
$\bar{X}_A = 77.8$	$\bar{X}_B = 83.4$	$\bar{X}_C = 66.8$
Grand average $(\bar{\bar{X}}) = 76$		

The inspectors are the *factor* or *treatment effect* we would like to investigate. For this experiment, the inspector factor (or treatment) has three qualitative levels, namely, Inspector A, Inspector B, and Inspector C. As we see later, factors can also have quantitative levels (for example, 15°, 25°, and 35°) or ordinal values such as 1, 3, 5, and so on. With ordinal levels, we only know that 5 is greater than 3 and that 3 is greater than 1, but we do not know by how much; in other words, unlike the scale obtained with a measuring instrument such as a thermometer, pressure gage, or a speedometer, for example, the distance between numbers is not known when using an ordinal scale.

In this example, each qualitative level of the factor Inspector is measured five times (n = 5). We therefore have three groups (A, B, C) and five observations.

Having computed the column (that is, within inspector) averages and the grand average (average of the 15 values), we can now compute two sets of sum of squares. Well over a hundred years ago, pioneers in statistical methods developed some clever methods to analyze numbers like these. The principle is rather simple and involves the computation of two sets of sum of squares known as *sum of squares between samples* (or *SSB*) and *sum of squares within samples* (which by definition is known as the error sum of squares, or SSE). These sums of squares are mathematically defined as follows:

$$SSB = n \sum_{i=1}^{k} (\bar{X}_i - \bar{\bar{X}})^2$$

where the summation (here from i = 1 to k) means summation over k levels. For this example, the summation will extend from i = 1 to 3, three inspectors. The term $\bar{X}_i$ refers to the average for each factor (that is, inspec tor) and the grand average $\overline{\overline{X}}$ (X double bar) is the average over all values. SSB measures the variability of the k sample means. If the k group means are nearly identical, then SSB would be small, reflecting little contribution, if any, from the groups. If, however, the group means were to differ greatly from one another, then SSB would be large, thus reflecting a contribution of the factor (or treatment) differences to the total variation.

$$SSE = \sum_{i=1}^{k} \sum_{j=1}^{n} (X_{ij} - \overline{X}_i)^2$$

where X_{ij} represents each individual value and the summations are for each inspector over the n observations (for this example n = 5 observations per inspector). The within sum of squares, or SSE, is a measure of the variation within individual samples or a measure of intrasample differences due to chance alone (hence the reference to error). This may seem very complicated, but as you shall now see, the computations are easy.

$$SSE = (73 - 77.8)^2 + (57 - 77.8)^2 + (95 - 77.8)^2 + (78 - 77.8)^2$$
$$+ (86 - 77.8)^2 = 818.8$$

$$+ (84 - 83.4)^2 + (95 - 83.4)^2 + (96 - 83.4)^2$$
$$+ (62 - 83.4)^2 + (80 - 83.4)^2 = 763.8$$

$$+ (69 - 66.8)^2 + (80 - 66.8)^2 + (73 - 66.8)^2$$
$$+ (62 - 66.8)^2 + (50 - 66.8)^2 = 522.8$$

SSE = 818.8 + 763.8 + 522.8 = 2104.8 = sum of squares within inspectors.

SSB = $5[(77.8 - 76)^2 + (83.4 - 76)^2 + (66.8 - 76)^2)] = 5[3.24 +$ 54.76 + 84.64] = 5 (142.64) = 713.2 = sum of squares between inspectors.

SST (or total sum of squares) = SSB + SSE = 2104.8 + 713.2 = 2818.

Having computed the sum of squares we next need to average these sums of squares. Indeed, the SSE term is computed over all 15 data points, whereas the SSB only compares the three group means with the grand mean. To correct for this discrepancy, statisticians have introduced another term known as the mean square. The *mean square* is the sum of squares divided by the appropriate *degrees of freedom*. The degrees of freedom for the between groups mean square is k − 1 (or the number of groups − 1). The degrees of freedom for the within group (or error) mean square is k(n − 1) (or 3 * 4 = 12). For this example we have:

$$MSB = SSB/(k - 1) = 713.2 / 2 = 356$$

$$MSE = SSE/3 * 4 = SSE/12 = 2105/12 = 175$$

You will recall that in order to compute the standard deviation of a set of n numbers you have to first compute the sum of the squared deviation from the mean divided by n − 1. This number is known as the *variance,* and the square root of the variance is the standard deviation. The preceding calculations for the mean squares are identical to those used to compute the variance and, in fact, *the preceding mean squares are nothing more than estimates of the variance of the observations.* The ratio MSB/MSE is used to determine whether a null hypothesis should be accepted or rejected. Recall that the null hypothesis is the hypothesis of no difference. In this example the null hypothesis states there is no inspector effect, meaning the average number of product defects for each inspector is equal. The alternative hypothesis would be that there is at least one average that is significantly different from the others.

How can we decide whether or not the null hypothesis should be accepted? We need to evaluate the magnitude of the MSB/MSE ratio. If the ratio is close to 1 this means the variation due to random error (or contributed by random error) is roughly equal to the variation contributed by the factor (that is, inspector). The obvious question is how far away from 1 must the ratio be before we can conclude there is *a factor effect,* that is to say that the means are different? In the preceding example, the ratio MSB/MSE = 356/175 = 2. Is this value (2) large enough to conclude there is an inspector effect? The answer to that question depends on the number of degrees of freedom of a distribution known as the F-distribution (see section 2.4 in Chapter 2). A computerized one-way ANOVA is reproduced in Table 4.4. Compare the table with Table 4.3. Note that the sum of squares for Inspectors (that is, the SSB, or between sum of squares) and the sum of squares for Error or within sum of squares (SSE) are equal to the values computed earlier. The ratio MSB/MSE (2.03) is listed under the heading F. This value is known as the F-ratio. Rather than printing the critical F-value (that is, the F-value needed to decide whether H_o should be accepted or rejected), the statistical software computes and prints F statistics and its associated probability (P). The P-value of 0.174 is the probability value associated with the F-value of 2.03. The decision rule (needed to either accept or reject H_o) is the same as the one described in Chapter 3:

1. If the probability value (P) is less than 0.05 (the significance level), reject the null hypothesis H_o and accept the alternative hypothesis H_a. This means there is a factor effect.

2. If the probability value (P) is greater than 0.05, accept the null hypothesis of no difference. This means there is no factor effect.

Table 4.4 One-way ANOVA: product defects versus inspectors.

Analysis of Variance for Product Defects					
Source*	**DF**	**SS**	**MS**	**F**	**P**
Inspectors	2	713	357	2.03	0.174
Error	12	2105	175		
Total	14	2818			

Term	Coefficient	SE Coefficient	T	P	
Constant	76.000	3.420	22.23	0.000	
Inspectors					
1	1.800	4.836	0.37	0.716	Note: 77.8 − 76 = 1.8
2	7.400	4.836	1.53	0.152	Note: 83.4 − 76 = 7.4

As for the third effect, it can easily be computed when we recall the sum of all effects is equal to 0 and therefore the third effect is equal to −9.2 (and indeed 66.8 − 76 = −9.2!).

*DF = degrees of freedom, SS = sum of squares, MS = mean square, F = F-ratio, P = probability

Although values of other significance levels can be selected (for instance, 0.01 or 0.10), 0.05 is the most often cited value for hypothesis testing.

Because $P = 0.174$ is greater than ($>$) 0.05, we must accept the null hypothesis H_o of no difference between inspectors. In other words, the F-ratio of 2.03 is not large enough to reject the null hypothesis. Stated differently, we can conclude that there is no inspector (factor) effect (that is, $Inspector_i = 0$) or the difference in the means among Inspector A, Inspector B, and Inspector C is *not* statistically significant. These statements are equivalent.

Optional explanation for Table 4.4: The bottom half of Table 4.4 is usually not reproduced in one-way analysis of variance tables. It was generated by running a separate program known as the general linear model. It shows P-values for three coefficients: constant (which is equal to the overall average $\overline{\overline{X}}$) and coefficients for Inspectors 1 and 2 (these are the effect values). Examining the P-values and comparing them to the alpha value of 0.05 we see that only the constant term of 76.000 (that is, the grand average $\overline{\overline{X}}$) is significant ($P = 0.000$); the other two coefficients (1.800 and 7.400) representing the Inspector effect are not significant. This information confirms what we already knew from the top half of Table 4.4, that is, there is no linear model [see Equation (4.2)] between number of nonconformances and Inspectors or, more accurately, that the number of nonconformances can only be predicted by the grand average $\overline{\overline{X}}$ + some error. If we refer back to Equation (4.2), we can see that because the Inspector effect (β_i in Equation (4.2)] is = 0, the equation (for this example) is as follows: Number of nonconformances = $\overline{\overline{X}}$ + error = 76 + error.

Table 4.5 is an extension of Table 4.4. It shows how the 95% confidence intervals for each inspector overlap. How are the limits computed? All the needed information is found to the left of the table. The three levels (under the heading Level), A, B, and C, are for the three inspectors. The sample size is N = 5 (five observations per inspector). The Means for each inspector are 77.80, 83.40, and 66.80, and the respective standard deviations are 14.31, 13.81, and 11.43. In addition the Pooled Standard Deviation is computed and equal to 13.24. The pooled standard deviation is the standard deviation computed for all three inspectors. If you recall that the standard error of a mean is equal to the standard deviation divided by the square root of the observations (N), or ($S/\sqrt{N}$), we can compute, using the pooled StDev of 13.24, that the pooled standard error of the means is equal to 13.24/ $\sqrt{5}$ = 5.92. To obtain the 95% confidence interval, simply multiply the standard error of the mean by 1.96 (that is, which is the $Z_{0.025/2}$ value): 5.92 x 1.96 = 11.60. For the first mean (77.80), we can now compute that the 95% confidence interval is equal to 77.80 +/− 11.60 or (66.19 to 89.40), which agrees with the plotted values. You can verify the limits for the other confidence intervals. You should also note that all of the confidence intervals overlap each other, signifying that the three means are statistically equivalent to each other (a result already confirmed by the ANOVA table).

The computational principles outlined for the one-way ANOVA (one variable) can be extended to 2, 3, 4, or N factors. The use of statistical software has greatly facilitated the sum of squares computations. This next example illustrates how a two-way ANOVA is analyzed.

Table 4.5 95% confidence intervals for the means.

				Individual 95% Confidence Intervals for Mean Based on Pooled StDev			
Level	N	Mean	StDev	-----+---------+---------+---------+			
A	5	77.80	14.31		(----------*----------)		
B	5	83.40	13.81		(----------*---------)		
C	5	66.80	11.43	(----------*---------)			
				-----+---------+---------+---------+			
Pooled StDev =		13.24		60	72	84	96

4.2 TWO-WAY ANOVA

The mathematical model for a two-way ANOVA is:

$$i = 1, 2, 3, \ldots, k \text{ (levels of } \alpha)$$

$$X_{ij} = \bar{\bar{X}} + \alpha_i + \beta_i + e_{ij} \quad \text{for}$$

$$j = 1, 2, 3, \ldots, n \text{ (levels of } \beta)$$

where alpha (α) and beta (β) represent two factors. The generalized analysis of variance table for two factors is presented in Table 4.6. The equations needed to compute the appropriate sum of squares and the detail of these computations are not shown. The generic two factors are labeled factor A and factor B. The source of variation is labeled "between levels of factor A" and "between levels of factor B." By levels we mean that the factors can represent, as explained in Example 4.1, either qualitative levels such as inspectors, departments, types of material, or quantitative levels such as different temperatures, different speed, or different humidity levels, for example.

Example 4.2: In Example 1.6 of Chapter 1, we analyzed various graphs to determine whether or not Workmen or Machine or both had an impact (an effect) on the number of defective parts produced. We can now restate the problem and analyze it as a two-way ANOVA.

The mathematical model for this example is:

$$\text{Defective-parts}_{ij} = \bar{\bar{X}} + \text{Worker}_i + \text{Machine}_j + e_{ij}$$

For $i = 1, 2, 3, 4$ workers and, $j = 1, 2, 3, 4$ machines

Hypotheses are as follows:

H_o: There is no worker effect (that is, Worker effect $= 0$)

H_o: There is no machine effect (that is, Machine effect $= 0$)

Table 4.6 Generalized two-way ANOVA table (factor A and factor B).

Source of variation	Degrees of freedom	Sum of squares	Mean square	F
Between levels of factor A	$k - 1$	SSA	$MSA = \dfrac{SSA}{k-1}$	$\dfrac{MSA}{MSE}$
Between levels of factor B	$n - 1$	SSB	$MSB = \dfrac{MSB}{n-1}$	$\dfrac{MSB}{MSE}$
Error (within factors)	$(n - 1)(k - 1)$	SSE	$MSE = \dfrac{SSE}{(n-1)(k-1)}$	
Total	$nk - 1$	SST		

H_a: There is a worker factor (that is, one or more workers is/are different from the others)

H_a: There is a machine effect (that is, one or more machines is/are different from the others) (Significance level (alpha) = 0.05)

The data plan is presented in Table 4.7. As you can see from the plan, each of the four workers is assigned to each of the four machines. For the purpose of this experiment, the process of assigning workers to machine is rather straightforward: the workers are simply rotated on each machine. For more complex experiments the process of assigning observations (or recording a measurement) for a particular combination of factors may need to be more carefully planned (see Chapter 5). The four levels for each worker are labeled W1–W4 and the four machine levels are labeled A1–A4. Table 4.7 shows how the data were entered into the computer using the usual spreadsheet format. The result of the analysis are presented in Table 4.8.

You will notice that the total sum of squares (SS) that is equaled to 199.0 is equaled to the sum of squares for Machine + the sum of squares (SS) for Workmen plus the SS for Error. You should verify the mean square

Table 4.7 Data for the two-way ANOVA.

Workmen	Machine	Defectives
W1	A1	26
W1	A2	19
W1	A3	23
W1	A4	22
W2	A1	27
W2	A2	21
W2	A3	28
W2	A4	26
W3	A1	31
W3	A2	27
W3	A3	26
W3	A4	25
W4	A1	26
W4	A2	18
W4	A3	24
W4	A4	19

Table 4.8 Two-way ANOVA: defectives versus machine, workmen.

Analysis of Variance for Defectives					
Source	DF	SS	MS	F	P
Machine	3	88.50	29.50	8.56	0.005
Workmen	3	79.50	26.50	7.69	0.007
Error	9	31.00	3.44		
Total	15	199.00			

(MS) values and the F-values. What are your conclusions? Should you accept or reject the null hypotheses?

4.3 HOW ABOUT INTERACTIONS?

The information contained in Table 4.6 tells us whether the factors Machine and Workmen have a significant statistical effect on the number of defective products being produced. Could there also be an interaction effect between Machine and Workmen? In other words, it could be that certain workers perform better or worse depending on which machine they operate on. The table does not provide us with this (interaction) analysis because it does not have the necessary information to do so. Looking at the number of degrees of freedom calculated in Table 4.6, notice that all of the degrees of freedom are accounted for and none are left to compute the mean sum of squares for interaction (MSI). To be able to compute the MSI we need to *replicate* each observation at least once, that is, take more than one observation for each combination of factors (see Table 4.9).

The mathematical model for a two-way ANOVA with interaction γ_{ij} is

$$X_{ijr} = \bar{\bar{X}} + \alpha_i + \beta_i + \gamma_{ij} + e_{ijr} \quad \text{for}$$

$i = 1, 2, 3, \ldots, k$ (levels of α)

$r = 1, 2, 3, \ldots, r$ (replicates)

$j = 1, 2, 3, \ldots, n$ (levels of β)

Example 4.3: Same as Example 4.2, but with replications. The mathematical model for this design is:

$$\text{Defective-parts}_{ijr} = \bar{\bar{X}} + \text{Worker}_i + \text{Machine}_j + \text{Worker} * \text{Machine}_{ij} + e_{ijr}$$

For $i = 1, 2, 3, 4$ workers; $j = 1, 2, 3, 4$ machines and $r = 1, 2$ replications

Table 4.9 Generalized ANOVA table for two factors (factor A and factor B) with interactions.

Source of variation	Degrees of freedom	Sum of squares	Mean square	F
Between factor A	$k - 1$	SSA	$MSA = \dfrac{SSA}{k-1}$	$\dfrac{MSA}{MSE}$
Between factor B	$n - 1$	SSB	$MSB = \dfrac{MSB}{n-1}$	$\dfrac{MSB}{MSE}$
Interactions	$(k - 1)(n - 1)$	SSI	$MSI = \dfrac{SSI}{(n-1)(k-1)}$	$\dfrac{MSI}{MSE}$
Error (or residuals)	$kn(r - 1)$	SSE	$MSE = \dfrac{SSE}{kn(r-1)}$	
Total	$rkn - 1$	SST		

Table 4.10 Number of defective parts produced over a period of two days (i.e., replication r = 2).

	Worker 1	Worker 2	Worker 3	Worker 4
Machine 1	26, 24	27, 26	31, 33	26, 24
Machine 2	19, 18	21, 20	27, 30	18, 17
Machine 3	23, 20	28, 27	26, 27	24, 25
Machine 4	22, 21	26, 26	25, 24	19, 20

Table 4.10 shows how the parts Defectives data was replicated a second day. Table 4.11 shows how the data were entered onto the spreadsheet. The results of the analysis are presented in Table 4.12. What are the hypotheses? What are your conclusions?

4.4 COMMENTS REGARDING THE SUM OF SQUARES FOR ERROR (SSE)

If you compare Tables 4.8 and 4.12 you will notice that although the SST has increased from 199.0 to 485.88 (which is not surprising because we have double the number of observations and hence the chance to increase the overall variation), the SSE has decreased from 31.0 to 20.0. Stated differently, we notice that in Table 4.8 the SSE represent approximately 15.6% of the SST, whereas in Table 4.12, the SSE represents only 4.1%.

Table 4.11 Number of defective parts produced: set of 32 observations represents 16 observations replicated twice (r = 2).

Workmen	Machine	Defectives
W1	A1	26
W1	A2	19
W1	A3	23
W1	A4	22
W2	A1	27
W2	A2	21
W2	A3	28
W2	A4	26
W3	A1	31
W3	A2	27
W3	A3	26
W3	A4	25
W4	A1	26
W4	A2	18
W4	A3	24
W4	A4	19
W1	A1	24
W1	A2	18
W1	A3	20
W1	A4	21
W2	A1	26
W2	A2	20
W2	A3	27
W2	A4	26
W3	A1	33
W3	A2	30
W3	A3	27
W3	A4	24
W4	A1	24
W4	A2	17
W4	A3	25
W4	A4	20

The variability attributed to chance in Table 4.8 is now mostly attributed to the Interaction between Machine and Worker and consequently we cannot simply say that a worker or a machine is better than another (worker or machine), but rather that the least number of defective parts is produced by

Table 4.12   Two-way ANOVA: defectives versus machine, workmen (with replication).

Analysis of Variance for Defectives					
Source	DF	SS	MS	F	P
Machine	3	156.63	52.21	41.77	0.000
Workmen	3	220.38	73.46	58.77	0.000
Interaction	9	88.88	9.88	7.90	0.000
Error	16	20.00	1.25		
Total	31	485.88			

Table 4.13   General linear model: wear versus rep(licate), A (= car), B (= wheel position), C (= compound).

Rep	fixed	2	1	2 (Two levels: 1, 2)		
A	fixed	4	1	2	3	4 (Four levels: 1, 2, 3, 4)
B	fixed	4	1	2	3	4
C	fixed	4	1	2	3	4

Analysis of Variance for Wear, Using Adjusted SS for Tests

Source	DF	Seq SS	Adj SS	Adj MS	F	P
Rep	1	3.125	3.125	3.125	2.08	0.164
A	3	5.250	5.250	1.750	1.16	0.348
B	3	1.000	1.000	0.333	0.22	0.880
C	3	194.500	194.500	64.833	43.05	0.000
Error	21	31.625	31.625	1.506		
Total	31	235.500				

an optimum worker-machine combination. This ability to reduce (or rather redistribute) variance attributable to chance (that is, error) is one of the important aspects of a well-designed experiment.

4.5 EXAMPLE 4.4 LATIN SQUARE (ADVANCED SECTION: REFER TO APPENDIX A)

In Appendix A, the potential effects of three factors on tire wear are analyzed. The design used for this experiment (a 4 x 4 Latin square) belongs to a class of designs known as randomized designs in that the tires were randomly assigned to each combination of car, wheel position, and rubber compound. The same problem is now analyzed using a three-way ANOVA.

The mathematical model for this design is:

$$\text{Wear}_{ijkr} = \bar{\bar{X}} + \text{Car}_i + \text{Wheel}_j + \text{Compound}_k + \text{Replicate}_r + \text{Error}_{ijkr}$$

For i = 1, 2, 3, 4 cars; j = 1, 2, 3, 4 wheel positions, k = 1, 2, 3, 4 compounds and r = 1, 2 (two replications)

Here are the hypotheses:

H_o: Car, wheel position and compound factors have no effect on tire wear

H_a: There is a car and/or wheel position and/or compound effect on tire wear (Significance level (alpha) = 0.05)

Table 4.13 on the preceding page shows the results of the analysis of variance. What are your conclusions? Which factor if any is (are) significant?

4.6 WHAT IS THE MEANING OF THE WORD *FIXED* APPENDED TO EACH FACTOR IN TABLE 4.13?

There are three types of ANOVA models: Model I for fixed effects, Model II for random effects, and Model III for mixed effect. What are fixed and random effects?

Fixed effects: A factor is said to be *fixed,* or Model I, if the experimenter is only interested in testing her hypotheses for a particular set of levels (or values). The discussion from section 4.1.1 is for fixed factor levels. Thus, for example, the conclusions regarding the compound effect (Example 4.4) are only valid for the four specific sets of compounds used during the experiment. If another experimenter wanted to verify the validity of the results he would have to duplicate the experiment using the *same chemical compounds* (that is, the same levels). That may seem obvious for testing chemical compounds but what about the cars? Are the results only valid for the four cars used in the experiment? One would hope not! But, as currently reported, this is what the model assumes. Similarly, the one-way ANOVA example for the three inspectors is only valid for these three inspectors; however, if the plant in question only has three inspectors then the fact that the qualitative factor levels for inspectors were fixed to these three inspectors is of no consequences whatsoever. If, however, the plant has seven or 10 inspectors and only three inspectors were selected at random from the population of seven or 10 inspectors, the factor levels would have to be treated as random levels (that is, random effects) and we would have to run a slightly different ANOVA.

Thus if we have k levels, the null hypothesis for fixed model is $H_0: \bar{X}_1 = \bar{X}_2 = \bar{X}_k = \bar{X}$ or $\beta_1 = \beta_2 = \beta_k = 0$ (that is, effects are equal to 0).

Random effect: For a random effect the levels are chosen at random from a vast array of possible values. Suppose for example you are the quality manager for a supermarket chain that has hundreds of stores throughout the state. Upper management wants you to conduct a customer survey. How can you proceed? Should you chose a Model I or a Model II? Because your population consists of hundreds of stores, you could select at random six or more stores from the region (or fewer, depending on your budget) and administer your customer satisfaction questionnaire to a sample of customers (let us say 30). For this simple one-way ANOVA example, the store factor is a random effect factor because the qualitative levels representing the stores are selected at random from a population of hundreds of stores. For random effect models (Model II), the nature of the hypothesis is different than for a Model I (fixed effect). With fixed effect ANOVAs, the purpose of the hypothesis is to test whether or not the effects are all zero. In random effect ANOVAs, the experimenter is not interested in a specific effect but rather in the variance s^2 (technically σ^2) of the population of differential effects. For example, if we had decided to select three inspectors randomly from a group of n inspectors, the null hypothesis would be:

H_0: variance (s^2) due to the inspector factor = 0, or, stated another way, there is no variation due to the inspector factor.

In the case of the four workmen working on four machines (Example 1.6, Chapter 1), if we had selected three workers at random from a population of n workers and four machines selected at random from a population of n machines, the analysis would have been a random effect model and we would have to test the following null hypotheses:

H_0: s^2 for workmen = 0 (that is, the variance due to the workmen factor is equal to 0)

H_0: s^2 for machine = 0

H_0: s^2 for workmen * machine interaction = 0

versus the alternative hypotheses that the variances (for workmen, machine, and workmen * machine) are not equal to 0.

To estimate the variances s^2 and to test H_0: $s^2 = 0$, we need to compute *expected mean squares* (EMS), which are derived for each source of variation (see section 4.7.1).The last model is known as the *mixed effect models* where some factors are fixed and some are random. No examples of mixed effect models are presented here.

4.7 ADVANCED TOPIC

This section is labeled advanced not so much because the subject matter is more complicated than what has been presented so far but rather because the material presented in this section is generally ignored or only covered superficially in Six Sigma Black Belt seminars. Knowing how to differentiate among the various types of levels (fixed vs. random vs. random and fixed) is important in understanding the different types of analysis of variances; this could in turn be of value to some data analysts. This section could also be valuable to those of you who need to perform a simplified Gage R&R study (explained in section 4.7.3).

4.7.1 Revisiting the Workmen Machine Example (4.2) Assuming the Factors Are Random Rather Than Fixed

Three workmen are picked at random from the population of 175 workers and randomly assigned to work on three machines picked at random (from a set of 17 identical machines).

The model is number of defective parts $= \bar{\bar{X}} +$ Workmen + Machine + Workmen * Machine + e

H_o: S^2 workmen = 0

H_o: S^2 machine = 0

H_o: S^2 workmen * machine = 0

versus H_a: S^2 not equal to 0 (as always, the alpha level is set at 0.05)

As you can see from Table 4.15, the analysis of variance table is slightly more complicated to interpret. Still, if we want to use a cookbook approach to explain Table 4.14 we can simply look at the P-values for each of the factors (0.008, 0.022, and 0.000) and conclude that the null hypotheses are rejected: there is a Workmen, Machine, and Workmen * Machine interaction effect or, stated differently, the variances for each factor and the interaction are not equal to zero. This can be verified by looking at the "Variance components using adjusted SS" listed at the end of the table. These estimated variances are:

Workmen = 7.948

Machine = 5.292

Workmen * Machine = 4.313

Error = 1.250

Table 4.14   General linear model: defectives versus workmen, machine.

Factor	Type	Levels	Values
Workmen	random	4	W1 W2 W3 W4
Machine	random	4	A1 A2 A3 A4

Analysis of Variance for Defective, Using Adjusted SS for Tests

Source	DF	Seq SS	Adj SS	Adj MS	F	P
Workmen	3	220.375	220.375	73.458	7.44	0.008
Machine	3	156.625	156.625	52.208	5.29	0.022
Workmen × Machine	9	88.875	88.875	9.875	7.90	0.000
Error	16	20.000	20.000	1.250		
Total	31	485.875				

Expected Mean Squares, Using Adjusted SS

Source	Expected Mean Square for Each Term (see also Table 4.15)
1 Workmen	(4) + 2.0000(3) + 8.0000(1)
2 Machine	(4) + 2.0000(3) + 8.0000(2)
3 Workmen × Machine	(4) + 2.0000(3)
4 Error	(4)

Error Terms for Tests, Using Adjusted SS

Source	Error DF	Error MS	Synthesis of Error MS
1 Workmen	9.00	9.875	(3)
2 Machine	9.00	9.875	(3)
3 Workmen × Machine	16.00	1.250	(4)

Variance Components, Using Adjusted SS

Source	Estimated Value
Workmen	7.948
Machine	5.292
Workmen × Machine	4.313
Error	1.250

If you compare the mean squares (MS) listed in Table 4.12 with the adjusted MS listed in Table 4.14 you will notice that with the exception of the MS for error, all other coefficients are slightly inflated. This is because in the random effect model the estimated variance for each factor is computed using a different assumption, which is explained in Table 4.15 (section 4.7.2).

If you would like to know how these variance estimates are computed, read the next section (4.7.2); otherwise skip to the next example.

4.7.2 How Are the Variances for a Random Effect Model Computed? (Optional)

You will recall that in Example 4.3 (section 4.3) we had two replications, four workmen, and four machines. If we denote Replication as R, A for Workmen, and B for Machines we have:

Replication (R) = 2

Workmen (A) = 4 = I (number of levels for factor A)

Machine (B) = 4 = J (number of levels for factor B)

Table 4.15 shows how the expected mean squares (EMS) are estimated for a two-factor random effects experiments. To compute the estimated variances for a factor we need to solve linear equations. For example, to find the variance for Factor A (that is, Workmen), proceed as follows:

$$MS_A = \sigma^2 + R\sigma^2_{AB} + IR\,\sigma^2_A$$

$$MS_{AB} = \sigma^2 + R\sigma^2_{AB}$$

Therefore, $MS_A - MS_{AB} = IR\,\sigma^2_A$ or, $\sigma^2_A = \dfrac{MS_A - MS_{AB}}{IR}$ (4.3)

Proceeding similarly for the other terms we would have:

$$\sigma^2_B = \frac{MS_B - MS_{AB}}{JR} \text{ and } \sigma^2_{AB} = \frac{MS_{AB} - MS_R}{R} \quad (4.4)$$

Referring to Table 4.15 and using equations (4.3) and (4.4), we have:

$$\sigma^2_A = \frac{73.548 - 9.875}{4 * 2} = 7.94$$

$$\sigma^2_B = \frac{52.208 - 9.875}{4 * 2} = 5.29$$

$$\sigma^2_{AB} = \frac{9.875 - 1.25}{2} = 4.313$$

These values agree with the values printed under the heading "Variance Components, Using Adjusted SS" found in Table 4.14. All of the necessary coefficients needed to compute the factor variances are reproduced under the heading "Expected Mean Squares, for Each Term" of Table 4.14 (see also the footnote in Table 4.15).

Table 4.15 EMS computation for a replicated random effects two-way ANOVA.

Source of Variation	EMS Model II
Workmen (A)	$\sigma^2 + R\sigma^2_{AB} + IR\ \sigma^2 A$
Machine (B)	$\sigma^2 + R\sigma^2_{AB} + JR\ \sigma^2 B$
Workmen $\times$ Machine (A $\times$ B)	$\sigma^2 + R\sigma^2_{AB}$
Error	σ^2

The section entitled "Expected Mean Square for Each Term" shows how the expected mean squares for each term are computed. Thus, for example, we see from Table 4.14 that the expected mean square for (1) Workmen = (4) + 2.0000(3) + 8.0000(1). The numbers in parentheses refer to the various sources of variation. Thus (1) = variation due to Workmen, (2) = variation due to Machine, (3) = variation due to Workmen * Machine, and (4) = variation due to Error. Translating this cryptic notation we have that the estimated mean square for workmen (1) is equal to Error variation (4) + 2 * Workmen * Machine variation (3) + 8 * Workmen variation (1) where the coefficients 2 and 8 are, respectively, equal to the number of replications (2) and the number of replication times the number of levels for workmen (2 * 4 = 8). To compute the estimated variation for the interaction term Workmen * Machine we have referred to Table 4.14: Error MS Workman * Machine = 9.875 = (4) + 2.0 (3) = 1.25 + 2 * $\sigma^2_{Workmen * Machine}$, or (9.875 − 1.25)/2 = 8.625/2 = 4.313 = $\sigma^2_{Workmen * Machine}$.

4.7.3 Gage Reproducibility and Repeatability Example Using a Model II (Random Effects) ANOVA (Optional) (See Also Section 8.12.3)

Suppliers, particularly suppliers to the automotive industry (but also others), are often asked to conduct costly studies known as Gage R&R studies (Gage Repeatability and Reproducibility studies). These studies, which are tedious and hence costly to conduct, consist of assessing the overall reliability of the measurement process, which includes the measuring equipment/instruments as well as the operators using the instruments. Within the manufacturing world where the practice of Gage R&R is most widespread, it generally consists of taking 10 or more parts of various sizes and assigning two or more operators, who should have some experience measuring the parts, to randomly measure the 10 parts at least twice (that is, repeatability = 2). By randomly measuring the parts, I mean the order in which the 10 parts are measured by each of the operators should be randomly assigned (for each operator) and the operators should not see the results of other operators.

In its most simplistic form, the purpose of Gage R&R studies is to determine what percentage of the variability attributable to (an inherent) part variation can be attributed to the *measurement process*. The measurement process itself consists of the ability of each operator to reproduce a measurement obtained by another operator (reproducibility) and the ability of each operator to obtain the same reading on the same part (repeatability). The variation attributable to repeatability and reproducibility is defined to be equal to the operator variability plus variation due to the repeatability (the error term), plus variation due to the interaction between operators and part.

$$R\&R = \sigma^2_{\text{Operator}} + \sigma^2_{\text{Operator * Part}} + \sigma^2_{\text{Repeatability or error}}$$

This R&R variation should not exceed 20% to 25% of the total variation where total variation is equal to:

Total variation = Variation due to parts + Variation due to R&R

To determine the Gage R&R capability, simply divide the variation due to R&R by the total variation and multiply by 100 to convert to percentage. If the R&R percentage contribution exceeds 25%, the measurement process should be reassessed, which could mean that operators may have to be retrained or perhaps some instruments may have to be recalibrated or possibly the measurement procedure needs to be reevaluated. Other causes may be found.

Naturally, the subject of Gage R&R is substantially more complicated than the brief description just provided, but nonetheless the main purpose of a Gage R&R study is to determine how much variability in the measurement process can be attributed to variability in operator, instrument error, and/or operator * part interaction. Table 4.16 shows the results of one such Gage R&R study. Ten parts were each measured twice by three operators. The order of measurement for each part and for each operator was randomly assigned. Because the assumption for the ANOVA model is that the operators were selected at random, the parts were also selected at random and the measuring order was also randomly assigned, and a Model II ANOVA was performed on the data. Note: If we only have three operators that specialize in measuring parts we could have assumed the levels for "operators" are fixed levels. This scenario would have required us to run a mixed model ANOVA.

Because the main purpose of a Gage R&R study is to determine whether or not the percentage contribution in variation due to repeatability and reproducibility is less than 25%, the hypotheses are not formulated for this example. What would be the hypotheses for this example? What would be your alpha level?

Table 4.17 is the analysis of variance for the Gage R&R study. Note that most statistical software packages offer a special routine design to perform Gage R&R study. This routine produces several tables and various graphics and analyses that are in substance the same as the analysis presented in this example but with much more information than shown in Table 4.17.

The results from Table 4.18 show that, as should be expected, the factor Part is statistically significant (remember that parts of *different* size were selected and therefore we would expect to find a significant part factor).

Table 4.16 Data for gage R&R study.

Part	Operator	Replicate	Measure
1	1	1	0.65
2	1	1	1.00
3	1	1	0.85
4	1	1	0.85
5	1	1	0.55
6	1	1	1.00
7	1	1	0.95
8	1	1	0.85
9	1	1	1.00
10	1	1	0.65
1	1	2	0.60
2	1	2	1.00
3	1	2	0.80
4	1	2	0.95
5	1	2	0.45
6	1	2	1.00
7	1	2	0.95
8	1	2	0.80
9	1	2	1.00
10	1	2	0.70
1	2	1	0.55
2	2	1	1.05
3	2	1	0.80
4	2	1	0.80
5	2	1	0.40
6	2	1	1.00
7	2	1	0.95
8	2	1	0.75
9	2	1	1.00
10	2	1	0.55
1	2	2	0.55
2	2	2	0.95
3	2	2	0.75
4	2	2	0.75
5	2	2	0.40
6	2	2	1.05
7	2	2	0.90
8	2	2	0.70

Continued

Continued

Part	Operator	Replicate	Measure
9	2	2	0.95
10	2	2	0.50
1	3	1	0.50
2	3	1	1.05
3	3	1	0.80
4	3	1	0.80
5	3	1	0.45
6	3	1	1.00
7	3	1	0.95
8	3	1	0.80
9	3	1	1.05
10	3	1	0.85
1	3	2	0.55
2	3	2	1.00
3	3	2	0.80
4	3	2	0.80
5	3	2	0.50
6	3	2	1.05
7	3	2	0.95
8	3	2	0.80
9	3	2	1.05
10	3	2	0.80

Also notice that there is a statistically significant Operator and Operator * Part interaction, which could indicate that not only operators measure parts differently but certain operators measure specific parts differently. To examine the nature of this interaction and to know which operator and which part are affected, we would need to produce a series of graphs (or more detailed tables), not reproduced here so as not to complicate this example unduly. Referring to the last heading of Table 4.17 entitled Variance Components, Using Adjusted SS, we see that the total variability (variance) is equal to $0.03694 + 0.00097 + 0.00222 + 0.00117 = 0.04130$. By definition, the variation attributable to Repeatability & Reproducibility is equal to the variation due to "Operator," plus variation due to the interaction "Part * Operator," plus the variation due to "Error" (which for this study consists of the variation due to "Repeatability" and due to "Error"):

$$R\&R \text{ variation} = 0.00097 + 0.00222 + 0.00117 = 0.00436$$

Table 4.17 General linear model: measure versus part, operator (combining replication with error).

Factor	Type	Levels Values
Part	random	10 1 2 3 4 5 6 7 8 9 10
Operator	random	3 1 2 3

Analysis of Variance for Measure, Using Adjusted SS for Tests

Source	DF	Seq SS	Adj SS	Adj MS	F	P
Part	9	2.045000	2.045000	0.227222	40.60	0.000
Operator	2	0.050083	0.050083	0.025042	4.47	0.026
Part × Operator	18	0.100750	0.100750	0.005597	4.80	0.000
Error	30	0.035000	0.035000	0.001167		
Total	59	2.230833				

Expected Mean Squares, Using Adjusted SS

Source	Expected Mean Square for Each Term
1 Part	(4) + 2.0000(3) + 6.0000(1)
2 Operator	(4) + 2.0000(3) + 20.0000(2)
3 Part × Operator	(4) + 2.0000(3)
4 Error	(4)

Error Terms for Tests, Using Adjusted SS

Source	Error DF	Error MS	Synthesis of Error MS
1 Part	18.00	0.005597	(3)
2 Operator	18.00	0.005597	(3)
3 Part × Operator	30.00	0.001167	(4)

Variance Components, Using Adjusted SS

Source	Estimated Value
Part	0.03694
Operator	0.00097
Part × Operator	0.00222
Error	0.00117

If we divide the R&R variability by the Total variability (0.04130), or $0.00436/0.04130 = 0.1055$, we see that only 10.55% of the total variability is attributable to R&R variability, which is less than 25% and therefore acceptable. As stated earlier, Gage R&R specialized software will produce much more information, but in the end the results are the same. However, you may not be able to convince your customer, who could demand that a more complete analysis be performed if only because the type of analysis just presented is unfamiliar to him or her.

4.8 CONCLUSION

As its name implies, the analysis of variance consist of breaking down the total variation (that is, the total sum of squares) found in a set of data into distinct parts known as within and between sum of squares. The partitioning of the total sum of squares is analyzed by computing mean squares. The ratios of mean squares are tested for significance using a statistical test known as an F-ratio. Although in theory one can analyze any number of factors (N-way ANOVAs), such experiments become increasingly more complicated to analyze. Moreover, it is also known that as the number of factors increases the probability of obtaining spurious significant tests (that is, probability of rejecting H_o) increases. It view of that limitation, it is important to resist the temptation of arbitrarily adding a large number of factors when performing analysis of variances.

5

Factorial Designs and Fractional Factorial Designs

5.0 INTRODUCTION

Design of experiments may be used to *confirm* our knowledge about the operating conditions of a process or to *explore* the effect of new conditions on a process. In both situations the purpose of the experiment(er) is to modify the routine operation of a process by readjusting a set of *factors* (hence the name *factorial designs*) and observe how one or more critical variables *respond* to the changes.

Until now the designs we have considered had factors with qualitative levels (number of operators or type of cars, for instance). But in many cases the factors affecting the response variable may be subject to either quantitative or qualitative changes. In many cases the experimenter wishes to investigate the relationship between two or more *factors* on a *response variable*.

Some examples of problems analyzed using factorial design type experiments would include:

1. Analyze the effect of temperature, concentration, and time on weight of metal recovered.

2. Analyze the effect of relative humidity, ambient temperature, and whether a pump is "On" or "Off" on the number of finished imperfections.

3. Analyze the effect of phosphorous, nitrogen, and carbon on algal population after 4, 6, 8, and 10 days of incubation (this is an example of a multiple response study).

4. Analyze the effect of a chemical brand, temperature, and stirring on the amount of pollutant discharged in a river.

5. Analyze the effect of concentration of a catalyst, concentration of sodium hydroxide, agitation speed, and temperature on the level of impurity.

6. Analyze the effect of daily deliveries: whether or not a uniform is worn, age of the deliverer, whether the delivery is before or after noon, on sales rating.

7. Analyze the effect of these seven factors: the presence or absence of a foreman, the gender of the packer, the time of day (morning vs. afternoon), whether the ambient temperature is normal or above normal, whether there is or is not piped-in music, age of packer (25 vs. > 25), and factory location (A vs B) on the time it takes to pack 100 standard items.

8. Analyze the effect of temperature and time on the tensile strength of a molded piece.

9. Analyze the effect of adhesive type (A vs. B), conductor material (copper vs. nickel), cure time (90 vs. 120 minutes), and integrated circuit coating (tin vs. silver) on bond strength.

Example: Suppose you wish to investigate how you could increase a process yield. Engineering has told you that three variables are likely to influence process yield: temperature, concentration of a chemical A, and whether or not the mixer is turned on. Because the process yield *depends* on the conditions set for the other three variables, we say that process yield is the *response* variable (also known as the *dependent* or *output* variable) and the three *independent* (also known as *input*) variables are the factors.

Generalizing, we have: $Y_i = F(X_1, X_2, \ldots, X_i,$ + all two-way interactions + ... + all n-way interactions) + e_i for i = 1, ..., n variables where the letter F reads as "(empirical) function of" and e_i is the usual error term. Note: I use the word *empirical* to differentiate the nature of the function from an exact mathematical function as found in physics, for example, $F = ma$. In other words, the equation says that Y is a function of some Xs, plus all possible interactions between these factors plus a (residual) error term that contains all unknown sources of variations not captured by the N variables (that is, factors) under investigation. In an ideal world, the error term e would be equal to 0, and we would explain 100% of the variation in the response variable Y. This would mean that the "behavior" (or variability) of the response variable Y is completely explained (or described) by the X independent variables (that is, factors) and their interactions. In reality, most investigators are quite happy if the factors can explain a percentage (30%, 50%, or sometimes 75% to 80%) of the response variable. For the process yield study we would have:

$$Y = F(X_1, X_2, X_3, X_1 * X_2, X_1 * X_3, X_2 * X_3, X_1 * X_2 * X_3) + e$$

or

Process Yield = F (temperature, concentration, mixing, temp * concentration, temp * mixing, conc * mix, temp * conc * mix) + e

The purpose of a design of experiment analysis is to investigate which factors if any, influence the response variable Y. As is the case with any statistical model, we would also formulate the following hypotheses:

H_0: There are no main factor effect and no interaction effect

or, $X_1 = X_2 = X_3 = 0$ and $X_1X_2 = 0$, $X_1X_3 = 0$, $X_2X_3 = 0$ and $X_1X_2X_3 = 0$

versus

H_a: One or more main factor(s) or interactions are significant

We would also specify a significant level alpha = 0.10 or 0.05. Next, we would run the design and verify the hypotheses via the ANOVA table.

5.1 FACTORIAL DESIGNS AT TWO LEVELS

The simplest factorial design is one in which the factors are set at two levels. Suppose that for the process yield experiment the process engineer suggests that the operative range for the temperature factor is 120°C to 145°C. Similarly, the chemical concentration factor can range between 5% and 12%. As for the last factor *mixing,* it can either be on or off. Thus for this experiment we have two quantitative factors and one qualitative factor *(mixing).* We would like to know how these three factors might affect the process yield.

It is important to note that if there is no factor effect this only means no effect was detected within the boundaries of the experiment but there could be a factor outside the boundary. Certainly one must also recognize that the area outside the experimental boundary may not be of any interest to the investigator. However, this unexplored area may well be where the optimum process performance could be found (you can explore this question a technique known as response surface analysis, presented in Chapter 7). To investigate this problem we need to design an experiment that will allow us to vary the temperature, concentration, and mixing factors and observe the process yield performance for each combination of temperature, concentration, and mixing. But how can we combine these factors in an orderly fashion? Statisticians have suggested specific ways to organize the data collection process. This organization process is known as a *design matrix* (hence the name *design of experiment,* or *DoE*). The design matrix for a three-factor experiment is shown in Table 5.1.

Table 5.1   Design matrix for a three factor two-level experiment.

Temperature	Concentration	Mixing
(C)	(%)	(On-off)
120	5	Off
145	5	Off
120	12	Off
145	12	Off
120	5	On
145	5	On
120	12	On
145	12	On

The pattern of the design matrix illustrated is said to be organized in the standard order form. A *standard order design* consists of alternating the values for each factor in a specific pattern: for the first factor, each value is alternated; for the second factor the values are alternated in pairs, and so forth. One important property of factorial designs is that they represent what is known as *orthogonal arrays*. Viewed geometrically, in an orthogonal array the columns are perpendicular to each other. This perpendicularity, in turn, implies that the columns are *independent* of each other, which in turn implies that the sum of squares used to estimate factor coefficients can also be estimated independently of each other. This turns out to be a very useful property. The subject of orthogonal arrays, although not complex, is beyond the scope of this book and only mentioned here because of its importance when computing the sum of squares (see note for Table 5.6). For computational convenience the values of each level can be recoded using minus and plus signs as shown in Table 5.2.

To conduct the experiment using the standard design matrix, one would first set the temperature at 120°C, concentration at 5% with no mixing, and observe what the process yield would be. The second run would set the temperature at 145°, concentration at 5% with no mixing, and the last or eighth run would set the temperature at 145°, concentration at 12% and mixing "On." Although one could use the order of the standard design matrix to run the experiment, it is usually recommended, if it is not expensive to do so, to *randomize* the runs as shown in the last columns of Table 5.2. Randomization allows for the redistribution of (potential) systematic source of error. If one uses the randomized run order suggested in the last columns of Table 5.2, the first run is equivalent to the fifth standardized run: temperature set

Table 5.2   Coded values from Table 5.1.

Standardized run order	Temperature	Concentration	Mixing run order	Randomized
1	−	−	−	5
2	+	−	−	2
3	−	+	−	1
4	+	+	−	6
5	−	−	+	4
6	+	−	+	8
7	−	+	+	3
8	+	+	+	7

at 120°, concentration of 5%, and "Yes" for mixing. One would then move on to the second run (145°, 5%, no mixing), and so on. Must one always randomize runs?

The advantage of running the experiment in a random order is that it allows for the reduction of systematic error. Systematic error *may* be introduced by the arrangement of treatments in a specific pattern as prescribed by the systematic design of the standard order matrix. However, as D. R. Cox points out in his excellent *Planning of Experiments,* "It should not be thought, however, that these remarks mean that systematic designs are never to be tolerated. If we have good knowledge of the form of the uncontrolled variation and if a systematic arrangement is much easier to work with, as when the different treatments represent ordered changes of a machine, it may be right not to randomize."[1] Randomization may not be required if the system under investigation is a state of statistical control (as defined by the well-known Shewhart process control charts). As the ever practical Cuthbert Daniel pointedly notes,

> We do not suggest that randomization be ignored just because "things appear to be going along all right." We may not know how nearly all right things have been going until some serious randomization trials have been carried out. We do suggest that randomization, although generally sufficient, may not always be necessary. . . . There are many cases in which randomization is difficult, expensive, inconvenient. The random allocation of differing experimental conditions to experimental units is sometimes upsetting to the experimenter. . . . If the system under study takes a long time to come to equilibrium after a sudden willful change

Table 5.3   A 2^3 factorial design for the process yield experiment.

	Standardized run order	Temperature	Concentration	Mixing Yield (%)
1	−	−	−	78
2	+	−	−	89
3	−	+	−	57
4	+	+	−	82
5	−	−	+	55
6	+	−	+	96
7	−	+	+	49
8	+	+	+	93

in the level of some factor, then experimental work, and even plant production, may be slowed to an unacceptable rate by such a change.[2]

This last observation by Daniel is very important. Suppose that for some technical reason the factor Temperature (see Table 5.2) is the most time consuming to change. How would you proceed? One way to address this difficulty would be to reassign the Temperature factor to the last column, the column for which values alternate the least.

Returning to our example, we see in Table 5.3 how the response variable "Yield" varied for each combination of values shown in the standard matrix.

One of the advantages of using + and − signs is that the computation for averages (as shown later) is easy. Another advantage is that the units of measurement are all the same. Finally, the use of coded values $(-1, +1)$ facilitates the calculation and explanation of main effects and interaction effects (however, note that computer software packages allow users to use coded or uncoded values). If, as shown in Table 5.4, one multiplies each factor, it is possible to calculate not only the *main effects* (that is, the effect for Temperature, Concentration, and Mixing) but also all of the interaction effects. Table 5.4 shows how these interaction factors are generated.

The mean is equal to the sum of the yield divided by 8 or 74.875. To compute the Temperature effect we simply multiply the sign of the Temperature factor with the corresponding Yield; referring to Table 5.4, we have:

$$\frac{-78 + 89 - 57 + 82 - 55 + 96 - 49 + 93}{4} = \frac{121}{4} = 30.25$$

Table 5.4   Main factors and all factor interactions.

Mean	Temperature (T)	Concentration (C)	Mixing (M)	T x C	T x M	C x M	T x C x M	Yield
+	−	−	−	+	+	+	−	78
+	+	−	−	−	−	+	+	89
+	−	+	−	−	+	−	+	57
+	+	+	−	+	−	−	−	82
+	−	−	+	+	−	−	+	55
+	+	−	+	−	+	−	−	96
+	−	+	+	−	−	+	−	49
+	+	+	+	+	+	+	+	93
Divide by 8	4	4	4	4	4	4	4	

Table 5.5   Fractional factorial fit: yield versus T, C, M.

Estimated Effects and Coefficients for Yield (coded units)		
Term	**Effect**	**Coefficient**
Constant		74.875
T	30.250	15.125
C	−9.250	−4.625
M	−3.250	−1.625
T * C	4.250	2.125
T * M	12.250	6.125
C * M	4.750	2.375
T * C * M	−2.750	−1.375

We divide by four because there are only four positive and four negative values. The Temperature * Concentration * Mixing effect is equal to:

$$\frac{-78+89+57-82+55-96-49+93}{4}=\frac{-11}{4}=-2.75$$

The remaining effect values were computed using a statistical software package (see Table 5.5). From Table 5.5 we can see that the largest effect is the Temperature effect (T = 30.25); all other effects are significantly smaller. The Temperature * Mixture interaction effect (T * M = 12.25) is the second largest effect but is less than 50% of the temperature effect. You will also notice that the T * C * M (three-way interaction factor) has the smallest value (-2.75). Small and therefore statistically insignificant values for three-way and higher order interactions are common and therefore usually not worth the analysis (also three-way interactions are difficult to interpret).

5.1.1 How to Interpret the Coefficients

As you compare the values listed under the heading Effect to the values listed under the heading Coefficient, you will notice the coefficient values are half the values of the Effects. This is because the effect is calculated over the range -1 to $+1$ (a range of 2) and therefore the real value of the effect is half. The value of 15.125 for the Temperature coefficient means there is a direct relationship between the yield and temperature: the yield is higher at higher temperature. A negative coefficient would mean there is an inverse relationship between the response variable (Y) and the factor. There seems to be a negative relationship between yield and concentration, meaning the yield is higher *at lower* concentrations.

5.1.1.1 Optional Reading

The complete mathematical equation for the response variable Yield is:

$$\text{Yield} = \text{Average (Yield)} + \text{Coefficient}_T * T + \text{Coefficient}_C * C +$$
$$\text{Coefficient}_M * M + \text{Coefficient}_{TC} * TC + \text{Coefficient}_{TM} *$$
$$TM + \text{Coefficient}_{CM} * CM + \text{Coefficient}_{TCM} * TCM + e$$

where Average (Yield) is the grand average (often denoted in textbooks as $\overline{\overline{Yield}}$).

Using the values listed in Table 5.5 we would have:

$$\text{Yield} = 74.875 + 15.125 * T - 4.625 * C - 1.625 * M + 2.125 * T *$$
$$C + 6.125 * T * M + 2.375 * C * M - 1.375 * T * C * M$$

Because the coded values for T, C, and M are -1 and $+1$, we would simply insert the appropriate coded value in the equation for each of the factors to estimate the yield. Thus, for example, for all factors set at their high ($+1$) value we would have:

$$\text{Yield} = 74.875 + 15.125 * (1) - 4.625 * (1) + 2.125 * (1 * 1) + 6.125 *$$
$$(1 * 1) + 2.375 * (1 * 1) - 1.375 * (1 * 1 * 1) = 94.624\%$$

What would have happened to the coefficients if the original values instead of the coded ($-1, +1$) values had been used? Because the original uncoded operational settings for Temperature are $120°$ (-1) and $145°F$ ($+1$) and 5% and 12% for Concentration, equation coefficients will need to be adjusted in the computation to account for the different units of measurement. And this is exactly what happens. When the same data is run with factor setting set at (120,145), (5,12), and (0,1) (for no mixing and mixing), the estimated coefficients for yields are adjusted appropriately as shown here:

Estimated Coefficients for Yield Using Data in Uncoded Units	
Term	**Coefficient**
Constant	88.2000
Temp	0.0400000
Concenc	−12.6000
Mix	−215.429
Temp * Concenc	0.0800000
Temp * Mix	1.51429
Concenc * Mix	9.68571
Temp * Concenc × Mix	−0.0628571

Thus if we had used original uncoded units, the equation now reads:

$$\text{Yield} = 88.2 + 0.040 * T - 12.6 * C - 215.0 * M + 0.080 * T * C$$
$$+ 1.51429 * T * M + 9.68571 * C * M - 0.0628 * T * C * M$$

where T is now equal to 120 or 145, C = 5 or 12, and M = 0 or 1. You will notice that the coefficients are now adjusted, as it were, to reflect the different range of values taken by each factor. As explained before, the advantage of using coded values is that it standardizes all units of measurement and in fact, when uncoded factor values (that is, levels) are entered in the design matrix, some software packages will automatically standardize the factor levels and generate effect coefficients based on the coded and uncoded values.

All of the yield values associated with each combination of factor settings can be generated by most computer software packages, but is it wise to use all of the factors in the equation? After all, it would seem that some coefficients are more significant than others. How do we know which factor(s) effect is/are statistically significant? Several methods are available; one can either:

1. Generate a Pareto chart (Figure 5.1).

2. Generate a normal probability plot (Figure 5.2).

3. Generate an ANOVA table and its associated P-values.

5.1.2 Pareto Chart

Figure 5.1 represents a Pareto chart of the effect. The dotted line represents the T-value associated with an alpha level of significance of 0.10. An effect

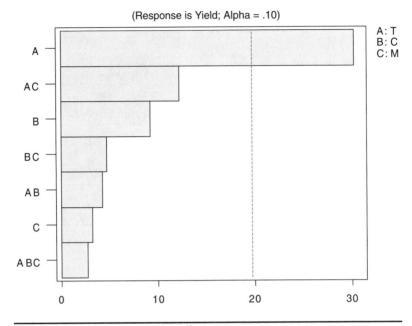

(Response is Yield; Alpha = .10)

A: T
B: C
C: M

Figure 5.1 Pareto diagram for effects T = temperature, C = concentration, and M = mixing.

larger than the dotted line represents a significant effect. The Pareto chart confirms that only the Temperature effect is statistically significant. The A, B, and C values are labels automatically assigned by the computer to each factor. The legend to the right of the Pareto diagram shows the correspondence among A: Temperature, B: Concentration, and C: Mixing.

5.1.3 The Normal Plot

The normal probability plot consists of a straight line and points representing each main effect and combination of factors (that is, two-way interaction, three-way interaction, and so on.) if these are included in the model. The simplest way to interpret a normal probability plot is:

1. If all of the effects line up approximately along the line, we can conclude that none of the effects (and hence none of the factors) are important; in other words, there is no relationship between the response variable and any of the factors.

2. If one or more points deviate significantly from the straight line, we can than conclude that the points representing these factors have an influence on the response variable. The further

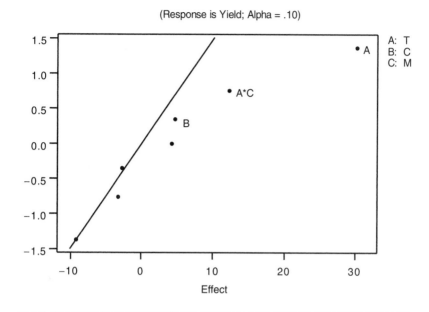

Figure 5.2   Normal probability plot for the effects.

an effect is from the straight line, the more likely it represents a statistically significant event. Unlike the Pareto diagram of Figure 5.1, the normal probability plot does not indicate which deviations from the straight line are significant (however, see the analysis of variance discussion that follows).

In Figure 5.2 we see that point A representing Temperature is way to the right of the straight line (this information is equivalent to the first bar of the Pareto diagram (Figure 5.1). The second point that is farthest from the line represents the AC, or Temperature * Mixture interaction—this may indicate the interaction may influence the response variable Yield.

5.1.4 The ANOVA Table

An ANOVA table cannot always be produced, and Table 5.6 shows why. Although the sum of squares needed for the ANOVA can be computed for each effect, the sum of square for the error term is equal to 0 because all of the degrees of freedom have been used to compute the main effects, the two two-way interaction and the one three-way interaction, and nothing is left to estimate the error term. Therefore, the ratios needed to compute the necessary t and F values cannot be computed.

Table 5.6   Analysis of variance for yield (coded units).

Source	DF	Seq SS*	Adj SS*	Adj MS	F	P
Main Effects	3	2022.37	2022.37	674.12	*	*
2-Way Interactions	3	381.38	381.38	127.13	*	*
3-Way Interactions	1	15.12	15.12	15.12	*	*
Residual Error	0	0.00	0.00	0.00		
Total	7	2418.88				

The sequential and adjusted sum of squares are always equal for orthogonal arrays.

One way to get around this difficulty is to use the three-way interaction term to estimate the error term. Table 5.7 shows how Table 5.6 can be modified to generate the appropriate t-values for each effect as well as the F-values and probability values shown in the ANOVA Table, by using the three-way interaction as a source of error. Notice how the three-way interactions sum of squares (Seq SS) of 15.12 (Table 5.6) is now found under the heading Residual Error in Table 5.7. The T column associated with each factor is the computed t values. The t value is obtained by dividing the effect coefficient by the standard error of the coefficient (1.375 in this example). For example, the T-value for factor M is equal to $-3.250/1.375 = -1.18$.

The ANOVA Table listed in Table 5.7 confirms the graphical display of Figures 5.1 and 5.2 because it shows that the only significant effect (assuming an alpha level of 0.10 as specified in Figure 5.1) is Temperature with a probability value of 0.058 (the grand average or constant term is also significant). What would happen to the coefficients if we had run the experiment (hence the ANOVA) on the original values instead of the coded values. Would they have changed (larger or smaller)?

5.2 THE USE OF REPLICATION TO ESTIMATE ERROR TERMS

Another method to obtain an estimate of the error sum of square needed to compute F-ratios would be to replicate the experiment twice. Table 5.8 show the first set of eight runs plus a second set of eight runs. Notice how the second set of Yield values only approximates the set of values obtained during the first run. This is to be expected because a model—remember the current model assumes only three factors—can approximate or estimate yield. The ANOVA of Table 5.9 shows there are now two significant main effects that influence process yield: Temperature and Concentration.

Table 5.7 Fractional factorial fit: yield (coded units) versus T, C, M.

Estimated Effects and Coefficients for Yield (Coded Units)					
Term	Effect	Coefficient	SE Coefficient	T	P
Constant		74.875	1.375	54.45	0.012
T	30.250	15.125	1.375	11.00	0.058
C	−9.250	−4.625	1.375	−3.36	0.184
M	−3.250	−1.625	1.375	−1.18	0.447
T * C	4.250	2.125	1.375	1.55	0.366
T * M	12.250	6.125	1.375	4.45	0.141
C * M	4.750	2.375	1.375	1.73	0.334

Source	DF	Seq SS*	Adj SS*	Adj MS	F	P
Main Effects	3	2022.37	2022.37	674.12	44.57	0.110
2-Way Interactions	3	381.38	381.38	127.13	8.40	0.247
Residual Error	1	15.12	15.12	15.12		
Total	7	2418.88				

The sequential and adjusted sum of squares are always equal for orthogonal arrays.

Table 5.8 Replicated design for the process yield experiment.

T	C	M	Yield	Run
−1	−1	−1	78	1
1	−1	−1	89	2
−1	1	−1	57	3
1	1	−1	82	4
−1	−1	1	55	5
1	−1	1	96	6
−1	1	1	49	7
1	1	1	93	8
−1	−1	−1	64	1 Replication 2 begins here
1	−1	−1	88	2
−1	1	−1	56	3
1	1	−1	80	4
−1	−1	1	71	5
1	−1	1	95	6
−1	1	1	66	7
1	1	1	90	8

Table 5.9 Fractional factorial fit: yield versus T, C, M.

Estimated Effects and Coefficients for Yield (Coded Units)					
Term	**Effect**	**Coefficient**	**SE Coefficient**	**T**	**P**
Constant		75.563	1.720	43.94	0.000
T	27.125	13.562	1.720	7.89	0.000
C	−7.875	−3.937	1.720	−2.29	0.051
M	2.625	1.312	1.720	0.76	0.467
T * C	2.125	1.063	1.720	0.62	0.554
T * M	6.125	3.063	1.720	1.78	0.113
C * M	3.125	1.562	1.720	0.91	0.390
T * C * M	−1.375	−0.687	1.720	−0.40	0.700

Analysis of Variance for Yield (coded units)

Source	DF	Seq SS	Adj SS	Adj MS	F	P
Main Effects	3	3218.69	3218.69	1072.90	22.68	0.000
2-Way Interactions	3	207.19	207.19	69.06	1.46	0.297
3-Way Interactions	1	7.56	7.56	7.56	0.16	0.700
Residual Error	8	378.50	378.50	47.31		
Pure Error	8	378.50	378.50	47.31		
Total	15	3811.94				

The Temperature effect is equal to 27.125, whereas the Concentration effect is equal to −7.878. This means there is a *direct relationship* between process yield and temperature and an *inverse relationship* between process yield and concentration. One can therefore conclude that, *within the current operating conditions,* the process yield is optimum when run at a temperature of 145°C and a chemical concentration of 5%. The expression *within the current operating conditions* is important because the temperature and concentration boundaries of the experiment were set based on the recommendation of the process engineer, and we do not know how the process behaves outside these boundary conditions. It could well be that the optimum process yield is outside this region and could be reached if one were to increase the temperature to 148° or perhaps 150°, for example. These questions can be investigated with a technique known as *response surface analysis.* Figure 5.3 shows how the 90% yield contour is found at the upper left corner of the contour plot (where T = 1 = 145°C and C = −1 = 5%). One could run another experiment in that region to see if a better yield could

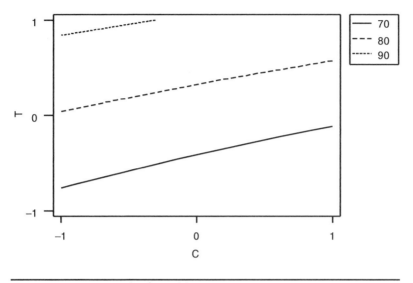

Figure 5.3   Contour plot for yield.

be obtained. We return to a more detailed explanation of this technique in Chapter 7.

5.3 FRACTIONAL FACTORIAL

A team of experts can sometimes suggest that as many as six or seven factors can potentially affect a response variable. Even if only two levels are considered for each factor, a seven-factor experiment will require $2^7 = 128$ runs. Regardless of the environmental conditions, 128 runs or even 64 runs is an expensive proposition for most industrial conditions. Most process managers or directors will likely refuse to have their process tied up for hours and maybe days to allow a team of experimenters to constantly readjust a process for the sake of observing the impact of some factors on a response variable. Fortunately, thanks to fractional factorials, one does not need to conduct 128 runs or even 64 runs to investigate the relationship among three or more factors on one or more response variables.

What is a fractional design? As its name implies, a fractional design is a fraction of the original design matrix where the fraction can be, depending on the number of factors considered in the design, one-half, one-quarter, one-eighth, or even one-sixteenth the length of the full factorial design. Thus, for example, a full factorial 8 run generated by a 2^3 full factorial design can be cut in half to generate a 2^{3-1} or 2^2 four-run design. Generally speaking, it is worth noting that every 2^p factorial experiment is a fraction of a larger 2^P (P > p) experiment for which some factors have not been considered and/or varied—in other words, held constant. For example, a 2^3 design requires half the runs of a 2^4 design, and we can assume that in the 2^3 design the (unknown) fourth (fifth, sixth, and so on) factors are held constant. Naturally, because it is either impossible or too costly to consider the potential effect of every possible factor on a response variable, we must accept the fact that all experimental designs are but an approximation (a model) of reality. The first question you might ask is this: "Out of N runs, how do I select half as many runs?" For example, out of an eight-row matrix (runs) generated by a 2^3 full factorial, which rows do you select to run the fractional design? Do you select the first four rows and ignore the last four rows, or do you select every other row, or do you select the four rows randomly such as 1, 4, 7, 8 or 2, 5, 6, 7 or some other combinations?

Here are two answers:

1. Statistical software can easily produce the correct fractional design. You simply enter the number of factors and ask the computer to generate a fractional design for you. In fact, if your budget is really tight or if your director or plant manager is really impatient or does not much care for experimental designs, you can even ask the computer to generate a quarter of the runs. Thus a 32-run 2^5 factorial experiment could be conducted with only eight runs. Naturally, as we soon see, this will result in the information being compressed, or *confounded*, among factors; obviously, nothing is free.

2. The best way to *generate* fractions of runs will be explained using the simple example of an eight-run 2^3 design.

We start with three factors that we generically refer to as A, B, and C. Multiply A by B and place the result of this multiplication into factor C. The design matrix shown in Table 5.10 represents a half-fraction of the design matrix shown in Table 5.1. How was this matrix generated? Column C was generated by multiplying column A with B, for example, $-1 \times -1 = 1$, $1 \times -1 = -1$, and so on, for the remaining two values. We now have C = AB. Having performed this simple operation the computer then selected the first four rows of the standard matrix (Table 5.1) replacing the original C plus and minus values with the transformed C = AB values.

Table 5.11 includes important information associated with the fractional design. From Table 5.11, we learn that the design is called a resolution III design (not a crucial piece of information), the Fraction is one-half, and there are no replicates and no blocking. The note warns us that "Some main effects are confounded with two-way interactions," and an "Alias

Table 5.10 Computer-generated half fraction for a three-factor design.

A	B	C = AB
−1	−1	1
1	−1	−1
−1	1	−1
1	1	1

Table 5.11 Fractional factorial design.

Factors:	3	Base Design:	3,	4	Resolution: III
Runs:	4	Replicates:		1	Fraction: 1/2
Blocks:	none	Center pts (total):		0	

NOTE: Some main effects are confounded with two-way interactions.

Design Generators: C = AB

Alias Structure

I + ABC
A + BC
B + AC
C + AB

structure is also printed along with a "Design Generator: C = AB." What does all this mean?

We already know about the design *generator* (C = AB), but what are these aliases? This is the part where we learn that a compromise had to be reached. Indeed, because nothing is free, there is a small price to pay for running fractional factorial designs, which is that the calculation of the effects are inflated (or deflated depending on whether the coefficients are positive or negative) by, in this case, two-way interactions. The alias structure describes the nature of this confounding by telling us that the grand average (I) is confounded with the three-way interaction and each of the main factors are in turn confounded by two-way interactions (BC, AC, and AB). Because C was generated by multiplying A with B, it is logical that C = AB; the other aliases are derived by a similar process of cyclical multiplication.

To illustrate the concept of fractional factorial, the example of Table 5.1 is now reproduced using only the half fraction shown in Table 5.10. Table 5.12 shows the data. The Yield data are taken from Table 5.1 and were

Table 5.12   Yield data taken from Table 5.1 to match the half replicate (2^{3-1}) design of Table 5.10.

T	C	M	Yield
−1	−1	1	55
1	−1	−1	89
−1	1	−1	57
1	1	1	93

Table 5.13   Fractional factorial fit: yield versus T, C, M.

Estimated Effects and Coefficients for Yield (coded units) Fractional factorial			Estimated Effects and Coefficients for Yield (coded units) from Table 5.7		
Term	**Effect**	**Coefficient**	**Term**	**Effect**	**Coefficient**
Constant		73.5000	Constant		74.875
T	35.0000	17.5000	T	30.250	15.125
C	3.0000	1.5000	C	−9.250	−4.625
M	1.0000	0.5000	M	−3.250	−1.625
I + T * C * M			T * C	4.250	2.125
T + C * M			T * M	12.250	6.125
C + T * M			C * M	4.750	2.375
M + T * C			T * C * M	−2.750	−1.375

Note: The left side of the table lists the coefficients for the fractional design; the right side of the table lists the coefficients for the full factorial design from Table 5.7.

selected to match the new (fractional) design matrix pattern. The results of the analysis are shown on the left side of Table 5.13; the right side of Table 5.13 has the coefficients for the full factorial obtained from Table 5.10.

If you compare the *coefficients* and look at the alias structure you will notice the following reading from left to right: 73.500 = 74.874 − 1.375 or, as the alias structure predicts, the coefficient for the grand mean (I = Constant) for the fractional design is indeed equal to the grand mean for the full factorial plus (in this case a −1.375) the three-way interaction factor. In this case the mean is deflated by the negative value of the three-way interaction. Similarly, you will notice (looking on the right side of Table 5.13) that 30.25 (the *effect* for T) plus 4.750 (the CM *effect*) = 35.000, which is the effect listed for T on the left side of Table 5.13 (the same observation about aliasing can be made by looking at the Coefficients instead of the Effects). And so on for the remaining values. The effect values of the fractional factorial

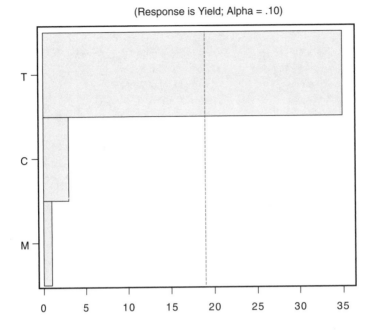

(Response is Yield; Alpha = .10)

Figure 5.4 Pareto diagram for the fractional design showing that temperature (T) is a significant factor.

design listed on the left side of Table 5.13 are *confounded* by three-way and two-way interactions. Despite this confounding of the main effects, the results are, interestingly enough, the same as can be seen from Figure 5.4.

The obvious advantage of fractional factorial is that they cost half as much to run and usually, almost the same amount of information can be obtained!

5.4 NONMANUFACTURING EXAMPLE

The following nonmanufacturing example shows how design of experiments can also be conducted in a nonindustrial setting. Having just returned from a four-week Black Belt training session, a plant manager decides to apply what he has learn. Having been particularly impressed with the topic of fractional factorial designs, he decides he could use such designs to study the potential effect of seven factors on the time it takes an assembler to assemble *standard* units.

Table 5.14 Factors and response variable.

	(−1,1)
1. Foreman	(absent, present)
2. Gender of packer	(man, woman)
3. Time of day	(morning, afternoon)
4. Temperature	(normal, above normal)
5. Music	(none, piped in)
6. Age of assembler	(under 35, above 35)
7. Plant location	(Temecula, Bellevue)
8. Response variable = Time to assemble standard unit (in minutes)	

Table 5.15 2^{7-3} fractional factorial with response variable time.

	Std Order	Run Order	Center Pt	Blocks	Foreman	Gender	Time Day	Temp	Music	Age	Location	Time
1	1	1	1	−1	−1	−1	−1	−1	−1	−1	46.1
2	2	1	1	1	−1	−1	−1	1	−1	1	55.4
3	3	1	1	−1	1	−1	−1	1	1	−1	44.1
4	4	1	1	1	1	−1	−1	−1	1	1	58.7
5	5	1	1	−1	−1	1	−1	1	1	1	56.3
6	6	1	1	1	−1	1	−1	−1	1	−1	18.9
7	7	1	1	−1	1	1	−1	−1	−1	1	46.9
8	8	1	1	1	1	1	−1	1	−1	−1	16.4
9	9	1	1	−1	−1	−1	1	−1	1	1	41.8
10	10	1	1	1	−1	−1	1	1	1	−1	40.1
11	11	1	1	−1	1	−1	1	1	−1	1	61.5
12	12	1	1	1	1	−1	1	−1	−1	−1	37.0
13	13	1	1	−1	−1	1	1	1	−1	−1	22.9
14	14	1	1	1	−1	1	1	−1	−1	1	34.1
15	15	1	1	−1	1	1	1	−1	1	−1	17.7
16	16	1	1	1	1	1	1	1	1	1	42.7

Because he knows he cannot afford to run a 2^7 experiment, he chooses a 2^{7-3} design matrix (16 runs). The complete alias structure for the 2^{7-3} design is shown in Appendix B. The seven factors are given in Table 5.14.

Table 5.16 Fractional factorial fit: packing versus foreman, gender, and so on.

Estimated Effects and Coefficients for Time (Coded Units)		
Term	**Effect**	**Coefficients**
Constant		40.037
Foreman	−4.250	−2.125
Gender	1.175	0.588
TimeDay	−16.100	−8.050
Temp	−5.625	−2.812
Music	4.775	2.388
Age	−0.000	−0.000
Location	19.275	9.638
Foreman * Gender	0.400	0.200
Foreman * TimeDay	−3.675	−1.838
Foreman * Temp	6.750	3.375
Foreman * Music	−3.300	−1.650
Foreman * Age	4.375	2.188
Foreman * Location	0.350	0.175
Gender * Temp	3.825	1.913
Foreman * Gender * Temp	−2.650	−1.325

Analysis of Variance for Packing (Coded Units)

Source	DF	Seq SS	Adj SS	Adj MS	F	P
Main Effects	7	2818.48	2818.48	402.64	*	*
2-Way Interactions	7	416.05	416.05	59.44	*	*
3-Way Interactions	1	28.09	28.09	28.09	*	*
Residual Error	0	0.00	0.00	0.00		
Total	15	3262.62				

Table 5.15 shows the design matrix with the associated response time. Table 5.16 lists all of the effects and Coefficients (equal to half the effects). The complex alias structure that explains the confounding structure is shown in Table 5.17. The alias structure is shown up to order 3. The complete alias structure is shown in Appendix B. (Note: The analysis of

variance cannot compute the F- and P-values because the experiment was not replicated to estimate the error variance; however, see the Pareto diagram in Figure 5.5.)

From Table 5.17 we see that all of the main effects are aliased with three-way interactions and four-way interactions (not shown in Table 5.17 but shown in Appendix B). Because it is generally assumed these three-way (and higher) interactions are insignificant, this confounding is a small price to pay to estimate the seven effects. The alias structure for the two-way interactions is such that all two-way interactions are confounded with other two-way interactions (and three-way interactions not shown in Table 5.17, but see Appendix B). However, as we can see from Figure 5.5, none of the two-way interactions are significant. Of course this could be because some interaction factors have a negative value and thus cancel any potential real effect.

Table 5.17   Alias structure (up to order 3).

Note: The complete structure is shown in Appendix B.

I

Foreman + Gender * TimeDay * Music + Gender * Age * Location + TimeDay * Temp * Location + Temp * Music * Age

Gender + Foreman * TimeDay * Music + Foreman * Age * Location + TimeDay * Temp * Age + Temp * Music * Location

TimeDay + Foreman * Gender * Music + Foreman * Temp * Location + Gender * Temp * Age + Music * Age * Location

Temp + Foreman * TimeDay * Location + Foreman * Music * Age + Gender * TimeDay * Age + Gender * Music * Location

Music + Foreman * Gender * TimeDay + Foreman * Temp * Age + Gender * Temp * Location + TimeDay * Age * Location

Age + Foreman * Gender * Location + Foreman * Temp * Music + Gender * TimeDay * Temp + TimeDay * Music * Location

Location + Foreman * Gender * Age + Foreman * TimeDay * Temp + Gender * Temp * Music + TimeDay * Music * Age

Foreman * Gender + TimeDay * Music + Age * Location

Foreman * TimeDay + Gender * Music + Temp * Location

Foreman * Temp + TimeDay * Location + Music * Age

Foreman * Music + Gender * TimeDay + Temp * Age

Foreman * Age + Gender * Location + Temp * Music

Foreman * Location + Gender * Age + TimeDay * Temp

Gender * Temp + TimeDay * Age + Music * Location

Foreman * Gender * Temp + Foreman * TimeDay * Age + Foreman * Music * Location + Gender * TimeDay * Location + Gender * Music * Age + TimeDay * Temp * Music + Temp * Age * Location

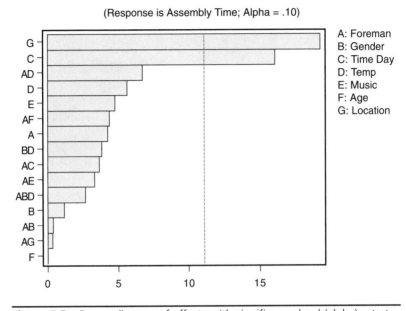

Figure 5.5 Pareto diagram of effects with significance level (alpha) set at 0.10.

Figure 5.5 shows that only two main effects, G = Location (Effect = 19.275) and C = Time of Day (Effect = −16.100), are significant. The positive effect means that assembly time increases with location but what does that mean? Because the value for locations is −1 for Temecula and +1 for Bellevue, the assembly time for Bellevue is *longer* (that is, slower) at the Bellevue plant. However, there is an inverse relationship between assembly time and Time of Day, which would indicate that assembly time is *slower* in the afternoon. All other factors do not appear to affect assembly time.

5.5 WHAT ABOUT TWO OR MORE RESPONSE VARIABLES? AN EXAMPLE FROM RESEARCH DESIGN

A design engineer would like to optimize three critical variables known as S, H, and Br. The desired operational criteria for these variables are as follows. Although there are no theoretical upper limits for S (larger = better), a value of around 13 or 14 is highly desirable. H should be equal to 20, and Br should be equal to 26.

During the last engineering meeting it was suggested the three response variables (S, H, and Br) would likely be influenced by six factors, labeled for the purpose of this exercise as A, B, C, D, E, and F. Unwilling to run a full 2^6 experiment, the project engineer decides that a 2^{6-1} (resolution VI) design would be adequate. The significant alpha level for all Pareto charts is set at 0.05. Table 5.18 shows the factorial design, design generator and alias structure. Table 5.19 shows the data matrix including the six factors (A–F) coded to the usual -1, $+1$ values and three response variables (S, H, and Br). The units of measurement for the response variables are not included and not really necessary for the analysis. As you can see from Table 5.18, all main effects will be confounded with five-way interactions. Because these interactions are very likely to be minimal, we can be reasonably sure the main effect estimates will not be seriously affected by these interactions. The same can be said about two-way interactions.

The factor estimates for each response is presented in Tables 5.20a–c. Significant effects for each response, as identified by the Pareto charts (Figures 5.6–5.8), are highlighted in bold letters.

5.5.1 Analysis of the Results Presented in Table 5.20 a–c

Using only significant factors we have for each response the following equations and their associated coefficients:

S = 11.3063 + 0.9563 * A + 1.7562 * D + 1.418 * F
(The average, A, D, and F are significant.)

H = 16.3750 − 4.937 * A + 6.50 * F
(Only the average, A, and F are significant.)

Br = 26.813 + −5.20 * F
(Only the average and F are significant.)

You will recall from the introduction to this example that response S is to be maximized (meaning the higher the better). Although no upper bound value was given for S, a value of 13 or 14 is considered very good. The optimum value for H is 20 and the optimum value for Br is 26. From the equations we see that to maximize S we only need to set all three factors (A, D, and F) to their highest values (coded as $+1$ in the design matrix). However, we can't really do that because we also notice that factor A has an inverse (-4.937) relationship with response H, so setting factor A to its highest value will reduce factor H. Therefore the only contradiction, as far as factors S and H are concerned, is with factor A. For factor F we see that if it is set to its maximum value, the Br response will be lower than its optimum of 26, so it would seem the best option would be to set factor F to its midrange coded value of 0. As for factor D, because it only impacts response S, it could be set to its maximum allowable value.

Table 5.18 Factorial design, design generator, and alias structure for a 2^{6-1} design.

Fractional Factorial Design

Factors:	6	Base Design:	6,	32	Resolution: VI
Runs:	32	Replicates:		1	Fraction: 1/2
Blocks:	none	Center pts (total):		0	

Design Generators: F = ABCDE (Note: Six letters, A–F, are used; hence the notation resolution VI.)

Alias Structure

I + ABCDEF

A + BCDEF
B + ACDEF
C + ABDEF
D + ABCEF
E + ABCDF
F + ABCDE
AB + CDEF
AC + BDEF
AD + BCEF
AE + BCDF
AF + BCDE
BC + ADEF
BD + ACEF
BE + ACDF
BF + ACDE
CD + ABEF
CE + ABDF
CF + ABDE
DE + ABCF
DF + ABCE
EF + ABCD
ABC + DEF
ABD + CEF
ABE + CDF
ABF + CDE
ACD + BEF
ACE + BDF
ACF + BDE
ADE + BCF
ADF + BCE
AEF + BCD

Table 5.19 Data matrix for factors A–F and responses S, H, and Br.

	StdOrderA	B	C	D	E	F	S	H	Br
1	−1	−1	−1	−1	−1	−1	3.4	15	36
2	1	−1	−1	−1	−1	1	10.5	10	34
3	−1	1	−1	−1	−1	1	11.3	28	30
4	1	1	−1	−1	−1	−1	10.6	8	34
5	−1	−1	1	−1	−1	1	8.1	22	30
6	1	−1	1	−1	−1	−1	7.9	9	32
7	−1	1	1	−1	−1	−1	10.3	13	28
8	1	1	1	−1	−1	1	12.9	16	25
9	−1	−1	−1	1	−1	1	14.6	38	20
10	1	−1	−1	1	−1	−1	10.5	1	32
11	−1	1	−1	1	−1	−1	7.8	11	32
12	1	1	−1	1	−1	1	12.9	16	25
13	−1	−1	1	1	−1	−1	9.4	15	34
14	1	−1	1	1	−1	1	14.6	14	15
15	−1	1	1	1	−1	1	13.3	25	19
16	1	1	1	1	−1	−1	15.8	1	28
17	−1	−1	−1	−1	1	1	11.0	31	22
18	1	−1	−1	−1	1	−1	8.0	8	30
19	−1	1	−1	−1	1	−1	7.9	16	35
20	1	1	−1	−1	1	1	13.1	23	18
21	−1	−1	1	−1	1	−1	7.2	25	32
22	1	−1	1	−1	1	1	8.6	20	20
23	−1	1	1	−1	1	1	11.8	18	20
24	1	1	1	−1	1	−1	10.2	8	32
25	−1	−1	−1	1	1	−1	10.3	10	20
26	1	−1	−1	1	1	1	14.6	30	11
27	−1	1	−1	1	1	1	14.9	31	20
28	1	1	−1	1	1	−1	15.1	4	36
29	−1	−1	1	1	1	1	15.6	33	16
30	1	−1	1	1	1	−1	15.1	4	36
31	−1	1	1	1	1	−1	8.7	10	36
32	1	1	1	1	1	1	15.8	11	20

Table 5.20a   Fractional factorial fit: S versus A, B, C, D, E, F.

Estimated Effects and Coefficients for S (Coded Units). Refer to alias structure of Table 5.18.

Term	Effect	Coefficient
Constant		11.3063
A	**1.9125**	**0.9563**
B	1.4375	0.7187
C	0.5500	0.2750
D	**3.5125**	**1.7562**
E	0.8750	0.4375
F	**2.8375**	**1.4188**
A * B	0.6375	0.3187
A * C	0.1500	0.0750
A * D	0.5625	0.2813
A * E	−0.2750	−0.1375
A * F	−1.6125	−0.8063
B * C	0.1000	0.0500
B * D	−1.4875	−0.7437
B * E	−0.5500	−0.2750
B * F	−0.3875	−0.1937
C * D	0.4000	0.2000
C * E	−0.7875	−0.3938
C * F	−0.8250	−0.4125
D * E	0.5250	0.2625
D * F	0.1125	0.0563
E * F	0.0250	0.0125
A * B * C	0.6125	0.3063
A * B * E	0.4500	0.2250
A * B * F	−0.0875	−0.0438
A * C * D	0.9500	0.4750
A * C * E	−0.1875	−0.0938
A * C * F	0.3250	0.1625
A * D * E	0.5750	0.2875
A * D * F	−0.9875	−0.4937
A * E * F	−0.3250	−0.1625

Analysis of Variance for S (coded units) Note: No replication; hence no residual error estimation and therefore no F nor P values calculated. However, see Pareto charts, Figures 5.6–5.8.

Source	DF	Seq SS	Adj SS	Adj MS	F	P
Main Effects	6	217.45	217.45	36.242	*	*
2-Way Interactions	15	62.77	62.77	4.185	*	*
3-Way Interactions	10	24.34	24.34	2.434	*	*
Residual Error	0	0.00	0.00	0.000		
Total	31	304.56				

Table 5.20b   Fractional factorial fit: H versus A, B, C, D, E, F.

Estimated Effects and Coefficients for H (Coded Units)		
Term	**Effect**	**Coefficient**
Constant		16.375
A	**−9.875**	**−4.937**
B	−2.875	−1.437
C	−2.250	−1.125
D	−1.000	−0.500 ←*Not significant but in italics for comparison*
E	2.500	1.250 *with other two responses*
F	**13.000**	**6.500**
A * B	1.750	0.875
A * C	0.125	0.062
A * D	−1.625	−0.812
A * E	1.625	0.812
A * F	−0.875	−0.438
B * C	−2.125	−1.063
B * D	−1.625	−0.813
B * E	−2.125	−1.063
B * F	−0.875	−0.438
C * D	−1.250	−0.625
C * E	−0.750	−0.375
C * F	−3.750	−1.875
D * E	−1.000	−0.500
D * F	4.750	2.375
E * F	1.000	0.500
A * B * C	0.500	0.250
A * B * D	−1.500	−0.750
A * B * E	−0.750	−0.375
A * B * F	−0.000	−0.000
A * C * D	−1.875	−0.938
A * C * E	−2.625	−1.313
A * C * F	1.375	0.687
A * D * E	1.125	0.563
A * D * F	-1.625	-0.812
A * E * F	1.875	0.938

Analysis of Variance for H (coded units)						
Source	**DF**	**Seq SS**	**Adj SS**	**Adj MS**	**F**	**P**
Main Effects	6	2296.8	2296.8	382.79	*	*
2-Way Interactions	15	498.5	498.5	33.23	*	*
3-Way Interactions	10	182.3	182.3	18.23	*	*
Residual Error	0	0.0	0.0	0.00		
Total	31	2977.5				

Table 5.20c Fractional factorial fit: Br versus A, B, C, D, E, F.

Estimated Effects and Coefficients for Br (Coded Units)		
Term	**Effect**	**Coefficient**
Constant		26.813
A	*−0.125*	*−0.062*←*Not significant but in italics for comparison*
B	1.125	0.563
C	−0.750	−0.375
D	*−3.625*	*−1.812*←*Not significant but in italics for comparison*
E	−3.125	−1.563
F	**−10.500**	**−5.250**
A * B	−0.125	−0.063
A * C	−0.750	−0.375
A * D	0.875	0.437
A * E	0.375	0.187
A * F	−1.000	−0.500
B * C	−2.000	−1.000
B * D	2.875	1.437
B * E	2.625	1.312
B * F	0.000	0.000
C * D	1.750	0.875
C * E	3.250	1.625
C * F	−1.125	−0.563
D * E	1.875	0.937
D * F	−3.000	−1.500
E * F	−3.250	−1.625
A * B * C	1.500	0.750
A * B * D	−0.125	−0.062
A * B * E	−1.375	−0.687
A * B * F	1.000	0.500
A * C * D	−1.500	−0.750
A * C * E	1.500	0.750
A * C * F	0.625	0.313
A * D * E	1.625	0.813
A * D * F	−0.750	−0.375
A * E * F	−1.500	−0.750

Analysis of Variance for Br (coded units)

Source	DF	Seq SS	Adj SS	Adj MS	F	P
Main Effects	6	1080.0	1080.0	180.00	*	*
2-Way Interactions	15	476.9	476.9	31.79	*	*
3-Way Interactions	10	124.0	124.0	12.40	*	*
Residual Error	0	0.0	0.0	0.00		
Total	31	1680.9				

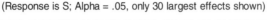

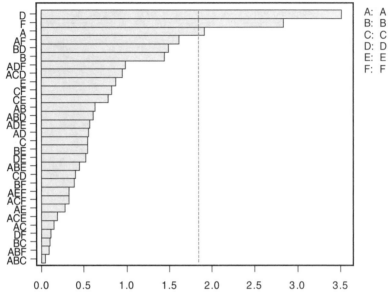

Figure 5.6 Pareto chart of effects for response S.

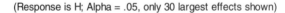

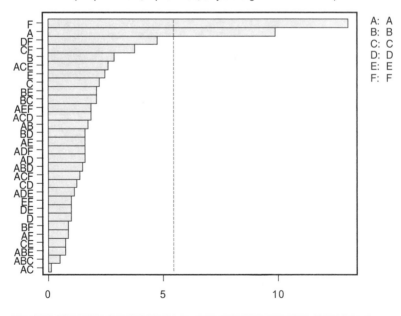

Figure 5.7 Pareto chart of effects for response H.

(Response is Br; Alpha = .05, only 30 largest effects shown)

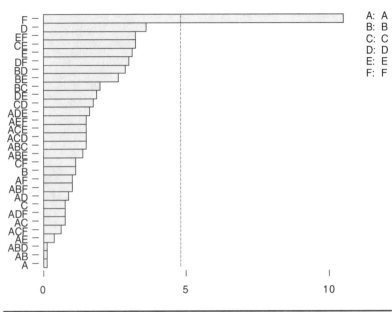

Figure 5.8 Pareto chart of effects for response Br.

If we set A to its lowest values (coded −1) and set F = 0, the response H is approximately equal to 16.37 (−1) * (−4.937) = 21, very near its optimum of 20. Response Br would equal 26.8, essentially equal to its optimum, and S would be equal to 11.3 + −0.95 +1.75 + 0 = 12.1. Of course these settings are approximate. However, for this particular example, we could go a little further in our analysis only because we are fortunate in that the equation for Br *appears* to be only influenced by one factor (F). I say "appears" because if we refer back to Figure 5.8, it seems that factor D may not be negligible. However if we start considering factors that are "almost significant" we would then have to consider the interaction factor AF for response S (see Figure 5.6) and DF for response H (see Figure 5.7), and if we were to do that, the complexity of the model would increase and so would the analysis for this simple example. If we set S, H, and Br to their optimum values of 14, 20, and 26 and we further assume that Equations 1–3 are a good representation of the relationship among the effects A, D, and F on the responses S, H, and Br, we can then estimate the values of the coefficients A, D, and F as follows:

$$S = 14 = 11.3063 + 0.9563 * A + 1.7562 * D + 1.418 * F \qquad (5.1)$$

$$H = 20 = 16.3750 - 4.937 * A + 6.50 * F \qquad (5.2)$$

Br = 26 = 26.813 + − 5.20 * F   (5.3)

or 14 − 11.3 = 2.7 = 0.9563 * A + 1.7562 * D + 1.4188 * F   (5.4)

20 − 16.4 = 3.6 = − 4.937 * A + 6.50 * F   (5.5)

26 − 26.8 = −0.8 = − 5.20 * F   (5.6)

All we have to do now is solve for F, A, and D. Using elementary algebra we have from (5.6), F = −0.8/−5.20 = 0.155 or rounding to 0.16. Inserting the value for F into (5.5) we have −4.937 * A + 6.50 * 0.15 = 3.6 or A = 2.62/−4.93 = −0.53 or −0.5. Inserting A = −0.5 and F = 0.16 into Equation (5.4) we obtain D = 1.7, but because the range of coded values for the factors is (−1, +1) we can set D = 1 that is its high value (however, this would indicate we could set D to a value higher than 1). These calculations suggest that for Equations (5.1)–(5.3), the optimum settings would be:

A= −0.5 and not −1 as suggested in the preceding discussion

D = 1 or perhaps higher

F = 0.16 or a little higher than the midrange value suggested in the preceding discussion; however, this slight difference in the setting for F may be of no importance

If we are now told that the actual operating ranges for A, D, and F are:

−1	0	+1	−1	0	+1	−1	0	+1

15 < A < 20	3 < D < 6 and	5 < F < 10

midrange values: 17.5   4.5   7.5

the engineer would set: A halfway between 15 and 17.5, or 16.25.

D to 6 or perhaps even higher (to be determined) and,

F equal to 7.9 because the range between 7.5–10 = 2.5 units and 0.16 * 2.5 = 0.40.

This discussion is continued in Chapter 7.

5.6 ECONOMIC CONSIDERATIONS

One of the many advantages of experimental designs is that it not only allows the experimenter to study the relationship between a set of factor effects on one or more response variables but it can also help the investigator conduct economic performance analysis studies. If, for example, a response variable can be optimized when *less* of a particular factor (or factors) is used, one could reap economic advantages and/or benefits. The performance of a process as measured by a set of one or more response variables may, for example, be improved if the concentration of a chemical is set at a lower percentage and/or if the temperature is set slightly below what was previously thought as the best temperature setting. All these small but cumulative optimizations can help improve the economic performance of a process. When applied throughout a company these series of optimizations can only help, among other things, customer satisfaction and, naturally, profitability.

5.7 CONCLUSION: HOW TO SET UP AN EXPERIMENT

Whenever an experiment needs to be designed, ask the following questions:

1. What is the purpose of the experiment? (For instance, to minimize or maximize a response Y; to maximize or minimize two or more responses; to minimize variability and satisfy a target value for a response.)

2. What factors shall be included in the experiment?

3. At what levels shall these factors be measured, and what shall be the range for each factor?

4. Are the levels qualitative or quantitative or mixed?

5. How many levels shall be selected for each factor (two or more or a mixture, depending on the factor.)

6. What design resolution shall be used? (For example, full factorial vs. fractional factorial or perhaps an N-way ANOVA with factors set at four or five levels.) If a fractional factorial design is preferred, what shall be the resolution? (That is, how much confounding are we willing to tolerate?)

The number of factors included in an experiment will depend on economic consideration, that is, the cost of running the experiment and prior knowledge of the process being investigated. Always remember that the more factors you add to an experiment the costlier it will be. Also, the more levels for each factor one wants to investigate, the greater the cost. It is always important to know which factor(s) is (are) easiest to change and which are hardest. The hardest or costlier factor should be assigned to the design matrix column with the least change.

The number of levels and range for each level will help define the boundaries of the experiment. The more levels are selected the more runs will have to be obtained and the more expensive the experiment. However, if too few

Table 5.21 Types of design associated with number of variables.

Number of variables	Number of runs	Type of design	Degree of fraction
5	16	2_V^{5-1}	1/2
6	32	2_{VI}^{6-1}	1/2
7	64	2_{VII}^{7-1}	1/2
8	64	2_V^{8-2}	1/4
9	128	2_{VI}^{9-2}	1/4

runs are obtained, the factors will be confounded and the result will be more difficult to interpret. For preliminary investigations with quantitative factors where the main objective is to first discover which factors are important and the direction of the effect, beginning with two levels is recommended. Once key factors have been identified, a follow-up experiment can be used with three-level factors to determine the shape of the response surface.

The nature of the experiment will determine whether the factor levels will be qualitative, quantitative, or both. Once the number of levels has been selected, it is preferable to have equally spaced levels with an equal number of observations at each level.

If you can afford it, try to run an experimental design that will allow main effects or interactions not to be confounded with any other main effects or interactions (these would be resolution V or higher designs). Table 5.21 shows the type of designs associated with 5, 6, 7, 8, and 9 variables.

Because it is unlikely that most experimenters will be able to afford the luxury of running a 64- or 128-run experiment (not counting replications), it is likely that for experiments with seven or more variables more fractionated designs (or saturated designs such as Placket-Burman) could be considered.

NOTES

1. D .R. Cox, *Planning of Experiments* (New York: Wiley, 1958), p. 77.
2. Cuthbert Daniel, *Applications of Statistics to Industrial Experimentation* (New York: Wiley, 1976), p. 24.

6

Regression Analysis

6.0 INTRODUCTION

The examples presented in Chapter 5 were such that the investigator or team of investigators conducting the experimental designs had some knowledge of the problem. By knowledge of the problem, I mean the investigators either knew something about the process under investigation or they knew whom to interview (generally process engineers and process operators) to help them select appropriate factors (that is, independent variables) and reasonable operating boundaries for each factor. As we have seen in Chapter 5 (and explore further in Chapter 7), the number of factors likely to influence a response variable depends on the complexity and/or *boundaries* of the process under investigation. Although it is probably true that most processes encountered in manufacturing or service sectors can be adequately described with two to five or perhaps six factors, it is also true that more complex systems are likely to require more independent variables to explain or understand their behavior.

Another characteristic of the processes presented in Chapter 5 is that the investigator had the ability to control or modify the "process behavior" by adjusting factors, and, in fact, as we have learned, that ability to see how a process responds to well-ordered changes (as defined by the *design matrix*) is the very essence of experimental design. There are times, however, when we simply cannot easily change, modify, or otherwise control factors (that is, independent variables). It may also be the case that a set of variables or factors are already collected (perhaps routinely) and we would like to know if there is a relationship between a response (dependent) variable and a set of independent (or factor) variables. If, for example, a statistical relationship is found between a response variable Y and one or more independent variables

X, we would not need to design an experiment to verify the nature of the relationship.

Suppose, for example, you are an economist and wish to investigate what (independent) variables influence the unemployment rate. You could perhaps begin by simply stating that the unemployment rate (Y) is, no doubt, a complex function of macro politico-economic factors + microeconomic factors.

At the macro level one could consider monetary policy factors (denoted by such terms as M1, M2, and M3 flows), demand (D), interest rate factor (R), exchange rate factor (E), national productivity factors (P), international politico-economic factors (P), and so on. At the micro level, also known as the economy of the firm, one could identify a host of other factors (productivity, solvability, financial factors, and so on.). As we begin to define and expand on these factors more specifically we will soon arrive at perhaps as many as 20 or even 50 or more independent variables. Designing an experiment for such a scenario would be impossible. Even thought governments try to adjust the economy by controlling, as it were, certain factors via the use of monetary and fiscal policies as well as interest rate manipulation, for example, it is impossible to control every factor. And yet this has not stopped economists from attempting to model the economy mathematically using very large sets of linear and nonlinear regression equations. Similarly, scientists in the field of biology, botany, geology, medical and social sciences, and in just about every field of scientific inquiry have, for decades, used regression and correlation analysis to try to understand the laws of nature and society in general.

6.1 RELATIONSHIP BETWEEN TWO VARIABLES (CORRELATION COEFFICIENT)

The topic of regression analysis covered in this chapter does not attempt to explain the economy but begins with a more modest proposal. The data shown in Table 6.1 consist of three variables labeled Month (where 1 = January and 12 = December), Therms, a measure of heat, and Kwh, the well-known measure of electrical consumption. Suppose we would like to know if there is a relationship between Therms and Kwh. How would we proceed?

If we remember the theme of Chapter 1 on intuitive statistics, one of the first things to do before performing any statistical analysis is to first ensure that the data are not corrupted (errors in data entry, for example) and then, if feasible, use one or more of the many graphing tools available in most statistical software to graph the data and see what the numbers might be telling us. Figure 6.1 shows a graph of the two variables across the 13-month

Table 6.1   Paired data of Therms and Kwh for a period of 13 months.

Month	Therms	Kwh
12	34	384
1	43	283
2	47	348
3	21	248
4	25	249
5	9	301
6	8	465
7	5	476
8	5	419
9	7	461
10	20	278
11	54	353
12	87	419

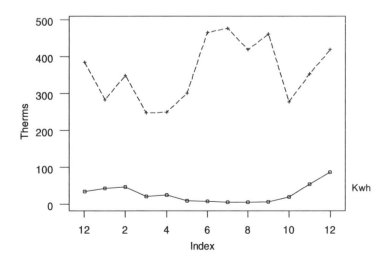

Figure 6.1   Graph of Therms and Kwh.

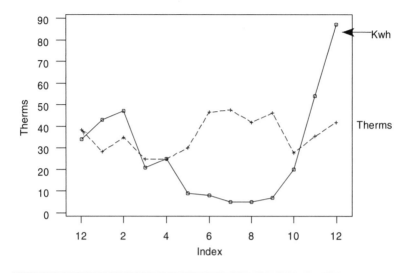

Figure 6.2 Graph of Therms and Kwh/10.

period. As you can see from the graph, the difference in scale between the two variables has a flattening effect on the variable Therms. To correct for this scale differential effect, the Kwh was divided by 10 and a second graph was produced (see Figure 6.2).

A different picture emerges: we can now see that from the 5th to the 9th month the two curves are opposite to each other. Could there be a relationship between Therms and Kwh? To answer that question we only need to produce a *scattergram* of the variable Therms versus Kwh (or vice versa for the inverse relationship). Figure 6.3 shows the result of the scattergram.

Each of the 13 pairs of data points (Therms, Kwh) shown in Table 6.1 are scattered in Figure 6.3 (hence the name scattergram). As we look at the scattergram, no obvious pattern emerges. Rather than rely on vague descriptions such as "no obvious pattern," statisticians have developed a statistical coefficient that measures the strength of a linear relationship between the two variables X and Y. The coefficient is known as the *Pearson (linear) correlation coefficient (r)*. If we can assume the two variables X and Y are normally distributed, the Pearson correlation coefficient r_{XY} is defined as follows:[1]

$$r_{XY} = \frac{\sigma_{XY}}{\sigma_X \, \sigma_Y} \tag{6.1}$$

where σ_{xy} is the covariance between X and Y and is defined as $\sum_{i=1}^{n}(x_i - \bar{x})(y_i - \bar{y})$, and σ_x and σ_y are the standard deviations for variable X and Y, respectively.

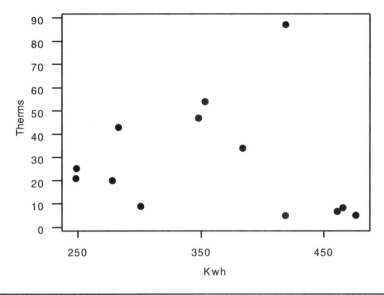

Figure 6.3 Scattergram of Therms versus Kwh.

Verbalizing Equation (6.1) we have: $r_{XY} = $ Covariance$_{XY}$/(Standard Deviation$_X$ * Standard Deviation$_Y$). The correlation coefficient r ranges from -1 to 1. A value of -1 indicates a perfect inverse or negative (linear) relationship, and a value of $+1$ indicates a perfect direct or positive (linear) relationship between X and Y. A value of 0 indicates no relationship. Naturally, in most cases, one usually obtains correlation coefficient values somewhere between -1 and $+1$. As is always the case with any statistics, one must state a null and alternative hypothesis. For this example we postulate the following hypotheses:

H$_o$: r = 0 (There is no correlation between Therms and Kwh.)

H$_a$: r $\neq$ 0 (Two-tailed test) (There is a correlation between
          Therms and Kwh.) As always, Alpha (α) = 0.05

Although one could, as prescribed by Equation (6.1), use a pocket calculator to compute the covariance and standard deviations to generate the correlation coefficient, it is easier and more reliable (assuming no typographical errors are made while entering the data) to use a statistical software package to calculate correlation coefficients. Table 6.2 shows that the correlation coefficient between Therms and Kwh is equal to -0.135, thus indicating a slight negative relationship. However, because the P-value of 0.661 is larger than alpha = 0.05/2 = 0.025 (remember that for a two-tailed test one must divide alpha by 2), we must accept the null hypothesis and

Table 6.2 Correlations: Therms, Kwh.

Pearson correlation of Therms and Kwh = −0.135
P-Value = 0.661

conclude that the correlation coefficient r is not significantly different from 0—in other words, there is no *linear* correlation between Therms and Kwh.

I have written the word *linear* in italics because we often forget that the Pearson correlation is a measure of linear association. As we look back at Figure 6.3, the assumption of linearity between Kwh and Therms is indeed questionable (as we soon see). The second error or misinterpretation is to interpret the value of a correlation coefficient as an indication of a cause-and-effect relationship. In other words, if the assumption of linearity between two variables (A and B) can be reasonably assumed and if one obtains a statistically significant correlation value, let's use 0.458, then the usual (but not necessarily correct) conclusion is to deduce that the two variables are somehow connected by a cause-and-effect relationship in that one variable causes the other variable to react. This may or may not be true. As we soon see, it turns out that, for this example, there is in fact a causal relationship between Therms and Kwh.

Using the same statistical software package one can also compute the covariance and standard deviations. Table 6.3 shows the covariance and standard deviations for Therms and Kwh (in bold letters). Using Equation (6.1) we can verify that:

$$r = \frac{-274.359}{24.43 * 83.4} = \frac{-274.359}{2037.462} = -0.13465 \text{ or rounding up to } -0.135 \text{ as}$$

shown in Table 6.2.

The correlation coefficient is limited to two variables; however, if several X variables need to be analyzed, it is possible to compute a multiple correlation coefficient. This is discussed in subsequent sections.

6.2 LINEAR REGRESSION ANALYSIS: AN EXAMPLE

If we try to place a straight line through the dispersed set of points shown in Figure 6.3, no evident linear relationship seems to emerge from the scattergram! The lone isolated point located at approximately (90, 425, actually

Table 6.3 Covariances, means, and standard deviations for Therms, Kwh.

	Therms	Kwh	
Therms	596.744		
Kwh	−274.359	6950.897	
Variable	**N**	**Mean**	**StDev**
Therms	13	28.08	**24.43**
Kwh	13	360.3	**83.4**

87, 419; see Table 6.1) does not help our interpretation. If we ignore that point, we could perhaps visualize a line trending down from left to right. But instead of guessing where the (*least-square*) best-fit negative trend line should be located, we could instead perform a linear regression analysis on the two variables. Given that we only have two variables (Therms and Kwh), the model is simple. However, because every model is a simplification of reality, the underlying assumption of every model is that one assumes all other (unknown or known) factors, obviously not included in the model, are held constant.

Because for this case we cannot really say which variable depends on the other, I have arbitrarily selected the dependent variable Y to be Therms and the independent variable X to be Kwh. Naturally, there are many cases where the decision as to which variable is Y and which is X is clearly defined. For example, if we wanted to look at the relationship between the Height and Weight of individuals, we would have to say the Weight of an individual will likely depend on the Height of the individual and not vice versa. Of course, a humorist would probably argue that in some cases, the weight of some individuals would appear to be inversely related to their height.

Returning to our example, the regression model would be as follows:

Dependent variable $= a + b *$ Independent variable $+ e$

$$Y = a + b * X + e \qquad (6.2)$$

$$Therms = a + b * Kwh + e$$

The mathematical model represented by Equation (6.2) suggests the (linear) relationship between Therms and Kwh is characterized by two parameters where *a* is the *intercept*, that is, the value for Therms when Kwh is equaled to zero, and the *regression coefficient b*, known as the *slope*, is a measure of the rate of change in Therms for each unit of Kwh. Because it is unlikely we will be able to explain all of the variation in the dependent variable Therms with only one independent variable (Kwh), the e(rror) term reflects all of the other unknown variables (or factors) that could affect (or influence) the dependent variable (Therms). Using a metaphor we could say that e represents all that is left unexplained either because we failed to include important (significant) variables or because we simply do not know what these other variables are, which is often the case.

As was the case in Chapters 3 and 4, when we postulate the existence of regression line between an independent variable Y and one or more independent variables X, we are proposing a set of hypotheses (H_o vs. H_a). In its simplest formulation H_o would state (as always) that there is no regression line. This statement is equivalent to saying that the regression coefficient b is equal to zero (or is not significantly different from 0). The alternative hypothesis H_a would state that there is a regression line or, similarly, that the regression coefficient b is either not equal to zero (or is significantly *different* from 0) or that b is larger than or smaller than a specified value (remember that all hypothesis tests can be either two-tailed or one-tailed). To test the significance of a regression coefficient we can either compute the confidence interval for the regression coefficient b and/or compute a t-value. The appropriate test for the regression coefficient is the t-test. Finally, as was explained in Chapter 3, whenever we formulate a set of hypotheses we must also propose a significant level (alpha) usually set at 0.05 or 0.10. We will set alpha = 0.05 or alpha = 0.05/2 = 0.025 for a two-tailed test.

H_o: The constant term a and the regression coefficient b are equal to 0.

H_a: The constant term and the regression coefficient are significantly different from 0.

The results of the regression analysis are shown in Table 6.4; the interpretation follows.

From Table 6.4 we can read that the regression equation is Therms = 42.2986 − 0.03947 * Kwh. Referring back to Equation (6.2) we learn that the intercept a = 42.2986 and that the regression coefficient is equal to −0.03947. The regression equation is an empirical equation derived from the data (Table 6.1); as such, it represents the best estimate for the relationship between Therms and Kwh. What does this mean? The regression coefficient b = −0.03947 tells us there is an inverse relationship between Therms and Kwh. The units for b are such that the equation must be dimensionally balanced. This means that because we have units of Therms on the left side of the equality sign and units of Kwh on the right side of the equality sign, the dimensional unit for b, which is multiplied by variable Kwh, must be equal to Therms/Kwh; in other words, (Therms/Kwh) * Kwh = Therms and the equation is dimensionally balanced.

Table 6.4 Regression analysis: Therms versus Kwh.

The regression equation is Therms $= 42.2986 - 0.0394710 *$ Kwh

$S = 25.2820$ R-Squared $= 1.8\%$ R-Squared(adjusted) $= 0.0\%$

$$S = \sqrt{MSError} \quad R^2 = \frac{SSRegression}{SSTotal} \qquad R^2(adj.) = 1 - \frac{SSError / (n - p)}{SSTotal / (n - 1)}$$

where n $=$ number of observations and p $=$ number of estimated parameters

$$S = \sqrt{639.179} \quad R^2 = \frac{129.95}{7160.92} = 0.01814 \quad R^2(adj.)^* = 1 - \frac{7030.97 / 11}{7160.92 / 12} = 1 - 1.07 = 0$$

Predictor	Coefficient	SE Coefficient	T	P
Constant	42.30	32.31	1.31	0.217 (Accept H_o)
Kwh	−0.03947	0.08754	−0.45	0.661 (Accept H_o)

Analysis of Variance

Source	DF	SS	MS	F	P
Regression	1	129.95	129.951	0.203309	0.661 (Accept H_o)
Error	11	7030.97	639.179		
Total	12	7160.92	596.743		

* Because R^2 adjusted is actually equal to a negative value $(1 - 1.07 = -0.07)$, it is not defined (i.e., set equal to 0). In the domain of real numbers, the square of a number cannot be equal to a negative value.

But is this regression equation statistically significant? Is the regression coefficient statistically and the constant term different from 0? Two types of analyses can be given to answer the question:

   1. Referring back to Table 6.4, we see two coefficients labeled R-squared and R-squared adjusted. The equations used to compute these values are reproduced in Table 6.4. R-squared (reported as a percentage), also known as the *coefficient of determination,* represents the percentage of the total variation about the mean $\overline{Y}$ (that is, *Therms*) that is explained by the regression of X with Y (Kwh with Therms for this example). You will notice from Table 6.4 that a pitiful 1.8% of the total variation about the average value of Therms is explained by the regression equation. When we adjust the coefficient of determination to correct for the number of estimated parameters (here two), we see the regression line explains nothing (0%); the equation represents nothing more than error! Therefore, although a regression *line* was indeed computed by the software package, it is a meaningless regression. This information is also reflected in the fact that the coefficient S (25.28), which represents the standard deviation about the regression line (or standard deviation of the residuals), is almost as large as the average for Therms, which is equal to 28.08 (and is not shown in Table 6.4).

2. If we look at the T values and Probability values listed just above the Analysis of Variance, we can see that for both coefficients we must accept the null hypothesis H_o. Similarly, if we refer to the analysis of variance table, we notice that the P-value for the regression is equaled to 0.661, which is much larger than a significance level of 0.05 (or 0.05/2), and therefore we must conclude that the regression line is *not* significant (that is, we must accept H_o); there is no linear relationship between Therms and Kwh, which is clearly shown in Figure 6.4. Figure 6.4 represents the line of best fit between the points. The line is calculated by using the regression equation. Table 6.5 shows the result of the calculation for the estimated Therms values (see the column labeled Estimated Fit).

For the first observation we have using this regression equation:

$$\text{Estimated Therms} = 42.2986 - 0.03947 * 384 = 27.14.$$

The difference between the actual or *observed* Therms value of 34 and the *estimated* (computed) Fit value of 27.14 is equal to 6.86, which is the first *Residual* listed in the next to the last column, and so on, for the remaining 12 observations. The residual are standardized in the last column (St Resid). This information can be useful in the event you want to compare dif-

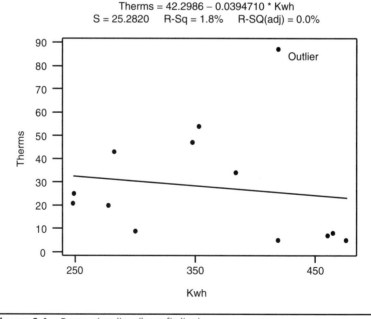

Figure 6.4 Regression line (best fit line).

Table 6.5 Actual and estimated values for Therms using the regression equation Therms = 42.2986 − 0.0394710 * Kwh.

Obs	Observed Kwh	Observed Therms	Estimated Fit	SE Fit	Residual	St Residual
1	384	34.00	27.14	7.31	6.86	0.28
2	283	43.00	31.13	9.75	11.87	0.51
3	348	47.00	28.56	7.09	18.44	0.76
4	248	21.00	32.51	12.08	−11.51	−0.52
5	249	25.00	32.47	12.00	−7.47	−0.34
6	301	9.00	30.42	8.72	−21.42	−0.90
7	465	8.00	23.94	11.54	−15.94	−0.71
8	476	5.00	23.51	12.32	−18.51	−0.84
9	419	5.00	25.76	8.69	−20.76	−0.87
10	461	7.00	24.10	11.26	−17.10	−0.76
11	278	20.00	31.33	10.05	−11.33	−0.49
12	353	54.00	28.37	7.04	25.63	1.06
13	419	87.00	25.76	8.69	61.24	2.58R

R denotes an observation with a large standardized residual.

ferent equations. The standard error (SE Fit) of each estimated value (each fitted value) is also computed.

6.3 CURVILINEAR REGRESSIONS

Is there any hope to improve on the regression introduced in section 6.1? As you look at Figure 6.3 (or Figure 6.4), you will notice one extreme point located at (87, 419). This is the point labeled as "an observation with a large standardized residual" in Table 6.5 (see observation 13 in Table 6.5). Extreme residuals are known as *outliers*. Because an outlier indicates a data point that is not typical of the rest of the data, the nature of this differentiation should be investigated because it may reveal some particularly interesting facts. One cannot simply reject from the database an outlier unless the erroneous value can be attributed to a recording error or perhaps some equipment malfunction.

Having said this, however, I will suggest that if you were to ignore the (87, 419) data point and visualize the scattergram (without the outlier), you may be able to see an inverted U-shaped curve. If you do not, you are not trying hard enough. Now that I told you about the inverted U-shaped curve, try again! I am sure you can see it now. If not, read on and you will eventually see it. Perhaps one of the reasons why the regression *line* performed so poorly is that the relationship between Therms and Kwh is not linear but rather curvilinear. After all, the graph shown in Figure 6.2 does indicate that both plots (for Therms and for Kwh) have some curvature. Encouraged by this observation, I decided to run what is known as a *polynomial regression*. The polynomial regression will include a quadratic term (Kwh^2) to the regression model. A cubic term could also be included, but let's keep things simple (and this is not required for this example). Table 6.6 shows the new regression equation along with the results of the analysis. Notice how the R-squared and R-squared adjusted coefficients have improved significantly to 29.5% and 15.4%, respectively. Of course, an explanation of 15.4% of the variation in the dependent variable is not all that great, but it is 15.4% better than 0%. We still do not have a significant regression (see the ANOVA table), but things have improved somewhat, not to say "significantly." As for the curve I mentioned earlier, can you now see it in Figure 6.5?

As you look at Figure 6.5 you will notice that point (87, 419) is still far from the regression line. In other words, this point still has a very high residual (or rather contributes to a very high residual). What would happen if, despite earlier warning not to arbitrarily do so, we were to ignore (delete) this point from our analysis? Table 6.7 and Figure 6.6 show the consequence of this act. The R-squared adjusted is now equal to almost 39%, and the analysis of variance shows we have a significant regression. Can we simply remove points from a database to improve artificially the explanatory power

---

Table 6.6   Polynomial regression analysis: Therms versus Kwh and Kwh**2.

The regression equation is
Therms = −277.298 + 1.82308 * Kwh − 0.00258 * Kwh**2

S = 22.4752   R-Squared = 29.5%   R-Squared(adjusted) = 15.4%

Analysis of Variance

Source	DF	SS	MS	F	P
Regression	2	2109.60	1054.80	2.08816	0.175
Error	10	5051.33	505.13		
Total	12	7160.92			

Source	DF	Seq SS	F	P	
Linear	1	129.95	0.20331	0.661	
Quadratic	1	1979.64	3.91906	0.076	

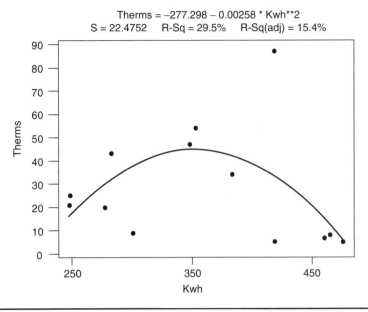

Therms = –277.298 – 0.00258 * Kwh**2
S = 22.4752   R-Sq = 29.5%   R-Sq(adj) = 15.4%

Figure 6.5   Regression plot for the polynomial regression.

of a model (regression or any other)? *Absolutely not,* unless of course it can be demonstrated that the point (or points) in question represent(s) a bad data point (a measurement error). In this particular example, I have no evidence to suggest the point (87, 419) represents a bad data point except to state that month 13, which represents point (87, 419), was a particularly cold month, and, as such, it could be argued (although this is a weak argument) that the point representing the Therms and Kwh consumption is "unusual" in that in represents an exceptional environmental condition. The removal on point (87, 419) from the database was mostly done as a pedagogical exercise to introduce the concept of quadratic terms and polynomial regression as well as to demonstrate how one point can have a significant effect on the validity or invalidity of a model.

6.4 USING DUMMY VARIABLES

The values taken by the independent variable X need not be from a continuous range such as Kwh, Therms, temperature, pressure, velocity, and a host of other possibilities. It is possible to introduce independent variables that have only two values (so-called *dichotomous* variables). For example,

Table 6.7 Polynomial regression analysis: Therms versus Kwh and Kwh**2.

The regression equation is
Therms = −186.549 + 1.31464 * Kwh − 0.0019369 * Kwh**2

S = 13.7504   R-Squared = 49.9%   R-Squared(adjusted) = 38.8%

Analysis of Variance

Source	DF	SS	MS	F	P
Regression	2	1698.01	849.006	4.49036	0.044
Error	9	1701.66	189.073		
Total	11	3399.67			

Source	DF	Seq SS	F	P
Linear	1	621.81	2.23845	0.165
Quadratic	1	1076.20	5.69199	0.041

Note: Polynomial regression analysis with the 13th data point (87, 419) removed.

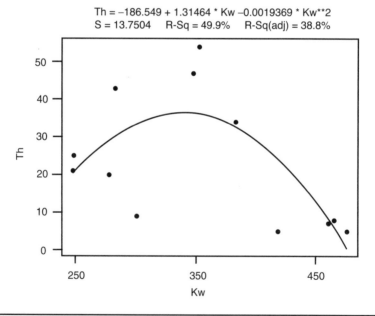

Th = −186.549 + 1.31464 * Kw −0.0019369 * Kw**2
S = 13.7504   R-Sq = 49.9%   R-Sq(adj) = 38.8%

Figure 6.6 Regression plot with point (87, 419) removed from the database.

we may want to look at the relationship between a response variable Y and two types of machines (A vs. B) or between two factories, two operators or by gender, or any other two *qualitative attributes*. When an independent variable can only assume two values, it is referred to as a *dummy variable*. The usual procedure to code dummy variables is to assign a 0 to one condition and a 1 to the other condition (for example, machine A = 0 and machine B = 1, or male = 0 and female = 1 or again, plant A = 0, plant B = 1, and so on.).

A dummy variable is a categorical or indicator variable. The "on" (1) and "off" (0) values of a dummy variable can be arbitrarily set by an investigator to reflect different conditions or states. Let us return to our Therms-Kwh example and see if we can reanalyze the data using a dummy variable. Looking at the original data listed in Table 6.1 or at the graph shown in Figure 6.3, you will have no doubt noticed that the values for the variable Therms are at a low during the middle (that is, summer months). What would happen if we were to introduce a new dummy variable that would be set equal to 0 for "winter months" and to 1 for all other (that is, summer) months? Table 6.8 shows the modified data set, and Table 6.9 shows the result. Notice how the R-squared adjusted has now increased to 62.0%.

Table 6.8   Regression with dummy variable.

Month	Therms	Kwh	Dummy
12	34	384	0
1	43	283	0
2	47	348	0
3	21	248	0
4	25	249	0
5	9	301	1
6	8	465	1
7	5	476	1
8	5	419	1
9	7	461	1
10	20	278	0
11	54	353	0
12	87	419	0

Table 6.9 Regression analysis: Therms versus Kwh, dummy.

The regression equation is Therms = −8.5 + 0.156 * Kwh − 50.8 * Dummy

Predictor	Coefficient	SE Coefficient	T	P
Constant	−8.47	22.22	−0.38	0.711
Kwh	0.15564	0.06736	2.31	0.043
Dummy	−50.79	11.09	−4.58	0.001

S = 15.07   R-Squared = 68.3%   R-Squared (adjusted) = 62.0%

Analysis of Variance

Source	DF	SS	MS	F	P
Regression	2	4890.4	2445.2	10.77	0.003
Error	10	2270.6	227.1		
Total	12	7160.9			

Source	DF	Seq SS
Kwh	1	130.0
Dummy	1	4760.4

Unusual Observations

Obs	Kwh	Therms	Fit	SE Fit	Residual	St Resid
6	301	9.00	−12.41	10.70	21.41	2.02R
13	419	87.00	56.74	8.52	30.26	2.43R

This is our best model so far. We now have two independent variables that tell us the variability in Therms can be (62%) explained by the independent variable Kwh and a dummy variable that represents time of year or, more specifically, winter versus summer months. Of course other variables such as ambient temperature could be added to the model to try to improve the R^2 value and hence the power of predictability of the model, but we shall stop here.

Can you interpret the regression equation: Therms = − 8.5 + 0.156 * Kwh − 50.8 * Dummy shown in Table 6.5? What is the estimated value of "Therms" for "Dummy" = 0 and Kwh = 275? (Answer: 34.4)

The regression actually consists of two equations:

For Dummy = 0 we have: Therms = −8.5 + 0.156 * Kwh

For Dummy = 1 we have: Therms = −8.5 + 0.156 * Kwh − 50.8 or, Therms = −59.3 + 0.156 * Kwh

Several dummy variables can be used to produce a blocking effect to reflect different conditions. In the preceding example the dummy variable

Table 6.10 Sales in millions of dollars for three plants.

Sales in million of $ S	X1	X2	
10	0	0	← Plant 1
15	1	0	← Plant 2
16	0	1	← Plant 3
11	0	0	etc.
15	1	0	
17	0	1	
11	0	0	
17	1	0	
17	0	0	
12	0	0	
17	1	0	
18	0	0	
13	0	0	
18	1	0	
18	0	1	

was turned "on" and "off" to reflect different months of the year, but suppose the Therms and Kwh data shown in Table 6.5 represent readings obtained at two different plants. In that situation, the dummy variable coding could have been used to categorize the two plants, for example, plant A = 0 and plant B = 1 (or vice versa). Because one dummy variable can be used to describe two conditions, categories, or states, two dummy variables can be used to defined three categories, conditions, or states. If X1 and X2 represent two generic dummy variables, the three conditions or states would be represented as follows:

X1	X2	
1	0	for condition or state one
0	1	for condition or state two
0	0	for condition or state three

Example 6.1: The data in Table 6.10 represents sales in millions of dollars for three plants. The regression analysis is presented without explanation in Table 6.11.

Table 6.11 Regression analysis: sales versus dummy1, dummy2.

The regression equation is Sales = 11.4 + 5.00 * Dummy1 + 5.80 * Dummy2				
Predictor	**Coefficient**	**SE Coefficient**	**T**	**P**
Constant	11.4000	0.5033	22.65	0.000
Dummy1	5.0000	0.7118	7.02	0.000
Dummy2	5.8000	0.7118	8.15	0.000
S = 1.125	R-Sq = 86.7%	R-Sq (adjusted) = 84.4%		

Analysis of Variance

Source	**DF**	**SS**	**MS**	**F**	**P**
Regression	2	98.800	49.400	39.00	0.000
Residual Error	12	15.200	1.267		
Total	14	114.000			

Source	**DF**	**Seq SS**
Dummy1	1	14.700
Dummy2	1	84.100

6.5 REGRESSION MODELS WITH AND WITHOUT INTERACTIONS

Suppose we want to find out if there is a relationship between a variable Y and three independent variables X1, X2, and X3. How would we formulate the regression model? Several options are available depending on whether or not we wish to investigate the importance of interactions. The simplest regression model would be:

1. $Y = a + b1 * X1 + b2 * X2 + b3 * X3 + e$. This model ignores all possible interaction effects.

2. $Y = a + b1 * X1 + b2 * X2 + b3 * X3 + b4 * (X1)(X2) + b5 * (X1)(X3) + b6 * (X2)(X3) + e$. This model includes all two-way interactions.

3. $Y = a + b1 * X1 + b2 * X2 + b3 * X3 + b4 * (X1)(X2) + b5 * (X1)(X3) + b6 * (X2)(X3) + b7 * (X1)(X2)(X3) + e$. This last model includes all interaction effects.

As was the case with experimental designs, model (3) is rarely used because three-way interactions are unlikely to be of any significance. Model (2) would be used if the experimenter or data analyst suspects possible interaction effects. If there is no prior knowledge as to the nature of the model, one may use model (2) to sort out what independent variables and/or interactions may have an impact on the response variable Y. If you should decide to use model (2) you need to ensure you have enough observations to estimate all of the parameters. For model (2) we see that a total of seven parameters need to be estimated (six regression coefficients plus the intercept). For such a model we would need to make sure we have a minimum of seven observations and preferably at least twice as many.

6.6 CONCLUSION: MODEL BUILDING WITH REGRESSION EQUATIONS

There are three types of models:

1. Functional models

2. Control models

3. Predictive models

A functional model is a model that explains the exact relationship between a response variable and one or more independent variables. As the name implies, functional models are described by mathematical functions that describe physical laws or physical principles, for example. These models belong to the domain of scientific investigation.

Control and predictive models are empirical models derived from data. Some examples of control models were explained in Chapter 5 (see also Appendix C, for an example of how a regression model can be used to analyze a designed experiment). However, if an experimental design is not practical, a regression model can still be used to predict the behavior of a response variable.

Here are the suggested steps to formulate a regression model:

1. Define the problem.

2. Select the response and independent variables.

3. Try various regression models to optimize R^2.

4. Review the model with people who have knowledge of the process associated with the problem to determine whether the model makes sense (that is, do the values of the estimated parameters make sense, does the regression equation make sense, are the parameters stable over the operational conditions?).

5. Verify the validity of the model.

NOTE

1. Unless the data are highly skewed (that is, not symmetrical), the assumption of normality can often be abused with no serious consequences to the estimation of the Pearson correlation. If the assumption of normality is not justified, other *nonparametric* correlation coefficients such as Spearman's rank-correlation coefficient, can be used. These nonparametric measures are available in statistical software packages under the tab labeled Nonparametric.

7

Response Surfaces

7.0 INTRODUCTION

In Chapter 5 we assumed that linear relationships geometrically represented by surfaces (or planes) were adequate representations of the possible relationships between a response variable and two or more factors. Although the assumption of linearity (also known as first-order) can be adequate in many instances, it is also possible, as shown in Chapter 6, that curvilinear (second-order) surfaces are better predictors than planes. To investigate whether or not a curvilinear surface (approximated by a polynomial fit) would be better to explain the relationship between a response Y and factors X_is, we need to use designs known as *response surfaces*. There are many types of response surface designs and only two are presented here: the *central composite* design and the *Box-Behnken* design. Because the Box-Behnken design requires fewer runs it is discussed first.

7.1 RESPONSE SURFACE DESIGNS: BOX-BEHNKEN

This next example shows how response surface designs can be used to find optimum factors settings to maximize multiple responses. Recall from Chapter 5 that a 2^{6-1} 32-run design was used to analyze the effect of six factors of three response variables: S, H, and Br. As a result of this analysis it was determined that only three factors had significant effects on S, H, and Br. The exercise concluded with an attempt to find the best setting for each factor to optimize the three factors: S = 14, H = 20, and Br = 26. We now reexamine the problem using a design matrix known as the Box-Behnken design.

Box-Behnken designs are the most efficient (least number of runs) response surface designs. One of their advantages is that all factors cannot be simultaneously set at the highest level. This property may be very useful for some designs when setting all factors at the highest level may be impossible or dangerous. For this example, I have selected the Box-Behnken design not for its safety feature but rather because of its efficiency in that it uses a minimal amount of runs.

Table 7.1 shows a computer-generated Box-Behnken design for three factors A, D, and F along with three response variables S, H, and Br. For three factors, only 15 runs are needed. You will notice that a new set of values (0) has not been added to the design matrix for factors A, D, and F. You might be wondering why I did not simply run a Box-Behnken design with the six original factors, and the reason is efficiency. The total number of runs using the initial 2^{6-1} and the Box-Behnken design is $32 + 15 = 47$. A Box-Behnken for 6 factors would have cost us 54 runs! You will remember from section 5.5.1 that the operating ranges for factors A, D, and F were:

$$-1 \quad 0 \quad +1 \qquad -1 \quad 0 \quad +1 \qquad -1 \quad 0 \quad +1$$

$$15 < A < 20 \qquad 3 < D < 6 \quad \text{and} \quad 5 < F < 10$$

midrange values: 17.5   4.5   7.5

This means that, if we are to use coded values in the design matrix for each factor, the operational settings for the Box-Behnken design shown in Table 7.1 will be as illustrated in Table 7.2.

For the first run A will be set to 15, D = 3 and F = 7.5. For this first setting the readings for S, H, and Br were, respectively, 3.4, 18.0, and 19.5. And so on, for the remaining 14 runs.

Table 7.3 shows the computer-generated response optimization settings and associated graph for factors A, D, and F. Although it is true that for response S, the optimum condition is "higher is best," a value of 14 for response S was deemed adequate for this study and consequently, the target value was set at 14. Notice that the optimum settings are a little different from those obtained in Chapter 5. The global solution suggested by the computer is to set A = 0.34629, D = −0.14933, and F = 0.83692 (the values obtained in Chapter 5 were A = −0.5, D = 1.0, and F = 0.16. However, at the time, we could not take advantage of the additional runs around the central values of 0,0,0 as suggested by the Box-Behnken design). Naturally, we will have to translate these coded optimum values back to optimum operational settings. Thus 0.346 (or 0.35 if we round up) would mean the operating setting for factor A should be approximately equal to 18.4 (or 17.5 + 0.35 * (20 − 17.50). D would be set slightly below 4.5, around 4.3, and F would be set at approximately 8.4. The complete response surface analysis and analysis of variance can be found in Appendix D.

Table 7.1 Response data (S, H, Br) and Box-Behnken design matrix shown in standard order format.

Std Order	A	D	F	S	H	Br
1	−1	−1	0	3.4	18.0	19.5
2	1	−1	0	11.3	15.0	18.7
3	−1	1	0	9.4	19.5	20.2
4	1	1	0	14.6	14.0	20.0
5	−1	0	−1	7.2	12.0	38.0
6	1	0	−1	15.8	6.0	28.0
7	−1	0	1	13.3	30.0	19.0
8	1	0	1	12.9	17.5	25.0
9	0	−1	−1	8.4	9.3	36.0
10	0	1	−1	8.9	21.0	34.0
11	0	−1	1	11.0	21.0	26.7
12	0	1	1	17.8	25.0	18.2
13	0	0	0	12.3	16.3	27.5
14	0	0	0	12.0	16.0	26.4
15	0	0	0	11.9	15.9	26.3

Table 7.2 Correspondence matrix between coded values and operating condition settings.

Factors (down)	−1	0	1
A	15	17.5	20
D	3	4.5	6
F	5	7.5	10

7.2 CENTRAL COMPOSITE DESIGN

Central composite designs are useful to analyze for the possibility of curvilinear response surfaces. As seen in the example that follows, central composite designs require a few more runs than the Box-Behnken design because factors have to be set at five levels rather than the three levels of the Box-Behnken design.

Suppose we wanted to analyze the effect of two factors A and B on the response variable PSI. More specifically, we would like to know how to

Table 7.3 Response optimization and associated graph.

			Parameters			
	Goal	**Lower**	**Target**	**Upper**	**Weight***	**Importance**
S	Target	13	14	16	1	1
H	Target	19	20	21	1	1
Br	Target	25	26	27	1	1

Global Solution

A = 0.34629

D = −0.14933

F = 0.83692

Predicted Responses

S = 14.0000, desirability = 1.00000

H = 20.0000, desirability = 1.00000

Br = 26.0000, desirability = 1.00000

Note: Desirability ranges from 0 (no optimum can be found) to 1 and varies depending on the goal. For this example, all goals were set equal to target. Other options for goals are to either maximize of minimize the response. The goals were also set to maximize S, but this had no effect on the results.

Composite Desirability = 1.00000

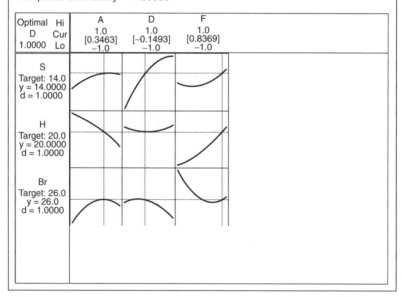

*Different weights can be assigned to each factor to control the importance of each target value. For this example, maximizing the target values are assumed to be of equal importance. The importance factor allows the analyst to rank (or prioritize) each factor in order of importance.

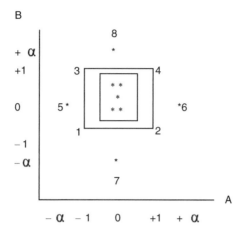

Figure 7.1 A central composite design for two factors. The "run order" from Table 7.4 is indicated by the numbers around the square. The five *'s in the center of the square represent the last five runs (runs 9–13) centered at (0,0). The alpha value (α) will vary depending on the number of factors (see Section 7.2.1).

maximize PSI and simultaneously develop a model that can predict the relationship between PSI and factors A and B. The design engineers are curious to know if there are some second-order interactions between the factor(s) and the response PSI and therefore, in order to investigate the problem, a central composite design matrix is set up. Geometrically, the star shape configuration of a central composite design is represented as shown in Figure 7.1.

After selecting the Central Composite design for a two-factor design matrix from the computer software, a design matrix with 13 runs is automatically generated. Table 7.4 shows the factor values and the associated response value PSI for all 13 runs. The experiment was run using the standard order instead of a randomized run.

7.2.1 How to Match Operational Values with Coded Values

Suppose the process experts have determined that the operational condition for factors A and B are as follows (the specification of units for A and B are not essential for the purpose of this example):

$$40 < A < 60 \qquad 200 < B < 260$$

Table 7.4 Central composite design for two factors A and B with coded and original operational settings (in parentheses) and response variable PSI.

Std	Run	A	B	PSI
1	1	−1.0000 (43)	−1.0000 (209)	210
2	2	1.00000 (57)	−1.0000 (209)	280
3	3	−1.0000 (43)	1.00000 (251)	365
4	4	1.00000(57)	1.00000 (251)	420
5	5	−1.4142 (40)	0.00000 (230)	250
6	6	1.41421 (60)	0.00000 (230)	380
7	7	0.00000 (50)	−1.41421 (200)	190
8	8	0.00000 (50)	1.41421 (260)	420
9	9	0.00000	0.00000 (230)	330
10	10	0.00000	0.00000	335
11	11	0.00000	0.00000	340
12	12	0.00000	0.00000	335
13	13	0.00000 (50)	0.00000 (230)	335

We see from Table 7.4 and Figure 7.1 that the range of coded values ($−1.414$ to $+1.414$) is equal to 2.828, and therefore for variable A we have:

$$60 − 40 = 20 = 2.828 \text{ or } 20/2.828 = 7.07 \text{ units/coded unit}$$

For B we would have: $260 − 200 = 60/2.828 = 21.2$ units/coded unit

Because 1.414 is the highest coded value we have for A, $60 = 1.414$, and for the lowest value we would have $40 = −1.414$. The midrange of 50 $= 0$ and because 7.07 of the original values $= 1$ unit of the coded value, we would have (rounding to the nearest digit), $57 = 1$ and $43 = −1$. The coded and uncoded (original) operational values are shown in Table 7.4. It is important to note that the coefficient values of $+/−1.412$ (α) used in the preceding computations are *only valid* for two factors central composite designs. For three factors the values changes to $+/−1.628$; for four and five factors it is equal to $+/−2.000$, and for six factors it is equal to $+/−2.378$. Statistical software packages automatically adjust the alpha coefficient to the appropriate value. Because this is only a two-factor design, we can plot a three-dimensional (3-D) response surface diagram of PSI versus A and B. Naturally if we had more than two factors, several sets of such 3-D diagrams

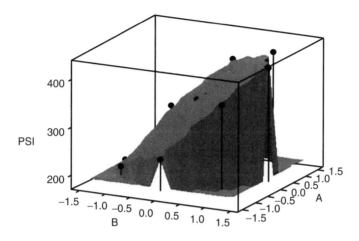

Figure 7.2 Three-dimensional diagram of the response surface for PSI versus factors A and B.

could be produced, but the interpretation would be more difficult. Figure 7.2 shows the 3-D diagram. The response surface shows where the range of maximum PSI occurs. We could stop here, but the predictive model of a graph is not all that accurate and also we would not learn how to interpret the results of a central composite analysis (simple as it is). So let us proceed to the analysis with the full support of our 3-D diagram.

Table 7.5 shows the result of the central composite design analysis. The statistical analysis is the same as for a polynomial regression. From the T- and P-values we learn that every coefficient except the A * B interaction is statistically significant. This means that not only are the A and B factors significant but so are the square of these factors. This information is confirmed (one could say duplicated) in the analysis of variance (for PSI) section of Table 7.5 where we can see the Square term is statistically significant with a P-value equal to 0.025. It is also encouraging to see that the model is very good because the adjusted R-squared is equal to 97.9% (an unusually high and certainly satisfying value).

As always the estimated regression coefficients could be used to predict the response value. The regression equation would be as follows:

$$PSI = 335.00 + 38.6060 * A + 77.5336 * B - 7.18125 * A^2 - 12.8125 * B^2$$

I have not inserted the coefficient for the A * B interaction term because it is not statistically significant. Remember that if uncoded levels had been used for the design matrix, most software packages will produce two sets of

Table 7.5   Central composite design.

Central Composite Design

Factors:	2	Blocks:	none	Center points:	5		
Runs:	13	Alpha:	1.414				

Response Surface Regression: PSI versus A, B

The analysis was done using coded units.

Estimated Regression Coefficients for PSI

Term	Coef	SE Coef	T	P
Constant	335.00	4.631	72.342	0.000
A	38.61	3.661	10.545	0.000
B	77.53	3.661	21.179	0.000
A*A	-7.81	3.926	-1.990	0.087
B*B	-12.81	3.926	-3.264	0.014
A*B	-3.75	5.177	-0.724	0.492

S = 10.35   R-Sq = 98.8%   R-Sq(adj) = 97.9%

Analysis of Variance for PSI

Source	DF	Seq SS	Adj SS	Adj MS	F	P
Regression	5	61480.2	61480.2	12296.0	114.68	0.000
Linear	2	60015.1	60015.1	30007.5	279.87	0.000
Square	2	1408.9	1408.9	704.4	6.57	0.025
Interaction	1	56.3	56.3	56.3	0.52	0.492
Residual Error	7	750.5	750.5	107.2		
Lack-of-Fit	3	700.5	700.5	233.5	18.68	0.008
Pure Error	4	50.0	50.0	12.5		
Total	12	62230.8				

Unusual Observations for PSI

Observation	PSI	Fit	SE Fit	Residual	St Resid
1	210.000	194.485	8.186	15.515	2.45R
5	250.000	264.778	8.186	-14.778	-2.33R

R denotes an observation with a large standardized residual.

regression coefficients; the first set would represent regression coefficient for the coded (−1, 0, +1 and + and −α) values and the second set would represent adjusted coefficients for the uncoded corresponding values (40, 60, 209, 251, and so on.) as shown in Table 7.4. Because the design matrix was entered using coded values, only one set of regression coefficients is reproduced here. Once the central composite design is analyzed the results could be run through a response optimizing routine, but the engineers, via the license of the author, decided against such an approach. Where (at what values) do you think factors A and B should be set?

Table 7.6 Factor design matrix and alias structure for a 2^{4-1} design with associated data for two replicated responses (Y1 and Y2), their average Ybar, and their standard deviation STDV.

Random order	A	B	C	D	Y1	Y2	Ybar	STDY
4	1	1	−1	−1	32.8	33.9	33.35	0.778
7	−1	1	1	−1	35.2	33.2	34.20	1.410
8	1	1	1	1	30.3	33.2	31.75	2.050
3	−1	1	−1	1	37.2	36.7	36.95	0.354
2	1	−1	−1	1	22.5	23.7	23.10	0.849
1	−1	−1	−1	−1	18.6	17.0	17.80	1.131
6	1	−1	1	−1	20.2	26.3	23.25	4.310
5	−1	−1	1	1	25.9	20.2	23.05	4.310

Alias Structure	Comments
I + A * B * C * D	(The mean (I) is confounded with the four-way interaction A * B * C * D.)
A + B * C * D	(Main effect A is confounded with three-way interaction B * C * D.)
B + A * C * D	
C + A * B * D	
D + A * B * C	
A * B + C * D	(Two-way interaction A * B is confounded with two-way interaction C * D.)
A * C + B * D	
A * D + B * C	

7.3 FINDING THE OPTIMUM SETTING TO CENTER A PROCESS AND MINIMIZE THE STANDARD DEVIATION

Objective: A process engineer needs to run a process at its optimum target value of 35. However for this study the engineer not only wants to know which factor(s) can affect the target value of the response variable Y but also which factor(s) have an effect on the variability of the response variable Y. The optimum solution would be to find a factor that can be used to run the process on target while at the same time minimize the standard deviation (hence the variability) of the response Y.

After a team meeting with the process operators and engineering staff it was decided that four factor labeled A, B, C, and D were likely to influence process performance represented by the response variable Y. Although a 16-run experiment was feasible (2^4) it was decided that a 2^{4-1} or a half fraction design would be just as efficient and less costly. You will have noticed that the name of the factors and the response variable are not given. This is done for two interrelated reasons:

1. The setup of the experiment and analysis of the results is the same irrespective of the nature of the data, and naturally this is true of *all* previous examples.

2. If you were told that, for example, factors A, B, C, and D represented flow rate, temperature of a polymer, roller setup, and supplier (A vs. B), and the response Y was thickness of the polymer in microns, you may not be interested in reading the example simply because the nature of your work has nothing to do with polymers. Unfortunately, this would be a mistake because of point 1.

Similarly, the operational conditions defining the range (or boundary) of operation for each factor is not stated. Suffice it to say that -1 and $+1$ have the usual meaning attributed to them. For this example we can assume the team of operators and engineers assigned to this problem have adequate knowledge of the ("their") process to determine what will be an appropriate high and low setting for each factor level.

7.3.1 Experimental Setup

The organization of the data is slightly different from other examples. First of all you will notice that unlike previous examples, the experiment was run using a randomized order suggested by the computer. As mentioned earlier, if it is economically feasible to do so, randomization is the preferred way to run experiments. You will also notice that the data are entered differently. Because one of the purposes of the study is to analyze the effect of factors on maintaining a target value of 35 while *at the same time* minimizing the standard deviation, two sets of observations will be required. In other words, the study will have to be replicated. Why? Because a minimum of two data points is needed to compute a standard deviation. The first set of observations listed under column Y1 represent observations for the response variable conducted in the morning session. The replication was conducted in the afternoon and these observations are listed under the column labeled Y2. The average Ybar and standard deviation STDY are reproduced in the last two columns, and *these are the two responses that will be analyzed with the design matrix.*

It is important to note that most statisticians would recommend that instead of analyzing the standard deviation (s) as a response one should

Table 7.7a Fractional factorial fit: Ybar versus A, B, C, D.

Estimated Effects and Coefficients for Ybar (Coded Units)		
Term	**Effect**	**Coefficient**
Constant		27.931
A	−0.138	−0.069
B	12.262	6.131
C	0.262	0.131
D	1.562	0.781
A × B	−2.887	−1.444
A × C	−0.987	−0.494
A × D	−2.438	−1.219

The analysis of variance for Ybar is not reproduced here; however, see the Pareto diagram in Figure 7.3.

Table 7.7b Fractional factorial fit: STDY versus A, B, C, D.

Estimated Effects and Coefficients for STDY (coded units)		
Term	**Effect**	**Coefficient**
Constant		1.8990
A	0.1955	0.0977
B	−1.5020	−0.7510
C	2.2420	1.1210
D	−0.0165	−0.0082
A × B	0.3365	0.1682
A × C	0.1245	0.0622
A × D	−1.0780	−0.5390

The analysis of variance for STDY is not reproduced here; however, see the Pareto diagram in Figure 7.4.

instead analyze $\log_{10}(s^2)$, which is the log base 10 of the variance. The reason for this transformation is that the standard deviation is not normally distributed, but the $\log_{10}$ of the variance (s^2) is or rather tends to be normally distributed. I have run the analysis shown in Tables 7.7a and 7.7b on both STDY and $\mathrm{Log}_{10}(STDY^2)$ and no significant difference in the results were obtained. Still, if one wants to be absolutely statistically correct, the standard deviation should be log transformed prior to the analysis.

The Analysis of Variance for Ybar is not reproduced here; however, see the Pareto diagram in Figure 7.3.

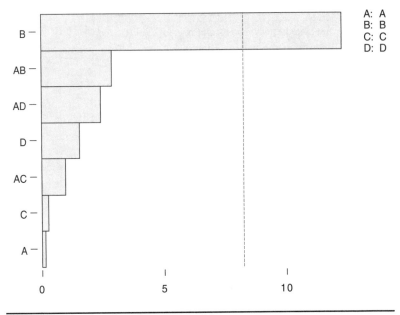

Figure 7.3 Pareto chart for response Ybar.

From Figures 7.3 and 7.4 we see that factor B has a significant effect on the response Ybar, and factors C and B have a significant effect on the standard deviation STDV. It is also interesting to note that the effect of factor B on STDV is an inverse relationship (-0.7510). One could look at the coefficients to try to determine what the optimum settings would be, or we could let a statistical software package do it for us. Table 7.8 shows the result of a response optimizing procedure. The target value for Ybar is set a 35 with a lower and upper limit of 34 and 36 and the target for STDY is set $= 0$ with an upper bound arbitrarily set at 0.5. However, I could have used a smaller upper bound value of 0.25 or 0.15.[1] The Weight of 5 (see the Weight column in Table 7.8) indicates that having a value on target for Ybar is important. The Global Solution indicates that setting factor B at its high setting and C at its low setting would optimize both Ybar ($= 35$) and STDV (0.5).

(Response is STDV; Alpha = .05)

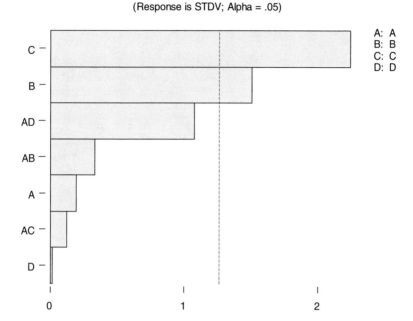

Figure 7.4 Pareto chart for response STDV (standard deviation).

Table 7.8 Response optimization.

		Parameters				
	Goal	Lower	Target	Upper	Weight	Importance
Ybar	Target	34	35	36.0	5	1
STDY	Minimum	0	0	0.5	1	1

Global Solution

A = −0.12847

B = 1.00000

C = −1.00000

D = 1.00000

Predicted Responses

Ybar = 34.9999, desirability = 0.99973

STDY = 0.0618, desirability = 0.87636

Composite desirability = 0.93601 (Values near 1.0 indicate that a good solution has been obtained.)

7.4 POTENTIAL PROBLEMS TO AVOID WHEN RUNNING A DoE

One must recognize that whenever an experiment is run, the best planning cannot anticipate unexpected factors that may creep in and possibly jeopardize results. The author once designed a simple two-factor experiment using four frames. The purpose of the experiment was to test the bonding strength of an epoxy used to bond wires to an aluminum frame. The preparation of each frame, itself a lengthy process requiring approximately 40 to 70 minutes per frame (depending on the conditions), went relatively smoothly. However, when the time came to begin the bonding process, the crucial step in the experiment, it was learned the operator who had expertise with the bonding process was too busy and could not assist the team. Because the experiment was already slightly behind schedule, it was decided the experimenter would, after a two-minute training session, bond the wires to the frame. The situation was actually slightly more complicated because two experimenters bonded two frames each and consequently, it is possible that an operator factor was also introduced. Not surprisingly, the quality of the bonds was not what they would have been had the operator—with about eight years of experience—bonded the wires. Although the experiment did reveal some interesting results it is also true that approximately three to four bonds out of 40 were of very poor quality and failed when barely touched!

7.5 CONCLUSION

We have come to the end of our quest for process analysis and improvement using a variety of data analysis techniques. More techniques are available but if you can learn to master the techniques presented in these first seven chapters you should be able to analyze most problems successfully, assuming of course that the problem has been clearly defined. The next chapter examines what can be done to ensure that problem statements are clearly formulated.

NOTE

1. A smaller value for the standard deviation of around 0.25 or 0.30 would have been better. Why? Hint: Three times $+/-0.3$ equals $+/-0.9$, which is within the stated upper and lower specification of $+/-1$.

Part II
The DMAIC Methodology

8

On Problem Definition

8.0 INTRODUCTION

The first seven chapters of this book explain how various statistical techniques can be used to analyze problems and subsequently test hypotheses. In all of the examples presented in these seven chapters, the problem is stated and the relevant data necessary for the analysis of the problem are already collected. All that remains to be done is to use the appropriate statistical technique(s) to analyze the data. This chapter explores what needs to be done prior to the data analysis phase when the problem is not yet defined and the data are not yet collected, the very scenario faced by every experimenter.

The essential steps presented in most Six Sigma Black Belt courses are covered here. In order to avoid making this chapter too long, I have avoided topics on group behavior, team psychology, conflict resolution, and other related psychological themes designed to help improve or facilitate the overall efficiency of a team of individuals confronted with the task of defining and analyzing a problem. The reason why some Six Sigma Black Belt courses spend a considerable amount of time teaching various facilitating skills is that in large corporations (where Six Sigma first evolved), teams of up to eight to 10 people are often involved in Six Sigma projects. In these situations group dynamics may be such that much time can be spent (wasted!) trying to resolve interpersonal conflicts, hence the need to train people on how to resolve conflicts. I do not deny that such information makes for interesting and even occasionally informative reading, but I also believe the essence of this information, which in some Black Belt courses can consume as much as two to three days of lectures and exercises, can be summarized in a few sentences.

When forming problem-solving teams, (1) select your partners carefully and make sure their expertise is absolutely necessary, and (2) try to keep your problem-solving teams to no more than two to five compatible people. When attending meetings, do not denigrate anyone. In other words, listen to what others have to say (that is, be open to suggestions and ideas); don't hesitate to ask for clarification; and respect the opinions of others.

I merely mention well-known tools of analysis such as the Cause-and-Effect and Pareto diagrams as well as Control charts (subjects covered in numerous books). If you wish to learn more about some of these and other classic tools, I encourage you to search the Web (by simply typing keywords such as "cause-and-effect diagram," "Pareto diagram," and so on), and visit the innumerable sites (some excellent) available on the Internet.

8.1 THE DMAIC MODEL: THE FOUNDATION OF SIX SIGMA

The acronym DMAIC, which stands for Define, Measure, Analyze, Improve, and Control, represents the five phases that are usually recommended when defining and analyzing a problem. In its most generic, condensed, and hence simplified representation, the DMAIC model proposes that one must:

    I. Clearly Define and cost the problem.

        A. Present the nature of the problem along with all of its associated costs to management and obtain approval from management to analyze and resolve the problem.

    II. Proceed to a *Measurement* phase that includes data collection.

    III. *Analyze* the data to uncover patterns and/or test hypotheses that will help explain the nature of the problem.

    IV. Suggest an *Improvement* process, and once the improvement has been verified to be adequate.

    V. *Control* the improved process,

        A. Formally document it.

        B. Conduct all necessary training (if required).

        C. Monitor the new improved process (via the use of control charts or other techniques such as internal auditing).

Entrenched within the DMAIC method is an extensive set of supportive tools and techniques, some simple or even trivial and others slightly more advanced but hardly more complex. Although the DMAIC methodology is efficient, like most methodologies it cannot be routinely applied to all or any situation. Indeed, one cannot assume that, when solving problems, the only way to proceed is to follow the DMAIC process mechanically. In many cases, one may already have data (hence measurements) that clearly define the nature of the problem. In such cases, one could even suggest that the D in DMAIC may also stand for Data, for it is with data that many problems are often defined.

8.2 DATA: THE SOURCE FOR MOST PROBLEM DEFINITIONS

In many cases problems are uncovered simply because the problem or processes speaks out, as it were, either through the well-known voice of the customer (VoC) or via some other performance indexes. For example, customers complain, products are returned, rejection rates increase, the rate of rework increases, work in progress fluctuates wildly, specifications are difficult to maintain, stubborn bottlenecks slow down productivity, and so on.

Problems usually speak out, or rather cry out, for attention whenever numbers or data often represented in the form of tables, charts, or graphs are analyzed. When a manager is shown a diagram that demonstrates customer returns for product XZ234 has increased by 12.7% over the past four weeks (or almost five times the average return for the past 18 months), he will most likely ask, "What has gone wrong?" When the average yield for a process drops from an average of 96.4% to 90.8%, management would likely want to know why. A problem has been defined.

8.3 TYPES OF PROBLEM OPPORTUNITIES

Within the vast systems of processes that make up an organization, there are always opportunities to improve process performance. For example, complex and often redundant processes can often be simplified; whereas processes characterized by a long cycle time can usually be shortened by eliminating nonvalue-added activities. Similarly, process bottlenecks known to reduce the overall efficiency of a system can be eliminated by analyzing the constraints responsible for the slowdown. Although it is relatively easy to identify a problem, coming up with a *well-defined* and not too ambitious project that can resolve the problem successfully is another matter. My experience has been that when people are first asked to propose a project and hence define a problem, they tend to define problems with a broad scope, in other words, problems that involve several departments or even the whole company. Unfortunately, when faced with an ambitious project the individual or project team usually does not know where to begin and a considerable amount of time must then be spent to reduce the *scope* of the project.

Novice problem solvers are faced with yet another difficulty in that problems come in various forms. There are three types of problem opportunities:

1. Internal problems—that is, opportunities driven by a need to improve internal efficiency. These opportunities may or may not be directly linked to any customer impact, but they invariably have a business or economic impact. These actions tend to be initiated by managers but may also be uncovered by so-called valued-added audits. Value-added audits (auditors) go beyond conformance enforcement and are designed to look for opportunities for improvement. A value-added audit may uncover that although a procedure is correctly followed as per standard operating instruction it may nonetheless be inefficient and in need of a revision (see also number 3, proactive opportunities). Examples of internal problems would include: cycle time reduction, which includes eliminating nonvalue-added process steps; eliminating or reducing (production/processing) bottlenecks to improve overall throughput and potentially profitability; and reorganization.

2. Reactive problems triggered by a need to react to a situation. One is usually confronted by these problems either via: (a) direct customer complaints—the noisiest and often the costliest form of the so-called Voice of the Customer (for example, product returns, warranty claims, customer complaints expressed via letters, or phone calls to an 800 number) or (b) routine internal audits (as required for example by the ISO 9001:2000 standard) that are designed to assess conformance to a quality management system (for instance, review and follow-up of corrective actions as specified by ISO 9001:2000). These corrective actions can include process, product, or procedures.

3. Proactive opportunities. These may be either: (a) uncovered by value-added internal audits, for example, preventive action value-added audits/auditors go beyond conformance enforcement and are designed to look for opportunities for improvement. A value-added audit may uncover that although a procedure is correctly followed as per standard operating instruction it may nonetheless be inefficient and in need of a revision; or (b) determined by assessing the voice of the customer. This activity may be driven by the need to develop or improve a new product. For example, several techniques made popular by software and IT developers integrate the customer in the design process. The technique of Participatory Design helps facilitate real-time customer interaction with the design engineer. Contextual design allows design engineers to assess how users handle or manipulate the product as well as determine environmental constraints that may affect how the product is used. Or it may simply be a general fact-finding opportunity designed to anticipate or improve one or more customer needs.

For example, interviews, focus groups, customer surveys, sales visits, or market research are some of the many fact-finding techniques.

8.4 TYPE I: INTERNAL EFFICIENCY OPPORTUNITIES

Because managers are more likely to be familiar with the internal processes of their organization, their first projects tend to be projects designed to improve some internal process. Some examples of internal efficiency opportunities would include:

- Reorganization of a department (for example, final assembly, or final inspection) to reduce process time

- Reorganization of the manufacturing process to reduce waste

- Analysis of a process to assess the effectiveness of standard operating procedures

- Energy utilization study to determine how consumption can be reduced

- Study of a machine to improve performance (that is, reduce variability and/or operate closer to a target value).

8.4.1 Problem Statement (the DEFINE Phase)

When faced with an internal efficiency issue, the first difficulty is the problem statement. Often the scope of the initial problem statement is too broad. Broad problem statements such as "We need to reorganize our department" are not focused, complex, and will likely require more resources and time to resolve or may never be resolved.

Any one of the opportunities just listed could be developed into a project; however, one first needs to clarify the intent. For example, the first statement, "Reorganization of final assembly to reduce process time" is a good first step but it is not yet an acceptable (that is, well-defined) project statement that could be submitted to upper management for review and (ideally) eventual approval.

8.4.1.1 What Is Missing?

If one were to submit to upper-management the following statement, what might be their reaction?

Project title: Reorganization of final assembly to reduce process time. Submitted by: John Knowlittle

Before approving this project, the review committee would like the project leader (Mr. John Knowlittle) to address the following comment and answer the following questions:

1. What is the current process time and by how much can it be reduced after the reorganization?

2. Will it suffice to reorganize final assembly?

3. What other departments may have an impact on the overall performance of final assembly?

4. What is the estimated timeline for this project?

5. What are the estimated resources and associated costs for this study (project)?

6. What savings (in thousands of dollars) would result from this reorganization?

The committee recommends that the project be resubmitted for a final review within 30 days. All of the questions just listed are reasonable, and Mr. Knowlittle needs to provide some specific answers if he wants his project to be approved during the next review.

8.4.2 What to Consider when Defining a Problem and Hence a Project

Let's examine each of the objections raised by the review committee:

1. What is the current process time and by how much can it be reduced after the reorganization? **Answer:** Measure, that is, collect data or review and analyze available data. It is always a good idea to quantify the problem. "Reduce process time" is too vague a statement. We would like to know what is the current process time and by how much it could reasonably be reduced. Depending on what types of data are currently available, this may be either easy or more difficult to assess. Assuming some process time data are available, the answer to the question may still be somewhat complicated because we cannot assume there is only one process time. Indeed, it is likely that process time (for final assembly) will depend on the nature (complexity) of the final assembly (unless, of course, only one type of product is assembled).

2. Will it suffice to reorganize final assembly?

3. What other departments may have an impact on the overall performance of final assembly? Because questions 2 and 3 are similar, we consider them together. **Answer:** Perform a process analysis (explained later in this chapter). The committee would like to know or perhaps suspects that

the alleged "efficiency problems" of final assembly may well be linked to one or more departments upstream from final assembly. To answer this request Mr. Knowlittle has a couple of tools and techniques available. He may want to prepare a high-level process flowchart of the final assembly process and/or use the *SIPOC model* (described later) or, better yet, prepare a *process map* (see later). However, because these techniques are usually used during the process analysis phase, he should explain that these analyses will be performed as part of the process analysis phases. Nevertheless, if Mr. Knowlittle is able to produce a generalized flowchart and perhaps a high-level process map for his presentation, the committee will likely appreciate this information.

4. What is the estimated timeline for this project? **Answer:** Produce a GANTT (or similar) chart. This reasonable request is to be expected for any and all projects. The committee would like to have some idea of how long this project will take (one, three, or six weeks).

5. What are the estimated resources and associated costs for this study (project)? **Answer:** Cost the project and estimate resources (staff and data processing) needed. This is another reasonable request. An attempt to answer this question demonstrates to the committee that the project leader has at least tried to cost the project. This is particularly important when considering the last question.

6. What savings (in thousands of dollars) would result from this reorganization? **Answer:** Estimate the cost savings. Estimation is always a tricky business, but the committee would like to have some idea of the cost to benefit ratio for this project. Also, when the time comes to distribute rewards to the project leader and his team members (if any), the cost savings are needed to compute the amount of the reward.

Review the other four project statements and write down your suggestions on what improvements are needed to improve the chance for approval.

8.4.3 Type II: Reactive Problems

These are perhaps the easiest problems to define because they are defined by the customer or by audit findings. When a customer calls about a specific complaint the problem is usually well defined. I say usually because one might still have to contact the customer for clarification. Still, if the complaint is not an isolated case but can be associated with other similar complaints, then an investigation as to the cause(s) for the recurrence is called for. When an auditor uncovers a pattern of corrective action problems, the causes of the problem are not yet clear but the scope and nature of the problem is usually understood.

In these cases, the same issues concerning problem statement apply. The same rules of problem statement definition outlined for internal efficiency problems/projects apply to so-called reactive problem statements. This leaves us with the last type of opportunity: proactive opportunities.

8.4.4 Type III: Proactive Opportunities: How to Assess the Voice of the Customer

When to use: This technique is most effective when you need to assess the customer perception of your service or products. This could include measuring customer satisfaction, identifying critical features of your service or product, and/or establishing key elements of customer satisfaction. It is also useful when you need to either design a new product or modify/improve an older product or service. The technique applies to either internal (that is, internal to your organization) or external customers (that is, the people purchasing your products).

Assumptions: An assumption often made by survey and/or product developers is that the customer knows what he or she wants. This may not always be true, and in fact, one of the purposes of the customer survey could be to help the supplier define customer needs more accurately.

Traditional technique used: The quantitative method that favors data collection and analysis consists of (1) designing a survey, (2) formulating a questionnaire, (3) administering the questionnaire to an *appropriate* sample of individuals, (4) tabulating the results, and (5) analyzing the results and formulating a conclusion.

The quantitative method is a well-established method and has proven to be popular for some years. However, over the past 15 to 20 years a method known as the qualitative approach has gained popularity.

8.5 THE QUALITATIVE APPROACH

The qualitative interview favors a face-to-face interaction with the customer. Prior to interviewing customers you must:

1. Define your topic by specifying the subject or purpose of your interview. If you can give a title to your project, you are already halfway there.

2. Decide how many customers you will need to interview. Usually 30 to 40 interviews will suffice; however, the size of sample can depend on one or more of the following conditions:

   • Whether or not you have multiple products

   • The type of clients (for example, large order vs. small orders)

- Geographic segmentation (for example, Europe vs. Latin America or major cities vs. rural areas or any other geographic division)

- Whether you have several plants or distribution centers

- Other conditions that may require you to consider how to *segment* your customer base

The idea of segmentation is to force you to ask the following question: Can I assume all of my customers are alike (that is, homogeneous)? If you have a homogeneous market and/or customer base, your task will be simpler. If however, you have reason to believe you have a heterogeneous market, you will have to take into consideration potential variability among customers, type of product purchased or geographic area, or other differentiating characteristics.

But what if you do not know whether or not you have a heterogeneous market? No problem. Simply collect the necessary information. For example, for each interview collect one, two, or three additional variables such as customer zip code, average amount of orders placed per year, product profile, and so forth.

Prepare a brief introduction that explains (to the interviewee) the purpose of your visit and interview. Prepare a list of questions (see open-ended questions later in the chapter). Try to organize your questions from general to more specific. Test your questions on co-workers. This is important because what you thought may have been clear questions may in fact be slightly confusing to the listener. Your co-workers may provide you with valuable suggestions on how you may want to rephrase questions. They may also recommend obvious questions you forgot to include.

Prepare a list of open-ended questions you think are relevant to the topic you wish to explore. Open-ended questions do not constraint the interviewee to a specific answer, and more importantly, they allow the interviewee to elaborate on what he or she perceives as important. Also, open-ended questions often offer you (the interviewer) the opportunity to ask follow-up questions.

Example: "Could you please tell me how (you place an order) or (how you operate this machine) or (how you take a sample), and so on . . ." "Could you please explain how . . ."

Follow-up example: "You said earlier that the sales representative did not seem to know how to answer your question. Could you please elaborate (or could you please be more specific)?" "When you described earlier how you used our product, you mentioned it was sometimes difficult to operate. Could you explain when this might occur?"

Your questions should be short and simply worded. Avoid questions that begin with *can, do,* or *are.* These questions invariably lead to a "yes" or "no" answer. Do not link questions.

Example: "Could you show me how you use the product? Do you use it with the XYZ adapter, for example, or do you prefer to use it with the extension feature turned off?" This question is in fact a three-part question that may be difficult or confusing for anyone. Whenever possible and when it is pertinent, encourage the interviewee to quantify his or her answers.

Example: Interviewee: "I often have problems placing an order on your website."

The interviewer needs to clarify two things before moving on: What type of problems and what is meant by *often*? Interviewer: "What do you mean by *often*?" or "Could you please approximate for me what you mean by *often*? After the clarification encourage the interviewee to explain the nature of the problems. Above all, learn to listen to the answers. During an interview the interviewee *must* do all of the talking and you (as the interviewer) should do all of the listening and writing (or taping if you can use a tape recorder).

8.5.1 Sample Generic Interview Questions

1. Please describe to me your experience with _____?
    (name of product or service)

2. What is important to you when you interact with the
    _____? (name department, service, or other)

2a. What has been your experience when you call the
    _____? (service, sales representative, and so on)

3. What do you like about _____?

4. What do you dislike about _____?

5. How can we improve with _____

5a. What specific recommendations would you make regarding
    our _____ (process, department, and so on)?

6. Could you please give me an estimate as to what you would
    consider to be a fast response? Note: If customer cannot
    answer, you can help by trying to bracket the response
    (for example, 24 to 48 hours, 2 to 3 hours, and so on).

Each of these questions can lead to many other unanticipated questions. No matter how much you plan an interview, there will always be surprises when the interviewee will take you on an unanticipated path of inquiry. You must learn to recognize these valuable leads and know how to explore them and when to stop asking for clarification.

8.6 ANALYZING THE RESULT: THE AFFINITY DIAGRAM

Once you have interviewed 30 to 40 customers, what do you do with the volume of notes or tapes you have amassed? If you have taped the interviews, you will need to transcribe them, that is, transfer the information to a computer file. Once transcribed you will need to sort the information to extract themes. One useful and easy to use technique for sorting and categorizing verbal data collected during an interview is the affinity diagram.

8.6.1 How to Prepare an Affinity Diagram

With the help of one or two co-workers, proceed as follows:

- Each person rereads the notes and highlights (perhaps with a marker) what they perceived as key statements.

- Once the important themes have been highlighted, begin your first round of association by grouping statements that express similar ideas. You will likely have to go through three or four iterations and some discussions to agree on the grouping. You may not be able to group all ideas into themes. Some ideas may have to stand alone and that is all right. Note: Some people code answers that are alike. A simple numeric code (for example, 1, 2, 3, 4, and so on) can be used. Some groups prefer to transfer the key sentences to index cards and then group the index cards into themes.

8.6.2 Example of Qualitative Interview and Affinity Diagram

The following statements are a sample of some of the statements collected during a phone interview conducted for a satellite television service provider. How many themes can you find?

"You charged me for a used receiver when I thought I was getting a new one." (1)

"I don't like your automated answering system." (2)

"Too many family channels." (3)

"Your technician was two hours late." (4)

"I can never speak to a manager." (5)

"I have to listen to that stupid music for too long." (2)

"Your assistants are very helpful." (6)

"Your programming is not flexible enough." (3 or 7)

"Too many channels repeat their films." (7 or 8)

"The same films are shown three or four times a week." (7 or 8)

"You offer too many programs that are of no interest to me." (7)

"I don't care for the way you split your Basic and Premium packages." (7)

"You have too many news channels." (7)

"You don't have enough news channels." (7)

"You should offer a more basic 'Basic' system." (7)

"You should let the customer select a set of channels." (7)

"You don't have an option (on your automated system) for policy cancellation." (2)

"You installation charges were more than you said." (1)

"There are too many options in your answering system." (2)

"Do I really need two dishes?" (4)

"Why do you keep certain channels off the Basic package?" (7)

"The technician who installed the dish gave me the wrong information regarding TV5." (4)

"Going through all the options can be very tedious." (2)

"I was told that I could not receive certain channels when actually I can!" (4 or 6)

"I always get good answers." (4 or 6)

"I waited all day for your technician." (4)

The numbers in parentheses represent the first-round coding for one participant. Notice that this evaluator is not always certain about his classification; some comments may belong to one or two categories. This is not unusual because some comments may have a double meaning or intent. Usually, these difficulties can be resolved after a brief discussion or after a second or third iteration. Also note that the number of comments in each category or theme can be interpreted as an indication of the importance of the category or theme. Thus, for example, if a category contains 30% of all the comments, it can be assumed it is an important category (issue) for customers. Naturally, the selection process that assigns comments to themes (categories) will influence (bias) the ranking of these themes.

Assuming for the sake of simplicity that for the majority of items the other members of the group agree with this preliminary grouping of seven major categories, the reorganized data will look as follows:

I. Pricing (2 out of 26 comments).

"You charged me for a used receiver when I thought I was getting a new one." (1)

"You installation charges were more than you said." (1)

II. Answering system (5 out of 26 comments)

"I don't like your automated answering system." (2)

"I have to listen to that stupid music for too long." (2)

"You don't have an option (on your automated system) for policy cancellation." (2)

"There are too many options in your answering system." (2)

"Going through all the options can be very tedious." (2)

III. Programming (2 out 26)

"Too many family channels." (3)

"Your programming is not flexible enough." (3 or 7)

IV. Technical or technician related (6 out of 26)

"Your technician was two hours late." (4)

"Do I really need two dishes?" (4)

"The technician who installed the dish gave me the wrong information regarding TV5" (4)

"I was told that I could not receive certain channels when actually I can!" (4 or 6)

"I always get good answers." (4 or 6)

"I waited all day for your technician." (4)

V. Access to management (1 out of 26)

"I can never speak to a manager." (5)

VI. Praise (1 out of 26)

"Your assistants are very helpful" (6)

VII. Programming flexibility (9 out 26). This category could perhaps be reorganized with Programming.

"Too many channels repeat their films." (7 or 8)

"The same films are shown three or four times a week." (7 or 8)

"You offer too many programs that are of no interest to me." (7)

"I don't care for the way you split your Basic and Premium package." (7)

"You have too many news channels." (7)

"You don't have enough news channels." (7) (Note: Opposite of preceding request. These two requests cancel each other.)

"You should offer a more basic 'Basic' system." (7)

"You should let the customer select a set of channels." (7)

"Why do you keep certain channels off the Basic package?" (7)

For this project, the voice of the customer consists of seven themes (voices) that are dominated by three (20 out of 26) demands or needs ranked as follows:

1. Programming flexibility (9 out of 26 comments)

2. Technical-related issues (6 out of 26 comments)

3. Frustration with the automated answering system (5 out of 26 comments)

The advantage of the qualitative interview is that it not only helps identify the voice of the customer (in this case three dominant voices have been identified), but it also simultaneously defines what are known as *key quality characteristics*. However, in this particular example and in most real case studies, especially in the service sector, the key quality characteristics have not been quantified yet. For example, if we look under the "programming flexibility" dimension, we note that some customers are not satisfied with the Basic programming system; they would like to select a set of channels but we do not know how many and what type of channels customers would like to be able to select and for what price. This information was not retrieved by the interviewers and it should have been! However, now that we have more information, a more specific survey can be designed to better assess these and other needs as demanded by the three requirements: (1) frustration with the automated answering system, (2) technical issues, and (3) programming flexibility. Still, even if we cannot afford to conduct another survey, a lot of information has already been obtained, enough to force decision makers to consider offering other options and to improve the answering system.

8.7 PROBLEM DEFINITION: THE KEY TO A SUCCESSFUL PROJECT

Because a well-focused problem with a clearly define scope and objective(s) is more likely to be resolved than a broadly defined problem statement, how can we ensure that the problem and hence the project definition will be clearly stated? The following set of questions can help when preparing a problem statement.

1. What is the nature of the problem? Is it an internal efficiency problem, a reactive problem driven by customer complaints, or a proactive opportunity driven by marketing studies or a voice of the customer survey?

2. What do you already know about the problem? Do you have a database you could analyze and from which you could establish a performance baseline? Will you need to collect new data?

3. Is it possible to *stratify* the problem by finding out *where* and *when* the problem occurs?

Regarding *where* questions:

• Does the problem occur at a particular plant (or process)?

• Does it concern a particular department and thus affect a particular process (or processes)?

• Does it concern a particular customer or a specific subset of customers and could it involve a specific supplier or suppliers?

• Is it a regional problem (which region)?

Regarding *when* questions:

• When does the problem occur (what time, day, week, month, shift, and so on)?

- Does the problem fluctuate or cycle with time (that is, can you prepare a time chart of the problem to see patterns across time or across space?)

8.8 WHAT TO CONSIDER WHEN SELECTING A PROJECT

Irrespective of the type of problem you wish to resolve, you should always:

- Define the problem as a business or financial opportunity that will improve profitability and/or improve customer satisfaction.

- Define the process(es) associated with the problem.

- Ensure that the process boundaries (that is, the scope) are not so broad as to minimize the opportunity for success.

- Find measures that will allow you to identify and quantify the type of defects that characterize the problem.

- Identify the impact of the problem on the internal or external customer.

- Ensure you have management support and approval to solve the problem.

If you can do all of the above, you will have a greater chance of solving the problem successfully. Once a problem has been clearly stated following the guidelines just specified, it is usually helpful to conduct a process analysis.

8.9 PROCESS ANALYSIS PHASE (ANALYZE)

A process analysis is a multiphased approach that consists in investigating how the current systems or processes may be related to the problem. Some of the principles and techniques available for process analysis include the following:

1. The **SIPOC** model.

2. Various types of flowcharting techniques used to represent a process graphically. Flowcharting is particularly useful to identify nonvalue-added steps (that is, areas of inefficiencies). These nonvalued-added steps may also be the cause of process

slowdown also known as bottlenecks, which affect the overall efficiency or yield and hence profitability of an organization.

3. Process mapping, a simple technique that matches input variables with output variables for each process.

4. The cause and effect matrix: an extension of process mapping whereby one or more persons familiar with the processes under investigation rank the importance of each input and output variable with respect to either customer requirements or a response variable under investigation. This can be useful when trying to identify which process (or processes) and more particularly which process input variables and/or which process output variables may affect the quality of the response (that is, problem) variable and by extension, the (internal or external) customer's perception of quality.

8.9.1 The SIPOC Model: Preamble to Process Analysis

Irrespective of the type of problem you wish to analyze (type I, II, or III), the same fundamental process analysis model applies. The acronym SIPOC stands for: **S**upplier, **I**nput, **P**rocess, **O**utput, and **C**ustomer.

Graphically, the SIPOC model consists of a diagram that represents the chain on interconnections linking suppliers to the customer via a system of processes.

The type of problem you wish to solve will define the nature of the customer. Suppose, for example, you are an internal auditor and have identified a Type II problem (reactive). In this case you or perhaps your manager becomes the internal customer. The "outputs" that feed into the customer perception of a problem can be:

1. A nonconformance report that tabulates the number of nonconformances for the week (either by department or process or by product category or some other form)

2. A list of customer complaints by type of complaints, dollar amount, percentage of weekly production or a host of other possibilities

3. A list of internal reworks (a nonvalue-added activity)

The processes would consist of the internal processes that produce these outputs. Identifying which process (or series of processes), or perhaps which step or procedure within a process (or series of processes), are responsible for producing these nonconformances, customer complaints, or internal reworks will become the responsibility of the investigating problem-solving team (see later).

The inputs consists of variables such as raw materials, information, test results, subassemblies, value-added transformations, and so on, that feed the system of processes that produces the final product or service.

Finally, the suppliers consist of all the internal and external suppliers that provide an organization with the necessary inputs required for the production of products or services.

8.9.2 Examples of Candidates for the SIPOC Model by Type of Problem

Table 8.1 lists examples of how the SIPOC model could be used with various types of problems.

8.9.3 What Is a Process?

A process is a series of value-added steps that transforms inputs (such as materials, information, or other process variables) into outputs (that is, semifinished or finished goods).

Processes consist of people, environment, machines, materials/ingredients, methods/procedures, and a measurement system (see Table 8.2).

8.9.4 Process Flowcharting

This technique is most effective whenever questions of process (in)efficiency or of bottlenecks need to be investigated. This simple technique is useful to uncover and eliminate nonvalue-added activities.

The technique of flowcharting originated at least 50 years ago when programmers began writing software codes for computers. As a software development tool, the technique of flowcharting helped conceptualize in a series of diagrams the logical flow of a series of computer commands that would have to be written to accomplish a certain task. The idea was that before writing a program from scratch, a programmer had to first design the program on paper to see how the logic would flow. Theoretically, the flowchart was supposed to help the programmer uncover errors in logic and thus avoid having to rewrite many revisions of the same program. In reality, most

Table 8.1 SIPOC applications by types of problems.

SIPOC components	Internal efficiency (I)	Reactive problem (II)	Proactive problem (III)
Suppliers	May or may not involve any suppliers. Can only be determined at time of study.	Usually involves one or more internal or external suppliers. Can only be determined at time of study.	May not involve any supplier. Can only be determined at time of study.
Inputs	Can only be determined at time of study.	Can only be determined at time of study.	Can only be determined at time of study.
Process	Tend to be at the department level or, more often, across a variety of departments.	Often is specific to a process but may also be linked to other processes.	Usually involves the engineering (design) department but, as with the case of value-added audits, may include any other department.
Output	Not necessarily linked to product defects, nonconformance or customer complaints but rather to efficiency measures often associated with throughput measures.	Internal audit report, customer complaints, warranty reports, final test reports, etc.	Customer surveys, focus groups, marketing surveys, etc. Or value-added audits that are designed to look for inefficiency or opportunities to improve (as opposed to the usual conformance audits—see Type II).
Customer	Managers (internal to the company) or value-added auditors.	Auditors (internal but also third-party); any internal customer or external customers.	Generally external customers (new product design or product improvement) but also value-added auditors whose focus is on process improvement.

programmers would first write the program, discover the errors, rewrite the program (often many times, known as *debugging* the program), and after the program was working satisfactorily but not necessarily optimally, they would then produce a flowchart to demonstrate the logical flow.

Table 8.2   Elements of a process.

A process consists of:	Potential variables or factors that may have an impact on product variation.
People *working* in an	People have various *skills* that are supposed to be standardized via *training* and *aptitudes* and that are assessed through job evaluation skills or job functional analysis.
environment and *operating*	Uncontrolled environmental conditions such as noise, humidity, or ambient temperature are referred to as *noise*. In certain situations, environmental conditions (e.g., air conditioning, humidity, and dust) can be controlled (e.g., as in a clean-room for example).
machines that *transform*	Machines of various age and *capability* and subject to a broad range of *maintenance* schedules.
materials or **ingredients** *according to a set of*	Materials or ingredients coming from various *suppliers* and therefore subject to variations in specifications.
methods or **procedures** to *produce a product* according to a set of specifications that is measured using a	Methods and procedures that may be in need of revision and/or that may have a high ratio of *nonvalue-added/value-added* steps.
measurement system.	Instruments that need to be *calibrated* and may have various levels of *accuracies, repeatability,* or *reproducibility* (etc.) In general, a measurement system that may not be adequate to measure specifications.

If we were to apply the original logic of flowcharts to the manufacturing world, we would first ask a manufacturing engineer to flowchart a process before implementing its design. This rarely, if ever, happens. In fact, most applications of flowcharting in the manufacturing or service world consist of flowcharting processes after they have been implemented, sometimes many years ago. Still the technique is useful because, as in the programming world, flowcharts can help problem solvers discover process inefficiencies that may be directly or indirectly responsible for a host of problems.

Several software packages are now available to flowchart processes (for example, Microsoft Word includes under the AutoShapes command a list of 24 flowchart symbols. However, when we are first confronted with the task of having to flowchart a process, we do not need a computer for the task. A packet of yellow (or any other color) self-stick notes can be very useful. Each note can be used to write a process step, and the notes can be rotated 45° degrees to create what are know as decision (IF) points. The advantage of the notes is that they can be moved around on any surface such as a wall or a whiteboard, for example, until the process is satisfactorily charted. Once the process is flowcharted the steps can then be transcribed to paper or onto a computer.

Basically, only two symbols are needed to flowchart any process: the square ☐ and the diamond ◇.

The square is used to identify steps or tasks and the diamond is used to identify what are known as decision points. A diamond always means that a question is asked, and there is usually only two branches coming out of a decision point: "yes" or "no." The series of squares and diamonds are linked with arrows to indicate the flow of a process.

Other symbols such as the circle are usually used to indicate a delay or an inspection (that is, a potential bottleneck) and can also be used to indicate nonvalue-added steps. As the name implies, nonvalue-added steps indicate inefficiencies and thus waste. Table 8.3 illustrates the use of a generic *deployment chart* across four departments. The elapsed time for each task across each department is also shown. Notice how the bulk of the time is spent when the task crosses departments (a cumulative percentage of the time spent could be calculated).

8.9.5 Process Mapping

This technique can be valuable when one needs to associate customer needs or demands with process variables and/or when one needs to understand how process input and output variables may affect or otherwise impact customer needs or expectations.

The technique of process mapping expands on the SIPOC model by allowing the investigator(s) to identify the inputs and outputs for each process. This technique can be useful in some situations where you need to associate specific (and preferably quantified) customer needs to specific processes input and/or output variables. However, the technique can, on occasion, unnecessarily complicate issues. Indeed, one of the advantages of the qualitative interview described earlier is that one can specifically determine, via the use of follow-up questions and open-ended questions, the nature of customer dissatisfaction.

Figure 8.1 is a generic illustration of a process map. It shows that some of the outputs from one process become the inputs form another process; however, not all outputs need to be viewed as inputs to the next process (for example, from Process A to Process B). Indeed, some inputs may be specific to a process. Examples would include additives in a chemical process, the anodizing of a part, painting or coating a chassis, and so forth. The list

Table 8.3 Generic of a deployment chart.

Department 1	Department 2	Department 3	Department 4	Elapsed time
	Task begins here			10–15 minutes
10–15 minutes		10 minutes	Step 2	Up to 4 hours
		Step 3		10 minutes
Step 4 10–15 minutes		(This is the only task performed by this department!)		10–15 minutes for steps 3–4 and steps 4–5
Step 5	Step 6			Up to 2 hours
	20 minutes			20 minutes
	Step 7		Step 8 30–45 minutes	Up to 4 hours 15 minutes for step 8 to end Total time: Up to 11:30 hours for about 75–90 minutes worth of tasks!
	Final step			

of needs under the title Customer indicates the expected needs or demands of internal or external customers. These demands may come in the form of a customer wish list for a new product or customer complaints or a manager's wish to reduce process inefficiency.

As a method, the process map facilitates the task of matching process outputs with customer needs. For example, let's assume Outputs 1 and 2 of Process B are directly linked to Customer Needs 2 and 3. Customer Need 1 may be associated with a process not yet identified, and so on. Once the needs have been matched with the various process outputs and hence process inputs, questions can next be formulated on how these outputs impact customer needs.

8.9.6 Another Example of Process Mapping

This next example illustrates the relationship between process input variables (PIVs), process control variables (PCVs), and process output variables

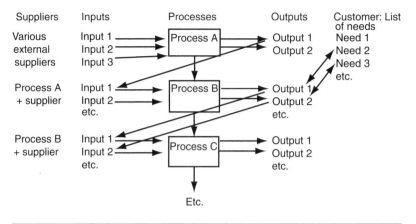

Figure 8.1 Generic example of a process map for internal or external customer needs.

(POVs) (see Figure 8.2). Within the manufacturing world, examples for PCVs would include temperature, flow rate, chemical concentration, pressure, acidity, and a host of other variables. For each process, each PCV is maintained within a specified operational range (for example, $150 <$ temperature < 175, $55 <$ flow rate < 65, $5.2 <$ acidity < 5.8, and so on).

PIVs would include a broad range of raw materials provided by various suppliers (hence the opportunity to stratify raw material by supplier, for example), as well as POVs coming from other processes. Each of these PIVs (and POVs) has a set of specifications that can (depending on the process) either be continuously monitored via a computerized monitoring system or via a sampling process (as required for example by control charts).

Within the service (or transactional) world, process input variables usually consists of forms that must be filled out. The process control variables could consist of data entry and/or data verification tasks and could also include laboratory analyses. The process output variables would include more forms, data entry/verification, and/or laboratory results.

Each POV produced by a process can in turn be viewed as a response variable (Y) that is the result of a transformation applied to a set of PIVs. Because in most cases, the transformation of the PIVs is achieved by adjusting a set of PCVs, the experimenter has an opportunity, should she deem it necessary, to conduct a design of experiment that will allow her to control, via the use of a design matrix, the range of operating values for each PCV. The use of such design matrices (presented in Chapters 5–7) allows the experimenter to observe how the response variable Y (that is, the process output variable) will "respond" (or not respond) to the set of control changes.

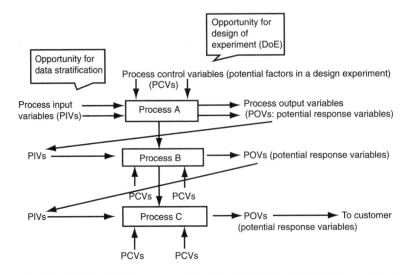

Figure 8.2 A process map with PIVs, PCVs, and POVs.

As shown in Chapters 5 through 7, such investigations can in turn lead to some valuable information.

8.10 THE CAUSE-AND-EFFECT MATRIX

This technique is often mentioned in Six Sigma classes but, like process mapping, it can often complicate an analysis unnecessarily. The technique outlined here is derived from Quality Function Deployment (and the House of Quality), a methodology developed in the early 1980s to determine what customer requirements are associated with what engineering variables and how they can be translated into engineering specifications.

The cause-and-effect matrix is most effective when specific customer requirements have been identified. The steps to built a cause-and-effect matrix are:

1. Rank the customer requirements. The usual scale is 1 = Low, 10 = High, but other values, 1 through 5, for example, can be used.

2. Identify all process input variables.

3. For each input and customer requirement, assign a subjective correlation using a numerical score of 1 = Low, 3, 5, or 9 = High).

4. Cross-multiply the correlation values with the customer ranking and add across all rankings to obtain a total score.

5. Select the first two or three highest scores.

8.10.1 Cause-and-Effect Matrix: An Example

A problem-solving team consisting of two individuals has identified five customer requirements. These five customer requirements have been ranked in the matrix (first row) from left to right. Note that the ranking can (should) be obtained from the customer interviews. For example, in the satellite television provider (developed earlier; see qualitative interview techniques), three general categories of complaints were obtained. Based on the number of citations (or customer comments), we can state that in order of preference the three categories of comments can be ranked as follows: (1) programming flexibility, (2) technical issues, and (3) automated answering machine issues. Therefore we could arbitrarily assign a 5 (or a 9) to programming flexibility, a 3 (or a 5) to technical issues, and a 1 to automated answering machine issues.

This example includes five customer requirements that are associated with a list of six process inputs across three processes (A, B, and C):

Process input steps	Lowest customer requirement (1)	Second lowest requirement (2)	Other requirements may be included here	Highest customer requirement (5)	Total
1 Process A	3 (3 × 1 = 3)	5 (5 × 2 = 10)		9 (9 × 5 = 45)	58
2 Process A	1 (1 × 1 = 1)	9 (9 × 2 = 18)		5 (5 × 5 = 25)	44
3 Process B	3 (3 × 1 = 3)	3 (3 × 2 = 6)		3 (3 × 5 = 15)	24
4 Process B					
5 Process C	5 (5 x 1 = 5)	3 (3 × 2 = 6)		3 (3 × 5 = 15)	26
6 Process C	5 (5 x 1 = 5)	9 (9 × 2 = 18)		9 (9 × 5 = 45)	68
etc.					

Based on these subjective estimates the team calculates that process step 6 in Process C and process step 1 in Process A are the two most important input variables to impact customer requirements.

8.10.2 Limitations of the Cause-and-Effect Matrix

The problem with the cause-and-effect matrix is that the numerical calculations give a false impression of scientific impartiality, when in fact many of the numbers (particularly the estimated correlation coefficients of association) are mere subjective evaluation. Because process experts subjectively estimate the correlation coefficients, there is no reason to assume a different set of so-called experts would have arrived at the same estimates. This is why I do not favor the use of pseudo-scientific methods often presented in the Six Sigma Black Belt course. A pseudo-scientific method is any method that gives the appearance of being rigorous by simply using subjective quantitative estimates. The difficulty with most if not all of these techniques is they fail to emphasize that the quantification is based on guesses or very rough estimates. In essence, all that is done is to quantify a series of guesses in the hope this quantification will bring more rigor to the decision process. Nevertheless, despite these limitations, it is true that when investigators have to sort our numerous issues, the use of these techniques can help bring some order to the chaos.

8.11 GENERIC TYPES OF PROBLEMS AND ASSOCIATED METHODOLOGY

There are two broad categories of problems: (1) problems relating to cycle time reduction and (2) problems relating to the performance of one or more process variables. By "performance of a process variable," I mean that given a set of specifications, a process variable has either too much variability, is too far from its ideal target value, or both. These types of problems are classic process capability studies:

1. If the problem is an administrative or manufacturing cycle time problem, the primary task will be to identify nonvalue-added activities—often redundant tasks as well as tasks that currently take "too long" to accomplish. These tasks usually lead to bottlenecks, which are well known to slow down the overall throughput efficiency of a production cycle. For cycle-type problems, the most useful tools tend to be interviewing techniques using either qualitative or quantitative survey methodology. These techniques can also lead to the generation of *activity flowcharts,* which allow for a detailed analysis of the tasks for each process and/or a *deployment flowcharts,* which allow for the tracking of a document across various departments. Once the process has been simplified or consolidated, one can use a variety of graphical or statistical techniques (for instance, histograms, time charts, control charts, or others) to show the cycle time has been successfully reduced.

2. If the problem relates to the performance of a process output variable (or variables), the problem can invariably be reformulated in terms of a response variable (that is, a process output variable or POV) whose variation needs to be analyzed using, perhaps, a design of experiment. As explained in previous chapters, these experimental designs can be conducted by controlling the setting of various process control variables (PCVs).

Naturally, experimental designs are but one of the many techniques available to an experimenter. As shown in Chapter 4, several statistical techniques can be used to analyze stratified data. Discrete variables can be cross-tabulated to search for patterns. Continuous variables can be analyzed using one-way, two-way or N-way analysis of variance, and so on.

In all cases, brainstorming techniques coupled with the use of simple analysis tools such as cause-and-effect diagrams, tree diagrams, or affinity diagram scan also be used to generate potential (nonquantitative) solutions that will have to be tested or otherwise verified and *validated* in the field (see section 8.14).

8.12 THE DEFINE-MEASURE-ANALYZE INTERPHASE

Once a project has been defined and approved successfully and the processes identified and, depending on circumstances, mapped and/or flow-charted, the next phase depends on the nature and extent of the data collection. In many (if not all cases) characterized by type I or type II problems, the project leader *will already have collected some data and may have already process the data through some data summarization or data sorting analysis*. For Type III (proactive) problem, a significant part of the project could be to analyze and summarize the data collected during interviews. Consequently, the sequence of events that follows is meant to be a guideline and will depend on the type of problems.

8.12.1 Data Summarization Tools

Several simple well-established and practical tools are available (see Chapters 1–4) for the analysis and/or summarization of data, as follows:

1. Data summarization table (for example, mean, median, standard deviation, minimum, maximum, and other statistics).

2. The *Pareto diagram,* which categorizes and ranks problem by types of problems and quantity. Do not forget to consider cost Pareto diagrams. One could prepare a Pareto diagram for the satellite television qualitative survey.

3. The histogram that reorganizes data into classes to see the overall shape of the data distribution. The nature of the shape can help the investigator estimate, among other things, the amount of variation.

4. The time series, which allows us to see the evolution of a variable across time.

5. Box plots, which are useful graphics that allows for a graphic estimation of variation. Box plots can also be used across time to visualize variation through time or across different variables (see Chapter 1).

6. Scattergrams are helpful to see the relationship between two variables measured on a continuous scale.

7. Cross-tabulations work on the same principle as scattergrams but used with ordinal variables such as those found in questionnaires (for example, Strongly like = 5, Strongly dislike = 1).

8. Control charts. A form of time series with control limits that bound the overall variation of a measured variable (for example, P-Chart, C-Chart, X-bar and R chart, and so on).

Prior to analyzing any data, always consider *when* the data was collected and *where* it was collected. These suggestions of *where* and *when* (two forms of data *stratification*) apply to data that have either been already collected or are about to be collected. In other words, when considering data as a source of information that can be used to solve a problem, always consider the "where" and the "when" of the data. An example of *where* would include location, broadly defined here to include geographic locations such as city, states, counties, different plants, different departments within a plant, or even different machines within a department or within a plant. An example of *when* would include: time, which in addition to the usual meaning of hours and minutes could also be expanded to mean: day of the week, week of the month or month, shift (1st, 2nd, and so on). Here are some other means of stratifying data:

1. Charting the data by type of customers, for example by sex (male or female), age (less than 20, 21–35, 36–45, and so on), income, or other categories.

2. Subdivide (or stratify) a particular type of problem by product types or some other category. The idea of data stratification is to slice the data to see if the problem under investigation may look differently when analyzed under a different set of conditions.

8.12.2 What Should Be Considered When Measuring Variables?

If an instrument (for example, a thermometer, a caliper, a gage, a scale, a potentiometer, and so on), is used to obtain measurements (that is, data), it is reasonable to ask how accurate the data (readings) are. If, for example, one were to measure the temperature of a solution or the weight in milligrams of a chemical residue, one would hope the instruments used to obtain these measurements are accurate and reliable. The topic of instrument reliability and repeatability is one of the favorite topics covered in the Six Sigma Black Belt course, but is it as important as some consultants would have us believe? To answer that question we must first define what is meant by a *measurement system,* which consists of a set of instruments, the people operating the instruments, and the environment in which the people and instruments are operating.

With regard to the instrument, we would like to know its *accuracy, precision, linearity, stability,* and *bias. Linearity* refers to the ability of an instrument to detect changes over a range of values (that is, different part sizes). For example, changes in concentration over a specified range, changes in temperature from 0° to 100°C and so on. *Stability* refers to the variation in a measurement of a standard (or master part) when measured over an extended period of time. A stable gage means that when used to measure a standard, the same reading will be obtain over a period of time. *Bias* refers to the tendency for the measurements to be too large or too small. *Accuracy* refers to the ability of an instrument to measure a true value. Or stated another way, accuracy is the discrepancy between the true value and the result obtained by measurement. To assess the accuracy of an instrument (or of an analytical method), acquire a standard (that is, the true value) and measure the standard with the instrument. If the measurement obtained equals the value of the standard, there is no discrepancy and the instrument is said to be perfectly accurate. *Precision* refers to the agreement among repeated measurements of the same quantity. Precision includes two components: repeatability and reproducibility (see later in the chapter).

With regard to the part-operator interaction, we would like to know the following:

1. If there is an operator-part *interaction;* that is, if the performance of the instrument depends on who operates the instrument with what part

2. If an operator can repeat over a short period of time a measurement (the instrument and/or method is said to be repeatable)

3. If two or more operators can reproduce (*reproducibility*) each other's measurements

To assess these three steps, we must conduct what is known as a *Gage R&R.*

8.12.3 Should a Gage R&R Study Always Be Conducted?

Some proponents of Six Sigma would have us believe a Gage R&R must always be conducted prior to performing any study. Is this a reasonable proposition? I propose that such an attitude is often not well advised because it has been my experience that in the majority of cases, both instruments and operators are very capable of obtaining very good, reliable, and repeatable measurements. However, if untrained operators are used to obtain measurements, then naturally, one would expect low repeatability and a Gage R&R study will very likely prove the obvious. Indeed, are the measurement needs of a furniture manufacturer who operates in a world defined in terms of $+/-0.25$ inch the same as a precision machinist who machines parts to a tolerance of $+/-0.0001$ inch, or the industrial chemist or environmentalist who has to measure infinitesimal concentrations in the ppm or even ppb ranges? I propose the answer is no.

For the furniture manufacturer and thousands of other manufacturers operating in the world of $+/-0.25$ inch, the accuracy of a tape measure and the skill and training required to operate, as it were, such a tape are more than adequate to obtain reliable and reproducible measures. Moreover, conducting a Gage R&R on a tape measure will likely prove to be a costly and futile exercise that would prove little. Naturally, the machinist and chemist require and use more precise and accurate instruments. In such cases, where there is likely to be disagreement as to the actual measurement of a concentration or of the outside diameter of a part, a Gage R&R could be a valuable exercise and may even spur some interesting debates between supplier and customers as to which instrument is more accurate or which method is the best. However, in many cases the problem may not have anything to do with the precision or reliability of an instrument but rather with the operator or perhaps the way the operator interacts with the instrument. How the instrument is used is very important because it may depend on the training of the operator. However, even in such conditions, the operator-instrument interaction is minimal (assuming of course, adequate training and equal skills) and may even be eliminated (using a pH meter, scales, or sophisticated scientific instruments when sample preparation may be important), via the use of automated procedures that essentially eliminate operator error.

Therefore, assuming proper training, the use of approved procedures and adequate instrument calibration and maintenance, most instruments will be found to be reliable, precise, and accurate, certainly accurate and precise enough for the purpose of most experiments, and not in need of any Gage R&R study. If, however, the experimenter does not have much confidence in the measurement process and therefore suspects that repeatability or reproducibility are likely to jeopardize the integrity of the data then he or she should conduct a Gage R&R study; this will in turn provide some valuable information as to what proportion of the error in measurement is attributable to the measurement system (that is, operators, instrument, method, and so on). Despite these observations suppliers to the automotive industry are required by their customers to perform costly Gage R&R studies for all of their instruments (see section 4.7.3).

Once data have been collected, they will need to be analyzed. Several nonquantitative techniques (as opposed to the statistical techniques already presented in Chapters 1–7) are available for the analysis of data.

8.13 IMPROVE

At the end of the analysis phase one should be in a position to offer some recommendations that will either solve a problem or *improve* a process. The nature of the proposed solution will depend on the method used to perform the analysis, which is in turn influenced by the type of problem under investigation. For example, if a design of experiments or some other statistical technique is used to analyze a particular problem, the solution or answer to the problem will be, in most cases, evident in that either the formulated hypotheses are verified or they are not and a new experiment will have to be conducted. Because statistical problems are formulated in terms of hypotheses that must be tested, one can either accept or reject the proposed hypothesis and move on to the next phase. However, if the analysis phase did not (or could not) require the use of some statistical technique (for example, regression analysis, analysis of variance, or others), other well-known (nonquantitative) techniques will need to be used.

Brainstorming is still a powerful technique that can be used by a team of process experts to suggest or generate ideas for potential solutions. Because the purpose of brainstorming is to generate as many ideas (solutions, suggestions) as possible, one needs a method to rank, evaluate, or otherwise sort out the ideas produced during a brainstorming session. Three techniques are proposed:

- Multivoting (used to reduce a long list of solutions down to two to six ideas)

- Prioritization matrix (a method used to rank evaluate several solutions)

- Pugh Matrix (method occasionally used to help designers select the best design)

Each of these techniques consists of assigning various weights and scores to a list of ideas. A multitude of methods have been suggested to prioritize pseudo-scientifically and thus reduce a list of options and/or suggestions. For each of these techniques, hundreds of websites can be found on the Internet by simply searching for *multivoting, Pugh matrix*, or *Prioritization matrix*.

8.14 VERIFY: PILOT RUN

A pilot run is necessary to test or otherwise verify the effectiveness of any proposed solution. The time required to verify the effectiveness of a solution will vary depending on the nature of the problem. Some solutions can be verified within one to three or four days; other solutions may take three to four weeks (or months) to verify. It could well be that the improved solution concerned a new assembly method and the cycle time from implementation—including documentation and training to product delivery and testing by customers—will take several months!

During the verification phase, one must demonstrate with data that the problem has either been reduced or (preferably) eliminated. An important phase of the improve-verify phase that is particularly relevant for all efficiency-related-type problems, such as, Type I or internal efficiency problems, is the documentation of the savings brought about by the process improvements. This is an important phase because in order for project improvements (Six Sigma or any other) to continue to be successful, the organization must learn to share all cost savings with its employees and especially with the team or individuals responsible for the savings. Unfortunately, the less than favorable economic conditions of the past few years have led some organizations to come up with ingenious methods to avoid having to pay any process improvement rewards. It is hoped that such practices will not become common, because if they do, one of the fundamental incentives of Six Sigma (or any other type) project improvements will be seriously affected and with it the future of Six Sigma.

8.15 CONTROL: THE LAST PHASE

Once the solution has been verified as being adequate it can be standardized and formally introduced into the system. This is known as Control because in some cases one may wish to monitor the effectiveness of the solution with control charts.

The control phase consists of the following actions:

1. Formal documentation of the new (improved) process.

2. Training of all staff affected by the new process.

3. Monitoring, as required, the effectiveness of the new process. Monitoring includes data collection and data summary to confirm effectiveness of the new process. Examples of some tools that can be used for monitoring include (a) Pareto diagrams, (b) Bar charts or histograms, or (c) Control charts.

The control phase can be considered the final phase of the DMAIC methodology.

8.16 CONCLUSION: INVESTIGATING THE DATA

We have come to the end of our data analysis journey. In most of the examples presented in the first seven chapters, the analysis revealed that some relationship or effect existed between a response variable (Y) and one or more factors (or independent variables X). Are these scenarios realistic? Although I can assure you the scenarios described in this book do approximate reality, not every project ends up with a solution. Indeed, although it has often been said that a well-defined problem is half-solved, it is also true that finding the remaining half may not be easily achieved or occasionally requires several iterations.

Consequently, I must admit that although the successful (or optimistic) scenarios presented in this book do reflect an aspect of reality, even after a problem has been clearly defined and the appropriate data have been collected and correctly analyzed, one may uncover nothing! In other words, the null hypotheses will have to be accepted and the experimenter is back to square one. In other words, the problem may have to be redefined and/or new solutions must be suggested (brainstormed), a new set of data may have to be collected and/or a new experiment will need to be conducted, and so on. Do not become discouraged if a solution to the problem is not found in the first round of data analysis, for that is often the case. The statistical methodology described in the first seven chapters and the problem-solving process suggested here in Chapter 8 provide a methodology designed to help reduce the risk of analyzing the wrong problem and/or analyzing the wrong data. And yet, even if a solution is discovered either on the first or second or third round, we cannot assume the solution is *the* final solution. We should always validate the results.

Many years ago I learned a valuable lesson regarding the need to validate results. As a young researcher I wanted to investigate the relationship between diet and arteriosclerosis. Medical researchers had, as early as the late 1960s or early 1970s, established a link between the risk of arteriosclerosis and food consumption. I wanted to see if this link could be shown to exist across nations. I was able to collect dietary and mortality data published by the Organization for Economic Cooperation and Development (OECD) and, running what is known as a factor analysis on the data, I was pleased to discover there was indeed a dietary factor (sugar, butter, fat, and so on) associated with a higher rate of arteriosclerosis. The research was eventually published. However, when I conducted a follow-up study the next year using data from the same organization (but for a different year), I was disappointed to find out the relationship that was so clearly evident the previous year was no longer exhibited by the new data set! I could not validate the result. The validation or confirmation of any research finding is an important step in any investigation and failure to do so may lead to serious financial or other unfortunate consequences.

Whenever possible, make sure you (and/or) the team have an opportunity to see the problem; in other words, if the problem is related to a defective part or transaction, examine the part and/or documents for possible clues. If, on closer examination, certain issues remain unclear or new questions emerge, do not hesitate to ask for clarification.

8.16.1 Potential Problems Relating to the Problem-Solving Team

Upper management may occasionally decide to appoint specific individuals directly to a problem-solving team. As long as management is careful to include all process owners, that is to say managers and people (that is, operators or staff) who have an intimate knowledge of the process, there should be no problem; however, this may not always be the case. Consequently, once a problem has been defined, include as soon as possible people that can, thanks to their knowledge of the process, contribute to the process of solving the problem.

Do not let a team member dominate the team. Domination can be exhibited in several ways:

- Constantly talking or talking for most of the time

- Constantly asking one question after the other and not allowing others to ask questions

- Offering immediate suggestions as to how the problem could be solved

- Working as if the problem was his or her personal problem

- Moving forward with the implementation of personal ideas with little or no input from others

Such behavior may lead a team to break into two or more problem-solving teams.

8.16.2 Do Not Forget the Importance of Validation

Validation is routinely performed in scientific research, especially in the medical field, but is unfortunately rarely performed in industrial or so-called transactional (service) applications where experimenters, who often are under tight scheduling pressures, tend to skip this step. Validation means that once you have proven some facts you, or preferably someone else, should validate these facts by being able to duplicate the results. (Note: I deliberately did not use the words "replicate your results" for fear it may confuse you). For example, if your experimental results (designed or not designed) demonstrate a relationship between the failure rate of some subassembly and the temperature of a variable X, you or a co-worker should be able to duplicate your findings. In order for anyone to duplicate results, a report detailing how the experiment was conducted should be written. The report should do the following:

- Identify which variables were analyzed.

- Explain how the data were collected (including, if appropriate, sample size and estimated time required for setting up the experiment and/or collecting the data).

- Present the original data matrix.

- Explain what transformation(s) (if any) were performed on the data.

- Include observations or comments relating to special or unique events.

- State how the data were analyzed using what technique(s).

- Present a summary of the results including conclusion.

- Include an estimate of costs savings if the experiment was a cost reduction study.

Finally, one must also admit that even after a problem has been well defined and the (ideally) relevant data has been collected, the search for and eventual discovery of the correct path to a solution is not always as clear cut as implied in the numerous examples presented in this book. Indeed, one must recognize that the analysis of a problem often resembles a criminal investigation where the role of the data analyst or experimenter, in many ways, is similar to that of a detective who, faced with a crime, must look for clues, evidence, or unusual or suspicious behavior patterns. When first faced with the task of analysis a graph, a control, chart or some other data summarization chart, one should, as explained in Chapter 1, spend some time looking at the numbers and search for any possible evidence. The case study presented in Chapter 9 will help illustrate the meaning of investigating the data.

9

Case Study

9.0 BACKGROUND INFORMATION

One of the many products manufactured by a supplier is a viscous substance whose specification, measured in Centipoise, is 7000 < Viscosity < 9000. Seven chemicals, provided by various suppliers, are used for the production of this viscous product. The supplier has had some difficulties maintaining the product within specification, and in fact, a major customer has often complained there is "too much variability in the viscosity," which, in turn, causes substantial difficulties in one of the customer's processes.

A team is formed to address the viscosity problem. More specifically, the team needs to address the excessive variability in viscosity.

Problem statement: There is too much variability in the viscosity.

Although the use of words such as *too much variability* may seem vague, little can be done until some viscosity data are collected. Nonetheless, regardless of the magnitude of the variability, the fact remains that, from the customer point of view, it is excessive and consequently the primary objective will be to reduce variability whatever its current value.

The manufacturer suspects that, out of the seven raw materials used for the production of the viscous substance, only two raw materials are likely to influence viscosity. Table 9.1 lists 149 production batch numbers and the associated batch numbers for the two key "ingredients," here labeled Ingredient 1 and Ingredient 2. These 149 batch numbers are equivalent to several weeks of production.

Table 9.1 Production batch numbers and associated batch numbers for ingredient 1 and ingredient 2.

Batch (1–51)	Batch ingredient 1	Batch ingredient 2	Batch (52–100)	Batch ingredient 1	Batch ingredient 2	Batch (101–149)	Batch ingredient 1	Batch ingredient 2
938522	1099	1076	504325	4089	5679	533588	8145	8040
952383	1664	1076	504326	5097	5679	533750	8145	8040
953547	2417	1189	504328	5097	5679	533921	8145	8040
955781	2417	2294	505564	5097	5679	533922	8145	8040
		1076	505968	5097	5679	535183	8145	8040
955782	2417	1189	505969	5097	5679	535184	8145	8040
955783	2417	2294	506691	5097	5679	535186	8145	8040
958589	2417	1421	506692	5097	5679	535190	8650	8040
974684	3610	2294	506939	5097	5679	535193	8650	8040
974685	3610	2294	507446	5097	5679	535196	8650	8040
974686	3610	2294	507447	5097	5679	535197	8650	8040
974686-X	3610	2294	507646	5097	5679	535421	8650	8040
978081	3610	2294	512142	5097	5679	535422	8650	8767
978082	3610	2294	512758	5097	5679	537107	8650	8767
978083	3610	2294	513133	5097	5679	537673	8650	8767
980114	4089	2294	513320	5097	5679	537674	8650	8767
980115	4089	2294	513683	5097	5679	538053	8650	8767
982573	4089	2294	513684	5097	5679	539450	8650	8767
982574	4089	2294	514838	5097	5679	539896	8650	8767
982575	4089	2294	515949	6299	5679	540050	8650	8767
982576	4089	2294		5097		541809	8650	8767
984122	4089	4144	515950	5097	5679	542458	9110	8767
984124	4089	4144	515952	5097	5679	542459	9110	8767
984125	4089	4144		6299	6204	542537	9110	9538
984126	4089	4144	516579	6299	6204	543530	9110	8767
984215	4089	4144	516580	6299	6204	545113	9110	9538
984280	4089	4144	517206	6299	6204	545551	9110	9538
985877	4089	4144	517207	6299	6204	546167	9110	9538
986109	4089	4144	517208	6299	6204	547290	9110	9538
987865	4089	4144	518496	6299	6204	548334	9110	9538
987866	4089	4144	518497	6299	6204	550700	9640	9538
989303	4089	4144	521752	6299	6204	550701	9110	9538
990689	4616	4144	521924	6299	6204	550876	9640	9538
990690	4089	4144	521925	6299	6204	552733	9640	9538
990691	4616	4144	522906	6299	6204	552734	9110	9538
990692	4616	4144	522907	6299	6204	552735	9640	9538
990693	4616	4144	526980	6299	7012	553620	10325	9538
990695	4616	4144	527659	6299	7012	553842	9110	9538
991297	4616	4144	527660	6299	7012	554418	10325	9538
992345	4616	4144	528000	6299	7012	555418	10325	9538
992791	4616	4144			6204	555419	10325	9538
992792	4616	4144	528091	6299	7012	556299	10325	9538
500778	4616	4144	528254		7012	559945-X	10656	9538
500938	4616	4144	528554	8059	7012	560289-X	10656	9538
500939	4616	5679	528554	8059	7012	560290	10656	9538
		4144	529197	8145	7012	560291-X	10656	9538
501981	4616	5679	529613	8145	7012	561060	10656	9538
501981	4616	5679	530856	8145	7012	561061	10656	9538
502621	4616	5679	530857	8145	7012	561062	10656	9538
502622	4616	5679	530858	8145	7012	561063	10656	9538
502623	4089	5679	532236	8145	7012	561064	10656	9538
504009	4616	5679	532237	8145	7012	561065	10656	9538
504010	4089	5679	532238	8145	8040	561066	10656	9538
504324	4616	4144	533162	8145	8040			

9.1 HOW SHOULD THE INVESTIGATOR PROCEED?

Several options are available to the investigator. As is often the case, various sources of information (or data) are usually available during the early stages of an investigation. What is often not available, however, is the process map (described in Chapter 8). Mapping the "viscosity process" would require the expertise of all those involved with the daily operation. The process mapping would consist of identifying the key process activities and the key input and output variables for each process activity. However, instead of proceeding with the process map, our investigator decides (wrongly or rightly) that because the scope (viscosity) and definition of the problem (variability) are well defined, there is no pressing need to extend the Define phase, and consequently he decides to proceed to the Measure and Analyze phases by first analyzing a database currently collected by the quality department. Table 9.2 lists the viscosity and pH (that is, acidity) measures for the 149 batches listed in Table 9.1.

The following scenario describes some of the steps undertaken during the data analysis phase. Having obtained the data listed in Table 9.2 from the quality engineer, the investigator decides to produce a control chart, a very convenient statistical tool to plot time-ordered data. Although there are many types of control charts, all control charts consist of a center line representing the average an upper and lower line equidistant from the average and representing what is known as the upper control limit (UCL) and the lower control limit (LCL).

Points above or below the control limits usually indicate the process is likely to be (perhaps only momentarily) out of control and therefore may not satisfy a customer (or process) specifications. However, in some cases, a point below (or even beyond) a control limit may actually indicate an exceptionally good product.

Because the database consists of 149 individual viscosity (and pH) measurements, the investigator decides to use an individual-moving range chart. Having selected the type of chart the investigator must then decide how the upper and lower control limits will be computed. As you may recall from Chapter 4, the standard procedure is to draw the control limits at $+/-$ 3.0 standard deviations. These lines represent approximately a one-sided alpha level (or Type I error) of only 0.001 (actually $+/-$ 3.09 standard deviation is the exact value for the 0.001 alpha level). Why one-sided? Because the alpha level is applied to each control limit (0.001 for the upper control limit and 0.001 for the lower control limit).

If you recall, setting the alpha level at 0.001 for the control limits is rather conservative in that it favors accepting the null hypothesis (H_0: process is in control). The *smaller* the alpha level the more the control limits will be drawn

Table 9.2   Viscosity data (Centipoise) and acidity measures (pH) for 149 production batches.

Batch	Visc. 22	pH	Obser-vation	Batch	Visc. 22	pH	Obser-vation	Batch	Visc. 22	pH	Obser-vation
938522	8988	6.90	1	504324	8298	6.70	51	533588	9774	6.55	101
952383	9811	7.00	2	504325	7265	6.60	52	533750	7631	6.20	102
953547	9429	6.90	3	504326	9768	6.85	53	533921	7296	6.40	103
955781	8996	7.00	4	504328	7401	7.00	54	533922	7044	6.95	104
955782	8988	7.00	5	505564	7626	6.50	55	535183	7177	6.45	105
955783	8473	6.70	6	505968	7362	7.00	56	535184	8221	6.05	106
958589	8092	6.80	7	505969	8222	6.70	57	535186	7775	6.30	107
974684	7069	7.00	8	506691	8020	6.50	58	535190	7523	6.15	108
974685	7314	7.55	9	506692	8061	7.00	59	535193	7387	6.10	109
974686	7858	0.00	10	506939	8010	6.70	60	535196	8382	6.45	110
974686	7858	7.25	11	507446	8010	6.85	61	535197	7461	6.35	111
978081	7739	6.80	12	507447	8020	6.55	62	535421	7662	6.35	112
978082	7550	6.70	13	507646	7129	6.80	63	535422	9000	6.45	113
978083	8673	6.95	14	512142	7638	6.95	64	537107	8105	6.40	114
980114	7340	6.90	15	512758	8688	6.50	65	537673	7921	6.80	115
980115	6951	6.55	16	513133	7063	6.75	66	538053	7132	6.70	116
982573	7281	6.45	17	513320	7176	6.95	67	539450	7154	6.40	117
982574	7977	6.75	18	513683	7241	6.50	68	539896	7812	6.85	118
982575	7787	6.80	19	513684	7048	6.45	69	540050	7542	6.80	119
982576	7777	6.45	20	514838	8244	6.55	70	541809	7149	7.00	120
984122	8430	6.70	21	515949	7808	6.75	71	542458	7061	6.90	121
984124	7806	6.35	22	515950	7465	6.85	72	542459	8668	6.20	122
984125	7087	6.35	23	515952	8559	6.55	73	542537	7089	6.20	123
984126	7957	6.50	24	516579	8847	6.55	74	543530	7291	6.90	124
984215	7087	0.00	25	516580	7866	6.65	75	545113	7046	6.15	125
984280	8489	6.65	26	517206	8645	6.45	76	545551	7247	6.70	126
985877	7856	7.65	27	517207	7964	6.55	77	546167	7272	6.75	127
986109	8600	7.25	28	517208	7551	6.55	78	547290	7526	6.45	128
987865	8029	6.85	29	518496	7066	6.50	79	548334	7117	6.95	129
987866	7988	6.95	30	518497	7700	6.45	80	550700	7661	6.80	130
989303	8646	6.25	31	521752	8596	7.00	81	550701	7344	6.65	131
990689	9570	6.95	32	521924	8627	6.40	82	550876	7679	6.35	132
990690	8185	6.80	33	521925	7839	6.60	83	552733	8031	6.95	133
990691	8653	7.00	34	522906	7171	6.55	84	552734	7156	6.85	134
990692	8161	7.00	35	522907	7479	6.80	85	552735	8729	6.95	135
990693	7988	7.00	36	527659	7002	7.00	86	553620	8709	6.25	136
990695	7704	6.90	37	527660	7351	6.45	87	553842	7049	6.45	137
991297	8164	6.90	38	528000	7473	7.00	88	554418	8209	6.40	138
992345	8627	6.70	39	528091	7469	6.60	89	555418	7004	6.85	139
992791	7295	6.85	40	528254	7056	6.50	90	555419	7878	6.80	140
992792	7782	6.85	41	528554	7518	6.70	91	556299	8214	6.70	141
500778	8775	6.15	42	529197	7645	6.65	92	559945	9589	6.40	142
500938	8910	6.90	43	529613	7429	6.00	93	560289	10158	6.90	143
500939	7209	6.45	44	530856	7281	6.55	94	561060	8204	7.00	144
501981	7421	6.30	45	530857	8070	6.95	95	561061	8148	6.60	145
502621	7160	6.60	46	530858	8553	6.45	96	561062	8212	6.65	146
502622	7002	7.00	47	532236	8242	6.75	97	561063	8792	7.00	147
502623	7376	6.85	48	532237	7714	6.85	98	561064	8675	6.90	148
504009	8762	6.55	49	532238	7380	6.90	99	561065	8171	6.75	149
504010	7489	6.70	50	533162	9476	6.35	100				

away from the average represented by the center line and the *less likely* we are to reject the null hypothesis. As the alpha levels are increased (that is, 0.005, 0.01, 0.05), the control limits are brought *closer* to the center line (that is, the average) and the more likely we are to *reject* the null hypothesis. In this case we already suspect and the customer has already told us that the process is not capable of meeting the viscosity specification, so our "objective" would be to favor rejecting the null hypothesis. Uncertain as to what should be the correct alpha level, the investigator decides to compute two sets of control limits, one for alpha = 0.005 and one for alpha = 0.01. For alpha = 0.005, the corresponding Z-value is Z = 2.58; for alpha = 0.01, Z = 2.33. Consequently, the first set of control limits (upper half of Figure 9.1a) is drawn as:

$\overline{X}$ +/− 2.58 * S where S = standard deviation. The second set of control limits (upper half of Figure 9.1b) is drawn as $\overline{X}$ +/ −2.33 * S.

The two-chart configuration shown in Figure 9.1a and 9.1b is known as an individual and moving-range chart (I-MR). The upper half of the chart is a plot of the 149 viscosity measures (labeled Visc. 22). The lower chart shows a plot of the ranges for each set of two consecutive viscosities. For

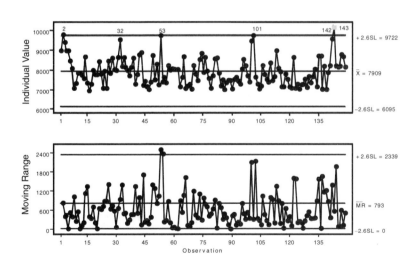

Figure 9.1a   Individual moving range chart for Visc.22 for
Z = 2.58*standard deviation.

When the standard deviation is used to compute upper and lower control limits, the control limits are labeled SL, meaning Sigma Limit. (For I-MR charts this notation is also referred by some authors as the upper and lower tolerance limits of the process.)

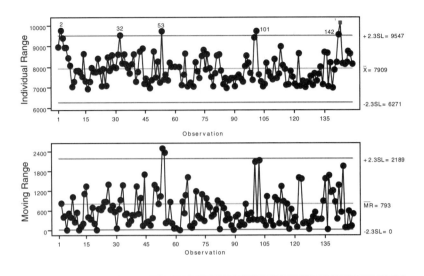

Figure 9.1b   Individual moving range chart for Visc.22 for
Z = 2.33*standard deviation.

When the standard deviation is used to compute upper and lower control limits, the control limits are labeled SL, meaning Sigma Limit. (For I-MR charts this notation is also referred by some authors as the upper and lower tolerance limits of the process.)

example, referring to Table 9.1 we see that the first two viscosity readings are 8988 and 9811. The difference between these two readings is 823 Centipoise, represented by the first Centipoise value plotted on the (bottom) range graph. The difference between the third and second viscosity readings is 382 Centipoise (which is the second range value, and so on). This process of computing and plotting consecutive differences is repeated for the other 147 differences to produce the (bottom) range graph shown in Figure 9.1.

9.2 WHAT DOES THE CONTROL CHART SHOW US?

From the upper half of Figure 9.1a, we can see the average viscosity is 7909 Centipoise (or 79.11 Poise) and the (alpha = 0.005) control limits are drawn at 9722 and 6095, respectively. The upper half of Figure 9.1b shows that for alpha = 0.05, the upper control limit and lower control limits are at 9547 and 6271, respectively (closer to the average of 7909).

Because the specification for viscosity is 7000 < Viscosity < 9000, the expected target value is 8000 +/− 1000 Centipoise. For both graphs the control limits are above and below the specifications, so we would naturally suspect that the process in not capable of maintaining the current specifications. This out-of-control condition is confirmed by the range charts, which show two points beyond the control limit (with a fourth and fifth point— 101, 102—very near the upper control limit). When a range chart has points beyond the control limits it is because the process is unstable, which is often exhibited by erratic variability in the data. A casual look at the range chart reveals that many ranges (approximately 15) are equal to 0, whereas many more ranges (at least 20) are in the 1000 to 1400 Centipoise range. The extent of this variability is also clearly visible when we look at the upper individual chart. An expert chartist would no doubt have noted great oscillation between points, a condition that generally indicates excessive operator intervention (a fact confirmed when a manager was interviewed). The expert chartist would also probably have noticed the distribution of point appears to be either bimodal or certainly skewed.

As we examine the individual chart shown in Figure 9.1a, we see six or possibly seven points that are very close to the upper control limit, and in fact, all these values are not only greater than the control limit but they are also greater than the upper specification of 9000 and therefore nonconforming. If we look at Figure 9.1b (alpha = 0.01), we see that six points exceed the upper control limit, indicating the individual chart is also out of control.[1] The six points are 2, 32, 53, 101, 142, and 143.

Because these points clearly represent what is known in the jargon of control charts as special (or assignable) causes, the investigator decides that, following well-establish procedures, the nature and/or cause of these special causes must be investigated. He has only two sources of information (Table 9.1 and Table 9.2), so he decides to match the six data points with the batch data listed in Table 9.1. The investigator then asks the following question: "Is there a transition in batch numbers for one or both of the ingredients?" In other words, one would like to know what happens to the batches as the chart transitions from a point that is in control to a point that is out of control or, more specifically: what happens to the batches as one transitions from point 1 to point 2, point 31 to point 32, point 52 to point 53, and so on, for the other three out-of-control points. Table 9.3 summarizes the result.

Examining Table 9.3 we see that for four out of six transitions (1 to 2, 31 to 32, 52 to 53, and 141 to 142) there was a change in batch number for Ingredient 1 (vs. only one batch change for Ingredient 2). This observation may or may not mean anything, but it is worth investigating further and the best way to proceed would be to interview the process operator(s). It is also true that between points 141 and 144 the process was brought under control with batch number 10656 for Ingredient 1 and consequently, it is possible

Table 9.3 Transition points and matching batch numbers.

Transition from in control to out of control	Batch number	Batch ingredient 1	Batch ingredient 2
From point 1 to point 2	952383	1099 → 1664	1076 → 1076
From 31 to 32	990689	4089 → 4616	4144 → 4144
From 52 to 53	504326	4089 → 5097	5679 → 5679
From 100 to 101	533588	8145 → 8145	6804 → 8040
From 141 to 142	559945x	10325 → 10656	9538 → 9538
From 142 to 143	560289	10656 → 10656	9538 → 9538
From 143 to 144	561060	10656 → 10656	9538 → 9538

the transition to a different batch number means nothing. You may wish to further analyze Figure 9.1 to see if other intriguing patterns of points can be uncovered.

Intrigued by the oscillation in viscosity, the investigator decides to generate a histogram for the 149 viscosity data points. The histogram shown in Figure 9.2, with a superimposed normal curve, indicates that, as suspected, the distribution of points is skewed to the right. The label to the right of the histogram informs us, not surprisingly, that the standard deviation is equal to 703.5 Centipoise (we now have a better idea of what is meant by "too much variability").[2] Using the standard deviation of 703 and the appropriate Z-values already cited (that is, 2.58 and 2.33), you may wish to verify the values of the control limits shown in Figures 9.1a and b.

We might also want to know why many viscosity values are toward the low end of the specification range. For example, the first three bars (reading from left to right) add up to 53 measurements (or 35.5% of all values) that are less than 7500 Centipoise. It would be interesting to interview the process operators to find out why the process is run at the low end of the specification. Looking at the values above the upper specification limit, it is interesting to note that if one removes the nine viscosity readings that are higher than 9000 Centipoise, the average viscosity decreases to 7798.5 Centipoise and, better yet, the standard deviation decreases to 565.5 Centipoise. Consequently, if these few high viscosities could be somehow avoided, the standard deviation would drop by 138 Centipoise.

9.2.1 Process Capability

The capability of a process is calculated by computing what is known as a *capability ratio.* If the process average is right on target (in this case 8000

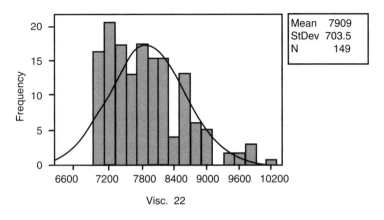

Figure 9.2 Histogram of 149 viscosity values.

Centipoise), we can easily estimate the process capability by computing the following ratio: (USL-LSL)/(6 * S) or (9000 − 8000)/(6 * 703) = 2000/4218 = 0.47. However, because for this case study the process average is slightly below the target value, we should compute the capability ratio from the lower end of the specification. This ratio, known as the *Cpk ratio,* is computed as follows: (LSL − process average)/(3 * S) or (6000 − 7909)/(3 * 703) = 909/2109 = 0.43. Note: If the process is above the target value, we must then use (USL − process average)/(3 * S). Because most customers require a Cpk of 1.3, it is evident the current process is not capable. To bring this process to acceptable capability, one can either widen the specification (an option not likely to be favored by the customer) or reduce the process variation (that is, reduce the standard deviation). By how much should the viscosity standard deviation (S) be reduced?

We need to have (USL − LSL)/(6 * S) = 1.30 or (USL-LSL)/(6 * 1.3) = S or S = 2000/7.8 = 256 Centipoise. Therefore if we can reduce the standard deviation from the current value of 703 down to 256 Centipoise, the process would be capable of satisfying the customer's specifications.

Instead of computing capability ratios we could also refer to Table 9.3 and count (or use the computer to do the task) the nine viscosities (or 6% of the data point) that are either less than the lower specification of 7000 (only one data point) or greater than the upper specification of 9000 Centipoise.

9.2.2 Additional Analysis

Rather than focus on the extremely high value (which have already been analyzed in Table 9.3), the investigator is curious about the 16 data points

Table 9.4 Data for 16 batches of Visc. 22 less than 7100 Centipoise and associated pH values.

Batch	Visc. 22	pH
974684	7069	7.00
980115	6951	6.55
984125	7087	6.35
984215	7087	0.00
502622	7002	7.00
513133	7063	6.75
513684	7048	6.45
518496	7066	6.50
527659	7002	7.00
528254	7056	6.50
533922	7044	6.95
542458	7061	6.90
542537	7089	6.20
545113	7046	6.15
553842	7049	6.45
555418	7004	6.85

shown in the histogram and represented by the first bar (after the value of 6600). A convenient feature of the statistical software reveals that these 16 viscosity values are below 7100 Centipoise (see Table 9.4).

As we scan the 16 sets of values listed in Table 9.4 we notice that the pH value for batch 984125 is 0. Because pH is a measure that varies from 1 to 14, this would indicate that either an incorrect value was entered or no pH measurement was obtained for batch 984215. It is presently impossible to obtain the correct pH measurement for batch 984215 so the pH reading is declared as a "missing value" and taken out of the database. Table 9.5 show the modified database with the 15 viscosity and pH measurements.

Curious as to whether or not there might be a relationship between viscosity and pH, the investigator decided to run a correlation analysis between Visc. 22 and pH for the 15 values listed in Table 9.5. Table 9.6 shows a negative correlation between Visc. 22 and pH; however, the correlation is not significant. Do you know why? Can you formulate the null and alternative hypotheses?

Table 9.5   Data for 15 batches of Visc. 22 less than 7100 Centipoise and associated pH values greater than 0.

Batch	Visc. 22	pH
974684	7069	7.00
980115	6951	6.55
984125	7087	6.35
502622	7002	7.00
513133	7063	6.75
513684	7048	6.45
518496	7066	6.50
527659	7002	7.00
528254	7056	6.50
533922	7044	6.95
542458	7061	6.90
542537	7089	6.20
545113	7046	6.15
553842	7049	6.45
555418	7004	6.85

Table 9.6   Results for Visc. 22 LT 7100 and pH GT 0 (15 observations). Correlations: Visc. 22 with pH.

Pearson correlation of Visc. 22 and pH $= -0.349$
P-Value $= 0.202$

Figure 9.3 is a scattergram of the 15 points representing the relationship between Visc. 22 and pH. Intrigued by the *possibility* of a negative correlation between Visc. 22 and pH, the investigator decides to look at the correlation for the complete database. However, before running the correlation analysis, the pH data is checked for 0 values. A review of Table 9.6 reveals two pH values are equal to 0 (the first value was already identified as associated with batch number 984215 of observation 25, and the second value associated with batch number 974686 of observation 10.

Table 9.7 shows the result of the correlation analysis and Figure 9.5 represent the scattergram for the 147 points (149 minus the two missing values for pH $= 0$).

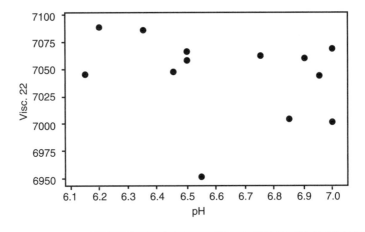

Figure 9.3   Scattergram of Visc. 22 with pH.

Table 9.7   Correlation results of Visc. 22 with pH GT 0 (147 observations). Correlations: Visc. 22 with pH.

Pearson correlation of Visc. 22 and pH = 0.063
P-Value = 0.445

As we can see from Table 9.7 and Figure 9.4, the correlation is now equal to 0.063 and the P-value of 0.445 indicates the null hypothesis of no correlation must be accepted. What looked like a possible negative correlation between Visc. 22 and pH is in fact (when all 147 values are considered) no correlation!

As you look at Figure 9.4, do you notice something unusual or odd (besides the fact that the scattergram represents a cloud of points typical of a zero or near zero correlation)? It might be interesting to obtain some information for the four points beyond pH 7.0.

9.3 SOME LESSONS LEARNED

The scale of the investigation can influence a result. We have seen that a semblance of a negative correlation exhibited by 15 points represent in fact no correlation when all 147 data points are analyzed. Still, we may be curious to know why there is a tendency (although not statistically significant) for a viscosity less than 7100 to be negatively correlated with pH!

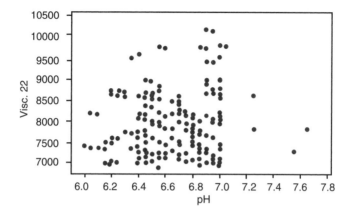

Figure 9.4 Scattergram for Visc. 22 LT 7100 and pH GT 0.

Table 9.8 A simplified descriptive statistics table for Visc. 22 and pH.

Variable	N	N*	Mean	StDev	Minimum	Maximum
Visc. 22	149	0	7908.5	703.5	6951.0	10158.0
PH	149	0	6.5960	0.8207	0.00	7.65

One should always run what is known as a *descriptive statistics* on all variables *before* performing any analysis. Such simple descriptive statistics will usually print averages, standard deviation, minimum and maximum values as well as a host of other simple descriptive statistics. If a descriptive analysis had been run on the database, we ideally would have noticed that the minimum value for pH was 0 (see Table 9.8). The next step would have been to eliminate (as was eventually done in this case study) these erroneous pH values.

Whether they are incorrect data entries or missing values, bad data can influence statistical results. In this particular case study, Table 9.9 shows that the inclusion of the two 0 pH values did not have a significant impact on the correlation coefficient (0.090 vs. 0.063 as reported in Table 9.7). However, a few more erroneous data points could have significantly changed the correlation coefficient and misled the investigator and eventually the investigation.

Histograms are valuable graphical tools that should be generated during the early stages of an investigation. As shown in this case study, asymmetrical distributions can readily be detected with a histogram. Histograms

Table 9.9 Correlations: Visc. 22 with pH for all 149 observations including the two pH 0 values.

Pearson correlation of Visc. 22 and pH = 0.090
P-Value = 0.277

can also complement time-ordered graphs (such as control charts, for example), in that they can reveal information not easily seen in control charts.

While investigating a problem one is often sidetracked by other questions: correlation between viscosity and pH, for example. Such activities are not detrimental and are part of the investigative nature of all problem-solving activities. Recognizing when an investigative trail is no longer worth pursuing is one of the keys to a successful investigation. Such skills can only be acquired with experience and the right team members.

9.3.1 Final Comments

Were all of the phases of the DMAIC methodology undertaken? Not yet, but that is to be expected because we do not have enough data and have just begun our investigation. This case study only covers the DMA phases.

Was the problem clearly defined? Yes. Was the process mapped? No. Was this a good idea? Probably not. It is usually a good idea to first map the process. However, we must also admit that when databases are already available it is not unreasonable to first look at the data. One might say, interrogate the data to see if some patterns emerge that can help reformulate the problem or perhaps better (re)define the problem statement.

Is the measure phase completed? No. Although the databases introduced in Tables 9.1 and 9.2 have helped the investigator ask more questions, the investigator has also learned that other measurements will likely have to be taken, but this is more easily achieved once the process map is completed. The process map will help the team of investigators and process experts identify the key input variables that are, in the opinion of the process experts, likely to influence the variability in viscosity.

Were the initial steps of the investigation wasted? Certainly not! In fact, some or all of the computations, graphs, and arguments presented in this case study could be used to better redefine the variability in viscosity project. For example, one could include the individual moving range chart (Figure 9.1) and the histogram (Figure 9.2) to quantify the extent of the problem. Moreover, the use of Figures 9.1 and 9.2 and any additional tables could be used to not only help management visualize the extent of the problem but to also quantify the meaning of the words *too much variability*. A standard deviation of 703 Centipoise is clearly too much if the specification calls for +/− 1,000

Centipoise, and this can be demonstrated mathematically and/or graphically. Whether or not the process standard deviation will be reduced to around 256 Centipoise remains to be seen, and it is possible that some of the design of experiment techniques described in Chapters 5, 6, and 7 could be very helpful in solving this problem.

NOTES

1. If we had selected an alpha value of 0.05 (Z = 1.96), the upper control limit would be 9287, and points 3 and 100 would now be out of control. I am not suggesting, however, that one keeps lowering the alpha level just to find more out-of-control points. It is clear from this example, however, that these six or seven points are out of control because they all exceed the upper control limit, which for this example happens to also be near the specification limit of 9000. Several other tests could be performed on the chart to detect what are known as special or assignable causes. These tests are not reproduced in this example.

2. Because the specification calls for 8000 +/−1000, we can see the specification range is included within +/−1000/703 or +/−1.42 standard deviations and not the expected +/− 3 standard deviations or even a +/−1.96 standard deviation.

Appendix A

Latin Square

A.0 LATIN SQUARES

The Latin-square design is named from an ancient puzzle that dealt with the number of different ways letters could be arranged in a square table so each letter appeared only once in each row and column. For example, for three letters A, B, and C one of the 12 possible arrangements of a 3 * 3 Latin square is the following:

A	B	C
B	C	A
C	A	B

Latin squares were first introduced in statistics in agricultural research where researchers needed to study the effect of various fertilizers on crop yields. Because the various concentrations of fertilizer (that is, the treatments) were to be used on plots of land it became necessary to find ways to assign the fertilizer randomly across plots in a way that would cancel (or *block*) any possible variation in plot soil fertility, for example. This practice of randomly assigning treatments to various blocks is known as a two-way (across columns and across rows) randomized block design.

Here are some examples of 3 * 3, 4 * 4, and 5 * 5 Latin-square designs:

A B C	A B C	
B C A	C A B	
C A B	B C A	

A B C D	A B C D	A B C D	A B C D
B A D C	D C B A	C D A B	B D A C

```
C D A B        B A D C        D C B A        C A D B
D C B A        C D A B        B A D C        D C B A

A B C D E      A B C D E      A B C D E
B C D E A      C D E A B      D E A B C
C D E A B      E A B C D      B C D E A
D E A B C      B C D E A      E A B C D
E A B C D      D E A B C      C D E A B
```

Latin-square designs are an efficient way to analyze the effect of an independent variable (often called a *treatment*) on a dependent (or response) variable while at the same time controlling two other sources of variation. These other sources of variation are sometimes referred to as *nuisance* variables. In the tread wear example found in Example 1.6 (Section 1.5), the four rubber compounds represent the independent variable (that is, the four treatments), and the tread wear is the dependent or response variable. Although the same type (model) of car is used to minimize the variation in cars, not all models can be assumed to be identical and there will certainly be some variability between the cars. Similarly, we can assume there will be some variability between wheels. The best way to *control,* or minimize, these external sources of variability induced by these two nuisance variables—one could speak of *noise,* which could mask any "rubber compound effect" on tread wear—is to randomize the assignment of rubber compounds to each car and each wheel position. Randomization can be viewed as a means to redistribute systematically (in an attempt to eliminate) the noise effect.

One of the obvious limitations of the Latin square is *that the number of rows and columns must be equal to the number of treatments.* Thus if the independent variable has four values (that is, if we have four treatments), we must use a 4 * 4 Latin square.

A.1 HOW TO ASSIGN TREATMENTS RANDOMLY USING A LATIN-SQUARE DESIGN

First select the appropriate N * N Latin square, append to it N columns and N rows and assign the treatment to each of the columns and rows as defined by the Latin square. A method for randomizing the columns and rows of a Latin square is described later.

Suppose we select the following 4 * 4 Latin square:

```
A B C D
B D A C
C A D B
D C B A
```

Table A.1 Latin-square design for tire experiment.

	Wheel position b1	Wheel position b2	Wheel position b3	Wheel position b4
Car a1	Compound c1	Compound c2	Compound c3	Compound c4
Car a2	c2	c3	c4	c1
Car a3	c3	c4	c1	c2
Car a4	c4	c1	c2	c3

The distribution of a's (rows) and b's (column) could have been randomized. For example, the cars could have been a3, a1, a2, a4, and the b's could have been b4, b3, b1, and b2.

Table A.2 Data matrix for tire tread wear measured in millimeters (with two replications).

	b1	b2	b3	b4
a1	c1 (3, 1)	c2 (4, 2)	c3 (7, 5)	c4 (7, 10)
a2	c2 (5, 3)	c3 (8, 6)	c4 (8, 10)	c2 (6, 2)
a3	c3 (7, 5)	c4 (9, 9)	c1 (3, 2)	c2 (4, 4)
a4	c4 (8, 11)	c1 (3, 2)	c2 (3, 3)	c3 (6, 6)

If we let A = Compound 1 (c1), B = Compound 2 (c2), C = Compound 3 (c3), and D = Compound 4 (c4), Columns = Wheel position, and Rows = Car, we can then randomly assigned each compound to each wheel position and car combination as shown in Table A.1. For this experiment there was no need to randomize the cars and wheel position. Naturally, if we had randomized the rows first and then the columns, adjusting each time the letter, we would have obtained a different Latin square (see end of the appendix).

To increase the precision of the measurements, the experimenter decided to *replicate* the study twice (r = 2). Replication simply means the experimenter conducted the experiment twice. The collected data are presented in Table A.2.

In Table A.2, c1 (3,1) means that for the first compound (c1), the first run produced a tread wear of 3 and the second run produced a tread wear of 1, and so on, for the rest of the table. The 32 data points (16 observations replicated twice) were stored in a computer using an Excel-type database as shown in Table A.3.

Table A.3   Tread wear data as entered in the spreadsheet.

Rep	A	B	C	Thickness
1	1	1	1	3
1	1	2	2	4
1	1	3	3	7
1	1	4	4	7
1	2	1	2	5
1	2	2	3	8
1	2	3	4	8
1	2	4	1	6
1	3	1	3	7
1	3	2	4	9
1	3	3	1	3
1	3	4	2	4
1	4	1	4	8
1	4	2	1	3
1	4	3	2	3
1	4	4	3	6
2	1	1	1	1
2	1	2	2	2
2	1	3	3	5
2	1	4	4	10
2	2	1	2	3
2	2	2	3	6
2	2	3	4	10
2	2	4	1	2
2	3	1	3	5
2	3	2	4	9
2	3	3	1	2
2	3	4	2	4
2	4	1	4	11
2	4	2	1	2
2	4	3	2	3
2	4	4	3	6

Rep = replication; A = car; B = wheel position; C = rubber compound

A.2 GRAPHICAL REPRESENTATION OF THE TREAD WEAR STUDY

The data will be statistically analyzed in the text, but for now, we can *look at* the data using box plot diagrams. As you examine the box plots reproduced in Figures A.1, A.2, and A.3, how would you answer the following questions?

1. Is there a difference in tread wear (that is, wear in tread) across compound?

2. Is there a difference in tread wear across cars (or stated differently, does the car affect tire performance)? Because all cars are of the same model, one would not expect any difference in tread wear.

3. Is there a difference in tread wear across wheel position (or does the wheel position affect tire performance)? Once again, we would not expect what is referred to as a "wheel position effect," in other words, we would not expect the tread wear to depend on the wheel position.

To eliminate more than two sources of variation, we can use Greco-Latin squares.

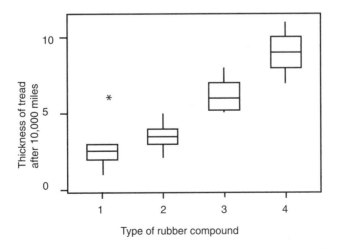

Figure A.1   Box plots of tread thickness by type of rubber compound.

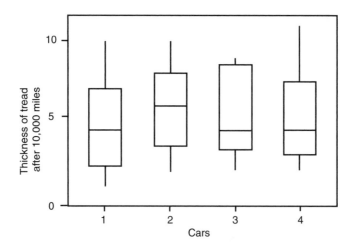

Figure A.2   Box plots of tread thickness by car.

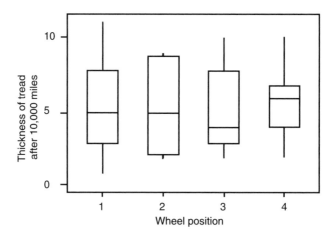

Figure A.3   Box plots of tread thickness by wheel position.

A.3 GRECO-LATIN SQUARES

Greco-Latin squares can be used to eliminate three sources of variability (that is, to control three nuisance variables). Referring back to the tread wear example, we could control for a third source of variation by having four different drivers drive each of the four cars. To obtain a Greco-Latin square, simply superimpose two Latin-square designs using Greek letters for the second Latin-square design.

We use two 4 * 4 Latin-square designs and superimpose the second Latin square onto the first (using Greek letters for the second Latin square):

			1 2 3 4
A B C D	Aα Bβ Cγ Dδ	1	Aα Bβ Cγ Dδ
B A D C	Bβ Cγ Dδ Aα	2	Bβ Aα Dδ Cγ
C D B A	Cγ Dδ Aα Bβ Leads to:	3	Cγ Dδ Bβ Aα
D C A B	Dδ Aα Bβ Cγ	4	Dδ Cγ Aα Bβ

The Latin letters could be used to distribute the rubber compound and the Greek letters could be used to assign the drivers to each car, wheel position, and rubber compound composition. As was the case for the Latin-square example, the columns (1–4) and rows (1–4) represent the wheel position and cars; the order of these numbers could also be randomized.

A.4 GENERATING LATIN SQUARES

1. Select the appropriate Latin square. For example, the example in Chapter 1 will test four compounds and therefore we will need a 4 * 4 Latin square. Suppose we select the following 4 * 4 Latin square:

                Columns
                1 2 3 4
            1 A B C D
    Rows   2 B C D A
            3 C D A B
            4 D A B C

The columns represent the first variable. For example, wheel position and the rows could represent the four cars.

2. Next randomize the rows, for example, 3, 1, 2, 4, to obtain the following square:

                Columns
                1 2 3 4
            1 C D A B
            2 A B C D
    Rows   3 B C D A
            4 D A B C

3. Finally, randomize the columns, for example, 4, 3, 1, 2, to obtain the following square:

                Columns
                4 3 1 2
            3 B A C D
            1 D C A B
    Rows   2 A D B C
            4 C B D A

Appendix B

Design Matrix for 2^{4-1} and 2^{5-1} 2^{5-2} and 2^{7-3} (Half Fractions)

Fractional Factorial Design

Factors:	4	Base Design:	4, 8	Resolution:	IV
Runs:	8	Replicates:	1	Fraction:	1/2
Blocks:	none	Center pts (total):	0		

Design Generators: D = ABC

Alias Structure

I + ABCD

A + BCD
B + ACD
C + ABD
D + ABC
AB + CD
AC + BD
AD + BC

This matrix was produced *without* randomization:

StdOrder	RunOrder	CenterPt	Blocks	A	B	C	D
1	1	1	1	−1	−1	−1	−1
2	2	1	1	1	−1	−1	1
3	3	1	1	−1	1	−1	1
4	4	1	1	1	1	−1	−1
5	5	1	1	−1	−1	1	1
6	6	1	1	1	−1	1	−1
7	7	1	1	−1	1	1	−1
8	8	1	1	1	1	1	−1

Note: No center point and no blocking factor were set for this experiment. This matrix was produced by asking the computer to randomize the runs:

StdOrder	RunOrder	CenterPt	Blocks	A	B	C	D
7	1	1	1	−1	1	1	−1
5	2	1	1	−1	−1	1	1
3	3	1	1	−1	1	−1	1
4	4	1	1	1	1	−1	−1
1	5	1	1	−1	−1	−1	−1
8	6	1	1	1	1	1	1
2	7	1	1	1	−1	−1	1
6	8	1	1	1	−1	1	−1

Note: No center point and no blocking factor were set for this experiment.

Fractional Factorial Design for a 2^{5-1} design

Factors:	5	Base Design:	5, 16	Resolution:	V
Runs:	16	Replicates:	1	Fraction:	1/2
Blocks:	none	Center pts (total):	0		

Design Generators: E = ABCD

Alias Structure

I + ABCDE
A + BCDE
B + ACDE
C + ABDE
D + ABCE
E + ABCD
AB + CDE
AC + BDE
AD + BCE
AE + BCD
BC + ADE
BD + ACE
BE + ACD
CD + ABE
CE + ABD
DE + ABC

StdOrder	RunOrder	CenterPt	Blocks	A	B	C	D	E
16	1	1	1	1	1	1	1	1
2	2	1	1	1	−1	−1	−1	−1
1	3	1	1	−1	−1	−1	−1	1
14	4	1	1	1	−1	1	1	−1
7	5	1	1	−1	1	1	−1	1
12	6	1	1	1	1	−1	1	−1
8	7	1	1	1	1	1	−1	−1
15	8	1	1	−1	1	1	1	−1
10	9	1	1	1	−1	−1	1	1
5	10	1	1	−1	−1	1	−1	−1
6	11	1	1	1	−1	1	−1	1
13	12	1	1	−1	−1	1	1	1
11	13	1	1	−1	1	−1	1	1
9	14	1	1	−1	−1	−1	1	−1
3	15	1	1	−1	1	−1	−1	−1
4	16	1	1	1	1	−1	−1	1

Fractional Factorial Design for a 2^{5-2}

Factors:	5	Base Design:	5, 8	Resolution:	III
Runs:	8	Replicates:	1	Fraction:	1/4
Blocks:	none	Center pts (total):	0		

*** NOTE *** Some main effects are confounded with two-way interactions

Design Generators: D = AB E = AC

Alias Structure

I + ABD + ACE + BCDE
A + BD + CE + ABCDE
B + AD + CDE + ABCE
C + AE + BDE + ABCD
D + AB + BCE + ACDE
E + AC + BCD + ABDE
BC + DE + ABE + ACD
BE + CD + ABC + ADE

StdOrder	RunOrder	CenterPt	Blocks	A	B	C	D	E
7	1	1	1	−1	1	1	−1	−1
2	2	1	1	1	−1	−1	−1	−1
5	3	1	1	−1	−1	1	1	−1
6	4	1	1	1	−1	1	−1	1
8	5	1	1	1	1	1	1	1
3	6	1	1	−1	1	−1	−1	1
1	7	1	1	−1	−1	−1	1	1
4	8	1	1	1	1	−1	1	−1

Fractional Factorial Design for a 2^{7-4} design

Factors:	7	Base Design:	7, 16	Resolution:	IV
Runs:	16	Replicates:	1	Fraction:	1/8
Blocks:	none	Center pts (total):	0		

Design Generators: E = ABC F = BCD G = ACD

Alias Structure

I + ABCE + ABFG + ACDG + ADEF + BCDF + BDEG + CEFG

A + BCE + BFG + CDG + DEF + ABCDF + ABDEG + ACEFG
B + ACE + AFG + CDF + DEG + ABCDG + ABDEF + BCEFG
C + ABE + ADG + BDF + EFG + ABCFG + ACDEF + BCDEG
D + ACG + AEF + BCF + BEG + ABCDE + ABDFG + CDEFG
E + ABC + ADF + BDG + CFG + ABEFG + ACDEG + BCDEF
F + ABG + ADE + BCD + CEG + ABCEF + ACDFG + BDEFG
G + ABF + ACD + BDE + CEF + ABCEG + ADEFG + BCDFG
AB + CE + FG + ACDF + ADEG + BCDG + BDEF + ABCEFG
AC + BE + DG + ABDF + AEFG + BCFG + CDEF + ABCDEG
AD + CG + EF + ABCF + ABEG + BCDE + BDFG + ACDEFG
AE + BC + DF + ABDG + ACFG + BEFG + CDEG + ABCDEF
AF + BG + DE + ABCD + ACEG + BCEF + CDFG + ABDEFG
AG + BF + CD + ABDE + ACEF + BCEG + DEFG + ABCDFG
BD + CF + EG + ABCG + ABEF + ACDE + ADFG + BCDEFG
ABD + ACF + AEG + BCG + BEF + CDE + DFG + ABCDEFG

Appendix C

Regression Analysis of Data Analyzed in Section 5.5

The technique of regression analysis can also be used to analyze data that were generated using a design matrix. One (small) inconvenience of using regression models is that all the second-order, third-order, and higher-order interaction terms have to be generated (using data manipulation operations) in order to be included in the regression model. For models with four or more factors, that process can be slightly tedious. Recall that the generation of interaction terms is done automatically with the design of experiments (DoE) module. Nonetheless, the data first presented in section 5.5 and analyzed using the DoE statistical module is reanalyzed using regression analysis. Note that the interaction terms (A * B, A * C, A * D, and so on) are *not included* in the regression models because (1) I was not inclined to enter all the interaction terms for each regression analysis (see Appendix D, however, which includes all second-order interactions), and (2) the primary purpose of this appendix is to demonstrate that regression analysis and DoE (which is a form of analysis of variance) both belong to the broader category of modeling known as the general linear model.

REGRESSION ANALYSIS: S VERSUS A, D, F

The regression equation is

$$S = 11.3 + 0.956\,A + 1.76\,D + 1.42\,F$$

Predictor	Coefficient	SE Coefficient	T	P
Constant	11.3063	0.3538	31.95	0.000
A	0.9562	0.3538	2.70	0.012
D	1.7562	0.3538	4.96	0.000
F	1.4188	0.3538	4.01	0.000
S = 2.002	R-Squared = 63.2%		R-Squared(adjusted) = 59.2%	

Analysis of Variance:

Source	DF	SS	MS	F	P
Regression	3	192.374	64.125	16.00	0.000
Residual Error	28	112.185	4.007		
Total	31	304.559			
Source	**DF**	**Seq SS**			
A	1	29.261			
D	1	98.701			
F	1	64.411			

Unusual Observations:

Obs	A	S	Fit	SE Fit	Residual	St Resid
1	−1.00	3.400	7.175	0.708	−3.775	−2.02R
R denotes an observation with a large standardized residual.						

REGRESSION ANALYSIS: H VERSUS A, F

The regression equation is

$$H = 16.4 - 4.94\,A + 6.50\,F$$

Predictor	Coefficient	SE Coefficient	T	P
Constant	16.3750	0.9544	17.16	0.000
A	−4.9375	0.9544	−5.17	0.000
F	6.5000	0.9544	6.81	0.000
S = 5.399	R-Sq = 71.6%	R-Sq(adjusted) = 69.6%		

Analysis of Variance:

Source	DF	SS	MS	F	P
Regression	2	2132.1	1066.1	36.57	0.000
Residual Error	29	845.4	29.2		
Total	31	2977.5			
Source	**DF**	**Seq SS**			
A	1	780.1			
F	1	1352.0			

Unusual Observations:

Obs	A	H	Fit	SE Fit	Residual	St Resid
26	1.00	30.000	17.938	1.653	12.062	2.35R*

*R denotes an observation with a large standardized residual.

REGRESSION ANALYSIS: Br VERSUS F

The regression equation is

$$Br = 26.8 - 5.25\ F$$

Predictor	Coefficient	SE Coefficient	T	P
Constant	26.8125	0.9122	29.39	0.000
F	−5.2500	0.9122	−5.76	0.000
S = 5.160	R-Sq = 52.5%	R-Sq(adjusted) = 50.9%		

Analysis of Variance:

Source	DF	SS	MS	F	P
Regression	1	882.00	882.00	33.12	0.000
Residual Error	30	798.88	26.63		
Total	31	1680.88			

Unusual Observations:

Obs	F	Br	Fit	SE Fit	Residual	St Resid
2	1.00	34.000	21.563	1.290	12.437	2.49R*
25	−1.00	20.000	32.063	1.290	−12.063	−2.41R
26	1.00	11.000	21.563	1.290	−10.563	−2.11R

*R denotes an observation with a large standardized residual.

Appendix D

Response Surface Regression: S, H, Br versus A, D, F, Box-Behnken from Chapter 7

RESPONSE SURFACE REGRESSION: S VERSUS A, D, F

The analysis was done using coded units.

Estimated Regression Coefficients for S:

Term	Coefficient	SE Coefficient	T	P
Constant	12.067	0.9018	13.380	0.000
A	2.663	0.5522	4.821	0.005
D	2.075	0.5522	3.757	0.013
F	1.837	0.5522	3.327	0.021
A*A	−0.808	0.8129	−0.994	0.366
D*D	−1.583	0.8129	−1.948	0.109
F*F	1.042	0.8129	1.281	0.256
A*D	−0.675	0.7810	−0.864	0.427
A*F	−2.250	0.7810	−2.881	0.035
D*F	1.575	0.7810	2.017	0.100
S = 1.562	R-Sq = 93.2%	R-Sq(adjusted) = 80.9%		

Analysis of Variance for S:

Source	DF	Seq SS	Adj SS	Adj MS	F	P
Regression	9	166.658	166.658	18.5176	7.59	0.019
Linear	3	118.167	118.168	39.3892	16.14	0.005
Square	3	16.496	16.496	5.4986	2.25	0.200
Interaction	3	31.995	31.995	10.6650	4.37	0.073
Residual Error	5	12.199	12.199	2.4398		
Lack-of-Fit	3	12.113	12.113	4.0375	93.17	0.011
Pure Error	2	0.087	0.087	0.0433		
Total	14	178.857				

Unusual Observations for S:

Observation	S	Fit	SE Fit	Residual	St Residual
5	7.200	5.550	1.353	1.650	2.11R
8	12.900	14.550	1.353	−1.650	−2.11R
R denotes an observation with a large standardized residual.					

Estimated Regression Coefficients for S using data in uncoded units:

Term	Coefficient
Constant	12.0667
A	2.66250
D	2.07500
F	1.83750
A*A	−0.808333
D*D	−1.58333
F*F	1.04167
A*D	−0.675000
A*F	−2.25000
D*F	1.57500

RESPONSE SURFACE REGRESSION: H VERSUS A, D, F

The analysis was done using coded units.

Estimated Regression Coefficients for H:

Term	Coefficient	SE Coefficient	T	P
Constant	16.067	2.086	7.702	0.001
A	−3.375	1.277	−2.642	0.046
D	2.025	1.277	1.585	0.174
F	5.650	1.277	4.423	0.007
A*A	−1.071	1.880	−0.569	0.594
D*D	1.629	1.880	0.866	0.426
F*F	1.379	1.880	0.733	0.496
A*D	−0.625	1.807	−0.346	0.743
A*F	−1.625	1.807	−0.900	0.410
D*F	−1.925	1.807	−1.066	0.335
S = 3.613	R-Sq = 86.8%	R-Sq(adjusted) = 63.0%		

Analysis of Variance for H:

Source	DF	Seq SS	SS	Adj SS	Adj MS	F	P
Regression	9	428.068	428.068	47.563	3.64	0.084	
Linear	3	379.310	379.310	126.437	9.69	0.016	
Square	3	21.811	21.811	7.270	0.56	0.666	
Interaction	3	26.947	26.947	8.982	0.69	0.597	
Residual Error	5	65.272	65.272	13.054			
Lack-of-Fit	3	65.185	65.185	21.728	501.42	0.002	
Pure Error	2	0.087	0.087	0.043			
Total	14	493.340					

Unusual Observations for H:

Observation	H	Fit	SE Fit	Residual	St Residual
10	21.000	17.375	3.129	3.625	2.01R*
11	21.000	24.625	3.129	−3.625	−2.01R

*R denotes an observation with a large standardized residual.

Estimated Regression Coefficients for H using data in uncoded units:

Term	Coefficient
Constant	16.0667
A	−3.37500
D	2.02500
F	5.65000
A*A	−1.07083
D*D	1.62917
F*F	1.37917
A*D	−0.625000
A*F	−1.62500
D*F	−1.92500

RESPONSE SURFACE REGRESSION: Br VERSUS A, D, F

The analysis was done using coded units.

Estimated Regression Coefficients for Br:

Term	Coefficient	SE Coefficient	T	P
Constant	26.733	1.2314	21.710	0.000
A	−0.625	0.7541	−0.829	0.445
D	−1.063	0.7541	−1.409	0.218
F	−5.887	0.7541	−7.808	0.001
A*A	−4.179	1.1099	−3.765	0.013
D*D	−2.954	1.1099	−2.662	0.045
F*F	4.946	1.1099	4.456	0.007
A*D	0.150	1.0664	0.141	0.894
A*F	4.000	1.0664	3.751	0.013
D*F	−1.625	1.0664	−1.524	0.188
S = 2.133	R-Sq = 96.1%	R-Sq(adjusted) = 89.2%		

Analysis of Variance for Br:

Source	DF	Seq SS	Adj SS	Adj MS	F	P
Regression	9	565.449	565.449	62.8277	13.81	0.005
Linear	3	289.457	289.457	96.4858	21.21	0.003
Square	3	201.339	201.339	67.1131	14.75	0.006
Interaction	3	74.653	74.653	24.8842	5.47	0.049
Residual Error	5	22.744	22.744	4.5488		
Lack-of-Fit	3	21.858	21.858	7.2858	16.43	0.058
Pure Error	2	0.887	0.887	0.4433		
Total	14	588.193				

Estimated Regression Coefficients for Br using data in uncoded units:

Term	Coefficient
Constant	26.7333
A	−0.625000
D	−1.06250
F	−5.88750
A*A	−4.17917
D*D	−2.95417
F*F	4.94583
A*D	0.150000
A*F	4.00000
D*F	−1.62500

Annotated Bibliography

Thousands of books have been published over the past 80 or so years on the subject of statistics and experimental designs. Many books published from the 1930s to the 1950s are excellent, but are now ignored because they are perhaps wrongly perceived as being outdated. And yet, even today, Walter A. Shewhart's *Economic Control of Quality of Manufactured Product* should be required reading for anyone interested in industrial statistics.

Rather than include a lengthy bibliography, I have selected from my own collection of over 80 books on statistics: a dozen books published over the past 45–50 years that I believe will be helpful to anyone who would want to learn more about the topics introduced in this book.

Automotive Industry Action Group. *Measurement Systems Analysis*. Southfield, MI: AIAG, 1990. Although this manual is often cited and is a must read for anyone that wants to understand gage repeatability and reproducibility, its poor organization makes it a rather unpleasant reading experience.

Box, George E.P., William G. Hunter, and Stuart J. Hunter. *Statistics for Experimenters: An Introduction to Design, Data Analysis, and Model Building*. New York: John Wiley & Sons, 1978. The reference work for design of experiments.

Box, George E. P. and Norman Draper. *Empirical Model Building and Response Surfaces*. New York: John Wiley & Sons, 1987. A more advanced text with several excellent and detailed examples.

Chou, Ya-lun. *Statistical Analysis: Experimental Design and the Analysis of Variance*. New York: Holt, Rinehart and Winston, 1975. An excellent introductory book with many examples and a broad range of topics useful to most quality professionals.

Cox, David R. *Planning of Experiments*. New York: John Wiley & Sons, 1958. An excellent book full of practical advice and knowledge ignored in today's book. Although written before the age of statistical software, this book is still very useful for its in-depth insights and explanations.

Cuthbert, Daniel. Applications of Statistics to Industrial Experimentation. New York: John Wiley & Sons, 1976. Similar to the practical style found in Cox's book.

Draper, Norman R. and Harry Smith. *Applied Regression Analysis*. New York, John Wiley & Sons, 1966. One of the classic references in regression analysis. An understanding of matrix algebra is required.

Freund, John E. *Mathematical Statistics with Applications*. Englewood Cliffs, NJ: Prentice Hall, 1962. An introductory text for those who are interested in learning more about the mathematical derivation of some of the theorems introduced in Chapter 2.

Gigerenzer, Gerd. *Calculated Risks: How to Know When Numbers Deceive You*. New York: Simon & Schuster, 2002. A very interesting book for anyone interested in the fashionable subject of risk analysis and risk management.

Montgomery, Douglas, C. *Design and Analysis of Experiments*. New York: John Wiley & Sons, 1984. This excellent book focuses on industrial applications; numerous examples.

Montgomery, Douglas, C. *Statistical Quality Control*. New York: John Wiley & Sons, 1985. A well-known reference for the industrial application of control charts.

Youden, W. J. *Experimentation and Measurement*. Washington, DC: National Science Teachers Association, 1985. The best short book (96 pages) on the subject. A must read for anyone interested in the measurement process in experimentation.

Wheeler, Donald J. and Richard W. Lyday. *Evaluating the Measurement Process*. Knoxville, TN: Statistical Process Controls, 1984. An invaluable, well-written complement to the AIAG manual.

Index